# ❧ *Previews* ✌

*Life Force* is a compendium of all that one needs to know about self-healing, written by a respected teacher who has been practicing and sharing the teachings of Paramhansa Yogananda for fifty years. Each book in this unique trilogy offers transformative techniques for those who seek better health, inner peace, and a harmonious life.

*–Padma Shri D. R. Kaarthikeyan, former director CBI and director general of the National Human Rights Commission; president, Foundation for Peace, Harmony and Good Governance, India*

Shivani and I grew up together spiritually, under the watchful eye of Swami Kriyananda. She preceded me by a few years, but both of us were founding members of the first Ananda community in California. She worked in the garden, I in the kitchen. It was simple living. Some might call it primitive. No amenities, very little money, and, in the eyes of many, no future. For us, it was heaven on earth. The foundation for all the blessings, opportunities, and accomplishments that have come in the fifty years since, is those first years of living for God.

From the beginning, Shivani had a passion for what we called "Paramhansa Yogananda's Original Teachings." Very little of his teaching was available then, and what did exist was highly edited to exclude, or water down, many of his most revolutionary ideas. Shivani was not satisfied with second-hand reports. She wanted the never published, or long-out-of-print original documents, hidden in dusty attics and bureau drawers of his direct disciples. Shivani bought a copy machine and as fast as she gathered these treasures, she shared them with kindred spirits who had the same passion for the original teachings of the master.

Much of what we have now of Yogananda's original written and spoken words, are a result of her determination to find and share them.

Shivani, however, did much more than collect. She studied, practiced, and gave her heart and soul to mastering the principles and techniques he taught. Her special interest, always, was Yogananda's healing methods. The fruit of those decades of unrelenting effort by

Shivani is this remarkable, unprecedented collection of teachings. No mere intellectual compendium, this is Truth explored, experienced, and shared by one who knows. A gift for the ages.

*—Asha Nayaswami, author, internationally renowned speaker*

For the past ten years, I have been using many of the self-healing techniques which author Shivani Lucki includes in the *Life Force* trilogy. These are surgical tools which can be used to heal not only physical, mental, and emotional illnesses, but also to eliminate the stubborn roots of past karma. The positive results I have seen—their efficacy in bringing about lasting change—have convinced me that every single word of these teachings is packed with truth and power. Thank you, Shivani, for compiling these techniques into a comprehensive and accessible resource.

*—Rashmi Krishnan, formerly Secretary*
*(Social Welfare), Govt of NCT of Delhi, India*

The Life Force trilogy is the ultimate collection of the physical and metaphysical techniques governing our health and happiness. The real-life stories throughout the books demonstrate what is possible when we determine to have a better life. Read it and experiment for yourself!

*—Dr. Abhilasha Kumar, PhD neurobiology, Basil, Switzerland*

In thirty years as a medical doctor, I feel health is our natural state. We get diseases when we create barriers. This book will help you to remove those barriers step by step and bring you back to your own natural state of pristine health and vitality.

*—Dr Amit Aggarwal, MD, professor of*
*medicine, Symbiosis Medical College, Pune*

# HEALING WITH
# LIFE
# FORCE

# HEALING WITH
# LIFE
# FORCE

## TEACHINGS AND TECHNIQUES
## OF PARAMHANSA YOGANANDA

VOLUME 1 PRANA

# SHIVANI LUCKI

## CRYSTAL CLARITY PUBLISHERS
Commerce, California

# HEALING WITH LIFE FORCE

## VOLUME ONE: PRANA

CRYSTAL CLARITY PUBLISHERS
1123 Goodrich Blvd. | Commerce, California
crystalclarity.com | clarity@crystalclarity.com
800.424.1055

ISBN 978-1-56589-047-3 (print)
ISBN 978-1-56589-528-7 (e-book)
Library of Congress Data available.

*Cover layout and interior design by*
Tejindra Scott Tully

Cover image by Apace on Freepik

*Please be advised: The content in this book is not intended to be a substitute for professional medical advice, diagnosis or treatment. Always consult with a qualified and licensed physician or other medical care provider, and follow their advice without delay.*

*Dedicated to*

**PARAMHANSA YOGANANDA**
*and*

**SWAMI KRIYANANDA,**

*whose lives and teachings inspire our journey
to radiant health and abundant joy.*

# ℒive or Die

## BASED ON TRUE STORIES

Although Samuel had been feeling distinctly unwell, he was reluctant to alarm his family, and so he had said nothing about the pains that were coming with increasing frequency and urgency. "Probably just age," he thought. Now in his sixties, he had considered retiring from a job that had long since ceased to hold any interest for him.

After a general checkup, the doctor referred him to an oncologist, who announced that he had an inoperable terminal cancer, and that he had perhaps six months to live.

Devastated, Samuel told his family that the doctor said he would die within six months. And from that day he began to die, quitting his job to sit before the television and take the medication the oncologist had prescribed for the symptoms. Profoundly depressed, he fended off the efforts of friends to cheer him with invitations to play cards, enjoy a family dinner, or spend time with his grandchildren. Why bother? He was going to die.

The six-month prognosis proved overly optimistic – after three months, Samuel was gone.

The oncologist who had diagnosed Samuel's cancer had another patient, Luca, who was roughly the same age as Samuel and had received an identical diagnosis and prognosis. But when Luca revealed the news to his family, he announced that he intended to live his final months to the full.

Luca loved his work and his colleagues. He reduced his hours and redefined his role as helping the others acquire the skills to carry forward the plans they had made together. In his spare time, he took a drawing class that he'd formerly been unable to find time for. The instructor soon discovered that Luca had talent, and within months he had enough sketches for a small exhibition.

Luca was happier than ever. Together with his wife, he traveled to exotic locales, where they experienced a diversity of cultures, food, and customs, making interesting new friends along the way.

Luca had found little time to share the lives of his two teenage sons, and now that he began to discover what wonderful youngsters they were, and wanting to leave them with happy memories, he made sure that they were able to share small adventures and spend meaningful time together.

After three months, Luca returned to the oncologist, who announced that the tumor had diminished. At six months, it was smaller still, and after a year it had vanished entirely. Follow-up exams at three, five, and ten years showed him completely cancer free.

*When we close the doors to life, life leaves us.*
*When we embrace life, life embraces us!*

# TABLE OF CONTENTS

## VOLUME I | PRANA

# FOREWORD

## DR. ADITYA GAIT

As a young surgeon in training, I experienced a life-changing moment when a patient whom I had been supervising suddenly left his body. I had hoped that he would recover, as he had shown signs of improvement. But when I rushed to his room I found only a lifeless form: a body that had just a few minutes before been vibrating with life as it spoke with me, but that was now limp in death. I had a sense that something sacred had taken place, but I didn't know what it was.

My medical books held no answers to the questions that now assailed me. Noticing my distracted state, my colleagues tried to cheer me up, inviting me to find relief in a cup of tea, and suggesting that I simply forget about it and move on. "This happens every day," they said.

Not convinced, I spent many months seeking answers to my questions about life and death: Who are we? Where do we come from? How can we remain in a state of perfect health in body, mind, and spirit?

My quest eventually led me to the teachings of a world-renowned spiritual master, Paramhansa Yogananda. For every question I asked, I found an answer. I dove deeply into his teachings, where I discovered healing principles that promised to take me beyond the frontiers of matter and demystify life and death.

I was fortunate to be helped along the way by a number of wonderful teachers whose lives and wisdom have deeply inspired me. One such treasured guide is Shivani Lucki.

I met Shivani for the first time in 2009, when I attended a weekend retreat on healing that she gave. The clarity and insights that she brought to her classes made me one of her most avid attendees. Over the ensuing years we have shared many deep conversations.

Dynamic and strong-willed, Shivani is an inspiration for me and countless others. I remember how she suffered a fall and fractured her ankle – and refused to allow the fracture to stop her daily practice of the Energization Exercises, which she did in her wheelchair.

As with her many other serviceful endeavors, *Life Force* is steeped in deep devotion to her subject, enriched with deep and persistent exploration, and permeated with meditation-born insights.

*Life Force* is a testament to the living wisdom of Paramhansa Yogananda, and to the deep desire to share the joy and healing that she has experienced while living the teachings for more than fifty years.

Shivani beautifully explores and elaborates on Yogananda's teachings. *Life Force* covers the vast spectrum of health, from the moment of our conception, through the journey of life, to the soul's final passage through the portals of death. Its three volumes are enriched by engaging real-life stories that illustrate the principles and convincingly demonstrate the role that we personally need to play in our healing.

The message of *Life Force* is one of immense hope and *true healing!* I feel deep joy in contemplating its far-reaching impact, as this blessed work awaits to share its inspiration with you and with countless other truth-seeking souls.

–**Dr. Aditya Gait**, *MBBS DNB(I)*

# PREFACE

The power to heal ourselves and to channel healing energy to others is too often considered a special talent of the rare few. In fact, it is a gift we all have, that we can discover and develop with the right practices. The human body, mind, and soul have tremendous resources to adapt, survive, and thrive in every circumstance.

Modern life is not conducive to good health. Pollution, climate change, sensory overload, all make this a time in which healthy, happy living is becoming harder to find, and a challenge to maintain. And we never know when a "karmic bomb" may explode in our lives. The techniques here will help improve your quality of life now, and prepare you to cope with whatever challenges may come.

If you are presently enjoying good health, this book will help you achieve an even more dynamic state of wellbeing.

If you are prone to illness, anxiety, fear, and disappointments, or if your energy reserves are flagging, this book can set you on a path to physical vitality, mental clarity, emotional stability, and inner peace.

Paramhansa Yogananda, author of *Autobiography of a Yogi*, repeatedly demonstrated a God-given power to heal. Yet his primary mission was not to show his uniqueness, but to empower all of us to heal ourselves: body, heart, mind, and soul. Simply stated, "To take charge of our own health."

In the fifty years that I have studied, practiced, and taught the techniques I share in this book, I have experienced their tremendous healing power countless times. The inspiring personal stories included throughout the book testify to their remarkable value.

*With daily Life Force techniques my crippling fatigue is a thing of the past, and I have enough vital energy again to garden and volunteer with needy children.* –**Jenny**, *Switzerland*

*After my near-fatal accident the doctors said my recovery would take at least twelve months. Lying in the hospital bed I did the Life Force exercises many times each day. After fifteen days I was dismissed from the hospital, and after three months I am back to my normal life.* –**Vinu**, *New Delhi*

*The treatment for the tumor close to my spine left me unable to walk. The doctor said I would need to stay in the hospital for a long time. I did the Life Force exercises mentally as I lay in the hospital. After three days, I started to walk, and very soon the amazed doctor dismissed me.* —**Rinus**, *Netherlands*

In this Life Force trilogy, my aim is to offer you a how-to-do-it manual of the full spectrum of Yogananda's teaching on self-healing, including materials not easily available before.

In Volume One you will learn how to access and channel the healing power of Life Force. In Volume Two you will learn mental superpowers to heal yourself and others. Volume Three teaches subtle laws of magnetism and attraction to improve relationships, increase financial abundance, and protect against harmful vibrational influences. An epilogue, "Transition and Transcendence," talks about death, dying, and the world beyond.

I wish you health, happiness, success, and Self-realization. As you read this book, keep in mind these words of the great Himalayan master, Mahavatar Babaji.

> "Even a little of this practice will save you from dire fears and colossal sufferings!"

# INTRODUCTION

he book you have in hand is the first volume in the Life Force trilogy—*Prana, Mind, Magnetism*—three guidebooks for your journey to better health. Together they represent an overarching view of Paramhansa Yogananda's teachings and techniques for self-healing and Self-realization.

Volume One, *Prana*, takes us back to the very beginning, when Life Force becomes the power that fashions creation. Yogananda shows us how to harness that power and use it to infuse our bodies with vitality. That force also gives rise to the eternal struggle between the soul and the ego, the root cause of all disease. Through the pages and practices of this book, you will learn how to reconcile these two protagonists through techniques of meditation; how to regenerate the cells and organs of your body with Yogananda's Energization Exercises; and how to nourish yourself and keep your body free from impurities with his dietary and detox recipes. A fascinating section in this volume presents Yogananda's techniques for utilizing the sun's power for self-healing.

Volume Two, *Mind*, highlights the superpowers of the conscious, subconscious, and superconscious dimensions of the mind. It offers extensive advice for breaking the stranglehold of negative habits, for using affirmations to carve new thought habits in the brain, and for learning to cooperate with the highest source of healing— Divine Love.

Volume Three, *Magnetism*, reveals how the Law of Attraction operates in our lives: how it draws us into contact with friends from past lives; and how we can use it to attract the economic and human resources for a successful career.

The final chapter of the trilogy demonstrates how we can attune ourselves to the subtle, vibratory healing frequencies of mantra and music; of nature, holy places, and inspiring people. Important techniques are given to reinforce the magnetic aura which protects us from negative influences that threaten our physical, mental, emotional, and spiritual health and well-being.

We are not alone in this quest. Some of those who have come before us, in ages past and in our times, those who have reached the summit of what it means to be a fully Self-realized being, have left for us guidelines for our own achievements.

One such recent guide is Paramhansa Yogananda.

## Paramhansa Yogananda

Author of the enduring spiritual classic, *Autobiography of a Yogi,*[1] Yogananda is universally regarded as an enlightened spiritual master of modern times. He had the remarkable gift of distilling the essential wisdom of India's great scriptures and presenting them in what he called "how-to-live teachings," useful and accessible to us today.

Yogananda was born in India in 1893, on the cusp of the beginning of Dwapara Yuga, the Age of Energy, which according to his guru, Swami Sri Yukteswar, started in 1899. Ushering in this new age were the discoveries of Albert Einstein and Nikola Tesla on the nature of matter and energy.

In the first decade of the twentieth century alone, the landmark inventions included radio, radar, and the electrocardiogram, to name a few. Energy now powers all our systems of transportation, communication, and the countless gadgets that simplify and enhance our daily lives.

When Yogananda arrived on the shores of the New World in 1920, around the time the Wright brothers had taken flight and Henry Ford had produced the Model T, the timing was right and people were eager to learn techniques of self-improvement that were based on principles of Energy.

Although Yogananda is not remembered primarily as a miracle healer, in his early lecture tours across America he gave many public demonstrations of the power of self-healing. On October 21, 1924, he held a first "public divine healing meeting" in Portland, Oregon. During a healing program at his headquarters at Mt. Washington in Los Angeles on November 1, 1925, he healed a woman of crippling neuritis, after which she was able to walk without crutches.

In Washington, D.C. in 1927, a reported 5000 people attended his healing program. It was at this time that he was invited to the White House where he met with President Calvin Coolidge.

Titles of his public talks reflect the scientific spirit of the new age:

*Practicing Religion Scientifically*
*Scientific Spiritual Healing*
*Law of Attracting Abundance and Health Consciously*
*The Mind: Repository of Infinite Power*
*Harmonizing Physical, Mental, and Spiritual Methods of Healing.*

When divinely guided, Yogananda would occasionally perform a healing, but his intention as a spiritual guide was to teach others the methods by which they could draw upon the inexhaustible Life Force to heal themselves. The gift that Yogananda gives us in these pages is the key to unlock the mysteries of life.

In addition to the five million copies of his *Autobiography* in circulation, his other books are widely read. Included in these volumes are important writings about health and healing which are not easily available. Of special note are his early correspondence lessons, written by his own hand between 1923 and 1935; the articles he wrote for his organization's magazines (*East-West* and *Inner Culture*), including his "Health, Intellectual and Spiritual Recipes," and his parallel commentaries on the Bhagavad Gita and the Christian Bible.

I draw on these sources abundantly in these books. It is Yogananda's  wisdom, in his voice and his words that I strived to convey as compiler, organizer, and annotator. All of his quotations are indicated in the text with a symbol of the spiritual eye.

## Swami Kriyananda

J. Donald Walters, later to become Swami Kriyananda, was accepted by Yogananda as a monastic disciple in 1948. On the master's request, Kriyananda carefully studied his writings, especially his commentaries on the Bhagavad Gita and the Christian Bible. He took copious notes of the master's public talks and their private conversations, which he later incorporated in his books *The New Path* and *Conversations with Yogananda.* Yogananda designated him as head of the monks, authorized him as a minister and teacher, and gave him the authority to initiate people into the science of Kriya Yoga. His life work, Yogananda told him, would involve teaching and writing.

During his sixty-five years as a disciple (1948-2013), Kriyananda gave lectures around the world, including daily talks on major Indian television channels. He published approximately 140 books in which he showed how his guru's teachings can be applied to improve and elevate our daily life activities—in business and leadership, relationships, education, music and the arts, and for achieving dynamic health and well-being.[2] Excerpts from these and unpublished articles and letters are included in the text, the Endnotes, and the Appendices.

I was trained by Kriyananda from 1969 until his passing, and have been practicing and sharing these teachings for the past fifty years. In addition to those of Yogananda, I have drawn profusely from Kriyananda's writings. Each of his quotations in the text is indicated with the Joy Symbol.

## Interactive

Throughout the three volumes you will find exercises to help you practice what you are learning. Your own experience of the techniques will give you an immediate awareness of their benefits.

Each exercise is aligned with a self-improvement goal, such as identifying our positive and negative, helpful and harmful habits. Doing the exercises at the points indicated will help you bring their benefits into your daily life.

Most of the exercises can be done, at your choosing, as you move through the book. Some of them are writing exercises that you will find in the online Appendices to download and complete electronically, or print and complete on paper.

## Value Added: A Treasure Trove of More Inspiration!

Available exclusively for readers of this volume is access to an online site: www.healinglifeforces.com/volume-1/ (or scan this QR code) where you will find:

* More than twenty articles written by Paramhansa Yogananda and Swami Kriyananda, many of which are offered publicly for the very first time.

* "Secrets of Spiritual Healing:" Three inspiring talks by Swami Kriyananda.

- *Detailed instruction videos* in Life Force Energization, recorded by the author.

- *Guided Practices* of meditation and visualization, in both video and audio formats.

- *Instruction videos* and *guided practice* of pranayama exercises.

- Exercises for spinal health, and much more!

**You're also invited to join the Online Healing Community** for regular healing tips, interactive sessions, and seminars with the author. Come visit us at *www.healinglifeforces.com*.

## Stories

Especially engaging, inspiring, and instructive are the stories that I have included throughout the books from people who have used these techniques for their own healing. Some of the stories are allegorical, some are drawn from mythology, while most of them tell of real-life experiences.

## Terminology

Because this is a handbook of spiritually based practices for improving health and finding healing, the central importance of **"Spirit"** cannot be overstated. Regardless of how we personally conceptualize and relate to the Supreme Reality, it must occupy a central position if we hope to understand and make effective use of these principles and practices.

Can an atheist find value in these teachings? Yes, because they are thoroughly grounded in the way human beings are made. Even if we reject the concept of "God," we may recognize the presence of a higher source of wisdom and inspiration. Many scientists, including physicist and cosmologist Stephen Hawking, and science-fiction writers like Isaac Asimov, have denied the existence of God while endorsing and popularizing cosmological principles that touch on the spiritual.

Yogananda urged us to be "spiritual scientists." He said that while the scientist approaches the Infinite from the outside, the spiritual scientist approaches it from the inside.[3]

Psychologist and researcher David DeSteno writes about "the science behind the benefits of religion."

*"I've come to see a nuanced relationship between science and religion. I now view them as two approaches to improving people's lives that frequently complement each other...If we ignore that body of knowledge, if we refuse to take these spiritual technologies seriously as a source of ideas and inspiration to study, we slow the progress of science itself and limit its potential to benefit humanity."* [4]

Whether we think of ourselves as scientists, technologists, or believers, we can all experience the practical results of these scientific healing practices.

## Energy

Yogananda uses a variety of phrases to refer to energy in its varied forms. His term "Cosmic Energy" refers to the universal energy by which all creation is manifested, and that is the source of all life. He describes this source also as the "Cosmic Electric Force," and the "Cosmic Intelligent Energy." [5]

As cosmic energy descends through the three universes and the three bodies that the soul inhabits (see Part I), it becomes what Yogananda termed "Life Force" or "Life Energy." When it enters the physical body, it becomes the "Lifetronic Force," synonymous with the Sanskrit term *prana*.

When quoting Yogananda directly, I have always used his exact words. In my commentaries and explanations, I generally refer to the healing force in the body as Life Force; interchangeably as *prana*.

## Energization Exercises

The primary Life Force healing technique described in these books is a practice that Yogananda developed in the 1920s that he originally called Yogoda Exercises. He later referred to them as Energization Exercises. Citations from Yogananda in the 1920s and 1930s use the term Yogoda, but I refer to them as Life Force Energization Exercises, and often simply as "energization exercises." Instruction in the practice of these exercises, in easy-to-follow videos, is included in the Appendices.

**Sanskrit** words appear sparingly throughout the text, usually when they capture a concept that is difficult to render in other languages. A glossary of Sanskrit terms is included at the back of each volume.

## LEGEND OF CITATIONS

*Each citation is referenced in the Endnotes.*
*These are the symbols used within the text.*

PARAMHANSA
YOGANANDA

HOLY BIBLE
(*King James*)

SWAMI
KRIYANANDA

SWAMI SRI
YUKTESWAR

BHAGAVAD
GITA

MAHAVATAR
BABAJI

*Now it's time to start your journey of self-healing.*
*May you make steady progress as you strive to*
*become what Yogananda describes as*
**"The master of your destiny."**

# NOTES INTRODUCTION

1 Selected as "One of the 100 Best Spiritual Books of the Twentieth Century", *Autobiography of a Yogi* has been translated into more than 50 languages, sold over 4 million copies, and is regarded worldwide as a classic of religious literature. It is available in its original edition from Crystal Clarity Publishers, www.crystalclarity.com, and from Ananda Sangha Publications in India, www.anandapublications.com.

2 Books of interest on this subject by Swami Kriyananda include *The Art and Science, of Raja Yoga, Affirmations for Self-Healing; Awaken to Superconsciousness; Living Wisely, Living Well; The Hindu Way of Awakening: Its Revelation, It Symbols, Secrets of Radiant Health and Wellbeing,* and *Material Success Through Yoga Principles.*

3 "The material scientist uses the forces of the body and of nature to make the environment of man better and more comfortable, and the spiritual scientist, who uses mind-power to enlighten the soul of man, can be of even greater service." –Yogananda, "Christian Science and Hindu Philosophy," *East-West*, May–June 1926.

4 DeSteno, David, *How God Works: The Science Behind the Benefits of Religion,* David DeSteno, 2021, Simon & Schuster, Inc.

5 Yogananda, *Praecepta Lessons*, Vol. 3:72/2. "Any method of healing is effective according to its Power to arouse or stimulate the Life Force. Medicines and physical manipulations are the grosser methods, while electricity and rays are of a finer nature and effect more directly the electronic constituency of the body, and harmonize the wrong vibratory condition. The Cosmic Electric Force is the direct source of Life."

# IN THE BEGINNING

The earth was a formless void and
darkness covered the face of the deep.
Then God said, "Let there be light";
and there was light. (GENESIS 1: 2,3)

# The Origin Story

> The Ocean of Spirit has become the
> little bubble of my little soul.... I am
> indestructible consciousness, protected
> in the bosom of Spirit's immortality.[1]
> —YOGANANDA

**In the Chinese** creation story, the god Pangu created Heaven and
Earth from the formless "Chaos" that existed before the world began.
In the Tao Te Ching, it is written that before heaven and earth were
created, there was formless silence, amorphous yet complete, existing
alone and unchanging. From this Unity there came Duality, the yin
and yang of which everything was created.[2]

Each culture has a story of how the manifested cosmos was created out of nothing. The indigenous Maori of New Zealand believe
that from nothingness (Te Kore) and darkness (Te Pō) the light was
born (Te Ao); the world was created from the interaction of these two
forces symbolized by Ranginui, the Sky Father, and Papatūānuku, the
Earth Mother.

The Iroquois tribes of North America tell of a Sky woman who
fell to earth and gave birth to twins, one being good and the other
evil, thus starting the human race.

Judeo-Christian cosmology refers to a formless void, and to two
opposing forces.

> The earth was a formless void and darkness covered the face of
> the deep. Then God said, "Let there be light"; and there was
> light. And God saw that the light was good; and God separated
> the light from the darkness. (GENESIS 1:2-4)*

* This and other Bible citations are from the King James Bible.

In India, the origin story is part of *Sanatan Dharma*,* the name given to the body of Vedic teachings.

*Sanatan Dharma* means that truth which
is eternal, and which is expressed in varying ways
in all the great religions of the world.[3]

According to *Sanatan Dharma,* the universe emerged from the unmoving state of pure existence, which the great philosopher-saint Swami Adi Shankaracharya described as "Satchidananda" – existence, consciousness, and bliss. Yogananda expanded this description: *ever*-existing, *ever*-conscious, *ever-new* bliss." indicating its dynamic yet unchanging nature.

The very universe was manifested out of
Absolute Spirit: ever-conscious, ever-existing,
*ever-new* Bliss, or Satchidananda.[4]

This state is variously known as the Infinite Spirit, the Cosmic Ground of Being, or Pure Consciousness, to mention just a few. In this book we will call it Cosmic Consciousness, or more simply, Spirit.

This pure consciousness is the building block of creation, and the essence of every atomic and subatomic particle. All life forms, from the minerals to the exquisitely designed human body, are created and sustained by the one Consciousness which vibrates at various rates their unique forms.

## Duality

To manifest a physical creation from the state of pure, motionless consciousness, there had to be a force that would create a movement outwardly. In Sanatan Dharma, this cosmic power is known as *Pranava*: the primordial cosmic sound of Aum. In the Christian tradition, it is known as the Word or the Amen, and in Islam as Amin.

* "The goal of *Sanatan Dharma* is twofold: the *upliftment* of human consciousness, on the one hand, and the *expansion* of our self-identity through love, on the other, that we embrace all life and all reality as our own. Any practice that inspires people in this *direction*, even if it doesn't define the goal so specifically, belongs rightfully within the domain of *Sanatan Dharma*." –Kriyananda, *The Hindu Way of Awakening*, 92-93.

"In the beginning was the Word, and the Word was with God, and the Word was God." (JOHN 1:1)

In Indian iconography, the primal power is portrayed in a female form as **Maha Shakti**, the forceful and sometimes fearsome power behind Creation. Maha Shakti is depicted as Saraswati, the "consort" of Brahma, the Creator, and as Maha Lakshmi, the consort of Vishnu, the Sustainer, and finally as Kali (also known as Parvati or Durga), the consort of Shiva, the Renewer. In all three cases, She represents the force that creates the manifested cosmos and everything in it. At the same time, She offers a path for all created beings to return to their Creator and merge their consciousness with His.

Another ancient term for the creative force is **Maya** – the cosmic Deceiver, the force that separates Creation from its Creator, and that will continue to do so until the end of the cycle of manifested Creation known as a Day of Brahma. We will meet Maya often in these pages, for She is the cause of all our ills.

*To summarize*: Cosmic Consciousness manifested this material creation by initiating a vibratory motion that was composed of two opposing forces, one of which is drawing all creatures back to their origin in Satchidananda, while the other is pulling them toward involvement with the entwining and entrapping, infinitely varied and enthralling manifestations of outward creation. The interplay between these forces rules our lives.

SPIRIT

⚡

COSMIC VIBRATION

SOUL  EGO

A great force of Divine gravitation is constantly pulling all units of energy toward God....
The Maya-force ... constantly tries to keep the creation in existence by the law of repulsion.
The collision between the creative force of Maya and the Divine gravitation force towards God causes inharmony in the universe, called disease in human beings.... Hence, "disease" is anything that keeps us from God-realization.[5]

## Meet the twins

Akin to the yin and yang of the Tao and the twin children of the Iroquois Sky Woman, the Cosmic Spirit (the Father) and the Cosmic Energy (the Mother) gave birth to twins: the Soul (in Sanskrit, the *atman*), and the Ego (in Sanskrit, *ahankara*). These two characters are the hero and villain of the Divine Drama as they interact to influence every aspect of our life, including – as we will see in these pages – our health.

> The **SOUL** is individualized spirit, as the wave is the individualized ocean. The spirit is Immortal, Omniscient, Omnipresent, Ever-new Bliss.
> So the soul is individualized immortal, omniscient, ever-new bliss.[6]

As human biological parents pass their genes to their children, Spirit endows its children with the rarified DNA of its own blissful Satchidananda. The soul, once fully awakened, recognizes its oneness with Spirit in the state known as Self-realization.

The scriptures of East and West descend from a common Truth which an ancient scripture of India, the *Yajury Veda* defines when it declares: *"Aham Brahmasmi"* – "I am Brahman, the Infinite Spirit." Jesus affirmed, "I and my Father are One." And in the *Bhagavad Gita*, God in the form of Krishna tells us:

> This Self is not born, nor does it perish.
> Self-existent, it continues its existence forever.
> It is birthless, eternal, changeless, and ever the same.
> The Self is not slain when the body dies.
> (BHAGAVAD GITA 2:20)*

How are these esoteric utterances relevant to our lives? Because, as Paramhansa Yogananda said, "As heirs of our Universal Father, we have access to perfect health, balanced prosperity, and deep wisdom." [7]

* This and other Bhagavad Gita references are from Yogananda, Paramhansa, *The Bhagavad Gita According to Paramhansa Yogananda*, Nevada City, California: Crystal Clarity Publishers, 2008.

Perfect health is our God-given inheritance. The Soul in us knows this truth and constantly tries to convey it to us through the quiet voice of intuition. If we could open our inner intuitive faculties to listen to its silent whispers, we would hear its constant affirmation.

*Affirmation*

"I am well! I am strong! I am a flowing river of boundless power and energy!" [8]

The voice of the Soul is one of the two driving forces of our existence. Let us now meet the other. Yogananda tells us: **"The ego is the soul identified with body"**

Whereas the Soul is identified with Spirit, the Ego is identified with the physical body and the material creation in which it exists. The Ego is an expression of the Soul that is looking in a different direction. While the Soul reflects unlimited pure consciousness, the Ego's gaze is directed fully toward limited material forms. Having identified its existence with matter, the Ego desires the satisfactions that it imagines it will find in material things.

The Ego is the voice in us that demands: "Buy me! Take me home!" "I am tired!" "I am ill!" "I am worried." "I am confused." "I can't handle it." The ego's constant demands express its obsession with its own existence and its desires.

Maya works her deceptive magic through the inner voice of the ego, and the ego works its hypnosis on us and entraps us through the five senses. A determining factor in our health – of lack thereof – is which of these two voices is dominant in us at a given moment.

To surmount *maya* was the task assigned to the
human race by the millennial prophets. To rise above
the duality of creation and perceive the unity of
the Creator was conceived of as man's highest goal.
Those who cling to the cosmic illusion must accept
its essential law of polarity: flow and ebb, rise and

fall, day and night, pleasure and pain, good and evil, birth and death. This cyclic pattern assumes a certain anguishing monotony, after man has gone through a few thousand human births; he begins to cast a hopeful eye beyond the compulsions of *maya*.[9]

---

*Affirmation*

Within my soul is the joy which my Ego is seeking. I suddenly become aware of His Bliss honey-combed in the hive of silence. I will break the hive of secret silence and drink the honey of unceasing blessedness.[10]

# Parallel Universes

God encased the human soul successively
in three bodies–the idea, or causal, body;
the subtle astral body, seat of man's mental and
emotional natures; and the gross physical body.
On earth a man is equipped with his physical senses.
An astral being works with his consciousness
and feelings and a body made of lifetrons.
A causal-bodied being remains in the blissful
realm of ideas.[1]–YOGANANDA

**SPIRIT**
*beyond creation*
(*Satchidananda*)

⚡

COSMIC VIBRATION

SOUL | EGO

CAUSAL UNIVERSE AND
OUR CAUSAL BODY
*Consists of Thoughts/thoughtrons*

↓

ASTRAL UNIVERSE AND
OUR ASTRAL BODY
*Consists of energy pulsations/
lifetrons/life force*

↓

PHYSICAL UNIVERSE AND
OUR PHYSICAL BODY
*Composed of physical vibrations
of electrons and protons*

**The Soul and the Ego** travel together through three separate universes: the causal, astral, and physical. In each of these realms, they assume a characteristic form. Our causal and astral bodies travel forward with us from life to life and are present with us today.

## Satchidananda

God is ever-existing,
ever-conscious,
ever-new bliss—
or *Satchidananda*.[2]

**The causal universe.** Cosmic Vibration in its most subtle frequency first creates the causal universe. The causal world is not an imaginary paradise or Shangri La. Swami Sri Yukteswar described the causal world when, after his death, he appeared in his physical form to his beloved disciple, Paramhansa Yogananda.

The causal world is indescribably subtle....
There one perceives all created things—
solids, liquids, gases, electricity, energy,
all beings, gods, men, animals, plants, bacteria—
as forms of consciousness, just as a man can
close his eyes and realize that he exists,
even though his body is invisible to his
physical eyes and is present only as an idea....
Causal beings realize that the physical cosmos
is not primarily constructed of electrons,
nor is the astral cosmos basically composed of
lifetrons—both in reality are created from the
minutest particles of God-thought, chopped
and divided by maya, the law of relativity
which intervenes to apparently separate the
Noumenon from His phenomena.[3]

## The causal body

Our causal body consists primarily of the thoughts and ideas we entertain, which Yogananda refers to as our "mental diet."

Psychological diseases give birth to physical
diseases. In fact, most physical diseases derive their
roots in the mind through disease convictions.[4]

If the mind can produce ill health it can
also produce good health.[5]

We will take a more extended look at our mental diet in Part VI, Volume Two, where we will discover how to fashion thoughts that will help us improve our health.

## The astral universe

As Spirit descends through the three realms of consciousness, it becomes increasingly solidified. From the causal realm of fluid thoughts, it enters the astral world, where it becomes encased in light and energy, and finally it enters the material plane where it is bound in rigid physical forms.

Sri Yukteswar's describes the astral plane in vivid detail:

> The astral universe, made of various subtle vibrations of light and color, is hundreds of times larger than the material cosmos... Just as many physical suns and stars roam in space, so there are also countless astral solar and stellar systems. Their planets have astral suns and moons, more beautiful than the physical ones.[6]

The astral plane, as part of manifested creation, is subject to the principle of duality. Thus the heavenly astral realm has its own matching dark planets.

> Astral beings of different grades are assigned to suitable vibratory quarters... These beings dwell in the gloom-drenched regions of the lower astral cosmos...friction and war take place with lifetronic bombs or mental mantric vibratory rays.[7]

## Our astral body

Sri Yukteswar continues:

> The astral body is not subject to cold or heat or other natural conditions. The anatomy includes an astral brain, or the thousand-petaled lotus of light,

and six awakened centers in the *sushumna*,
or astral cerebro-spinal axis. The heart
draws cosmic energy, or *lifetrons*, as well as
light from the astral brain, and pumps it
to the astral nerves and body cells.
Astral beings can affect their bodies by
lifetronic force or by *mantric* vibrations.[8]

Yogananda adds an interesting footnote about the word "lifetron":

The "Lifetron [is] the finest ultimate unit of
intelligence and energy.... Each microcosmic
lifetron contains in miniature the essence
of all the macrocosmic creation.[9]

Sri Yukteswar used the word *prana*;
I have translated it as lifetrons. The Hindu
scriptures refer not only to the *anu*, "atom,"
and to the *paramanu*, "beyond the atom,"
finer electronic energies; but also to *prana*,
"creative lifetronic force." Atoms and electrons
are blind forces; *prana* is inherently intelligent.
The pranic lifetrons in the spermatozoa and
ova, for instance, guide the embryonic
development according to a karmic design.[10]

In Part Three we will discover how we can use life force to animate, purify, and regenerate our body and harmonize our thoughts and feelings.

### The physical universe

Spirit descends first to thought, then to energy, whereupon it assumes its most concrete form in the material plane, where its pure vibrations are encased in physical forms.

> The material universe is no mere copy of
> the astral: It represents, rather, the necessary
> end product of cosmic creation. Without it,
> the subtler manifestations of energy, light,
> and thought would dissolve back again into
> Pure Consciousness. The material universe is,
> so to speak, the anchor of creation....
> The existence of matter is necessary for
> holding it all together.[11]

Although the physical plane is the smallest of the three manifested universes, it is nevertheless vaster than the human mind can
conceive. Our Sun is only one of hundreds of billions of stars in the
Milky Way, which is just one of several hundred billion galaxies in
the universe. These planets and galaxies are not dead rocks floating
in empty space: "Countless planets there are... and endless numbers
of them are fairly teeming with life." [12]

Yet this vast physical cosmos is a pallid expression of Creation's
glory. It is the ten percent of an iceberg, about the hidden portions
of which we know nothing. We can think of the physical plane as a
Sahara where water must be carefully harvested from the dew on the
sparse vegetation – compared to the lush Hawaiian paradise of the
astral and causal worlds.

## Our physical body

Our physical world and our physical bodies are constricted by the
limitations of weight, mass, and gravity. Astral beings, in contrast, inhabit bodies of energy and light, while causal beings live in bodies of
thought. When a soul incarnates on a physical planet, it is confined
in a body that is subject to the physical laws of nature, and must pass
through unavoidable stages of birth, growth, deterioration, and death.
The difference between the gross physical body and the subtler bodies
of the astral and causal planes is that the material body perishes, whereas the subtler bodies accompany the soul to the end of its journey.

All of these bodies can suffer from disease.

There are diseases which result from breaking hygienic laws and consequent bacterial invasion. There are maladies which come from disobeying the mental laws of being, and the consequent attack of mental bacteria of fear, anger, worry, greed, temptation, and lack of self-control. There are diseases which arise from the soul's ignorance.[13]

# The Day of Brahma

"God sleeps in the rocks," proclaim the Indian
scriptures, "dreams in the plants, stirs toward
wakefulness in the animals, in mankind is awake
to his own ego-individuality[1]... and in the
superman He regains His lost omnipresence."[2]

A professor visiting Yogananda at his Mt.
Washington headquarters asked: "Is there any
end to evolution?" The Master replied, "No end.
You go on until you achieve endlessness."[3]

—KRIYANANDA/YOGANANDA

**Yogananda explains** that in the grand scheme of creation, the physical cosmos emerges from pure Consciousness and is withdrawn again into pure Consciousness, to re-emerge in yet another cycle of creation. Yogananda called these grand cycles of creation and dissolution the Day and Night of Brahma, each of which lasts for billions upon billions of years.

At the beginning of each Day of Brahma, individual souls emerge as newborns or begin their evolution for the first time.

A "Day of Brahma" is described in the Indian scriptures.
It is one complete period of cosmic manifestation,
lasting billions of years. The "Day of Brahma" is
followed by a period of equal duration, called
the "Night of Brahma." During Brahma's "night," all
creation is withdrawn from outward manifestation.

Beings that are not yet liberated rest in "seed form" for that time, in the consciousness of Spirit, awaiting the Creation's next manifestation. When the following Day of Brahma dawns, they resume whatever state they attained formerly. [4]

Yogananda tells us that every soul is endowed with individuality. Each soul is a unique expression of the infinite Spirit. The purpose of our long journey of spiritual evolution is to re-discover our unique nature in its purest form. The soul does not evolve, being perfect. It is our awareness of our original perfection that needs to awaken.

A newly created soul is unaware of its perfect nature – the scriptures describe it as sleeping. Before reaching the human level, it slowly awakens through successive stages of evolution in the form of minerals, plants, and animals.

Omnipresent Spirit becomes buried in matter and vibration, just as the oil remains hidden in the olive.... When the olive is squeezed, tiny drops of oil appear on its surface, so Spirit tries to squeeze its way out of matter as the souls of gems, beautiful minerals, plants, men, and supermen. Spirit expressed itself as beauty, magnetic and chemical power in gems; as beauty and life in plants; as beauty, power, life, motion, and consciousness in animals; as comprehension and expanding power in man; and again returns to omnipresence in the superman.[5]

The intelligent life force in every atom of creation also slowly awakens through the stages of evolution.

All matter is composed of living intelligent electrons. All minerals, plants, and animal bodies are made of intelligence and electrons.[6]

As the soul takes on various forms of minerals, plants, and animals in its spiritual evolution toward birth in a human body, it is impelled forward automatically according to the mass karma of those lower forms, as if its progress were driven not individually but according to a mass metaphysical plan.

> Evolution of the soul up to this level is a more or less automatic climb; the intelligence reaches out for continually greater awareness, but is not yet sufficiently developed to become caught in the countless bypaths that open up to a more inquiring mind. The Hindu scriptures state that it requires from five to eight million lives for the soul to evolve to the human level.[7]

At each stage, the soul undergoes a long arc of development: through untold incarnations as a mineral, to a gemstone, then from algae to medicinal and edible plants, and from a simple protozoon to a monkey.

> When that physical vehicle is destroyed, its individual vibration of energy is simply impelled outward again into matter. It is the infinite creative impulse, not material desire, that pushes it toward the experience of greater clarity in its expression of awareness.[8]

## Minerals

The soul evolves at the mineral level by taking a unique path through the thousands of known minerals. In time, it will take the form of a higher mineral such as a crystal, then it will gradually assume the forms of precious gems such as sapphires, emeralds, and diamonds.

Minerals in all forms, lower and higher, play important roles in life on earth. Minerals are essential for the life and health of the human body. As we will see in Part XII, we can use various gemstones to protect our subtle energy aura from negative influences, and even to mitigate the effects of our personal karma.

The soul at the mineral stage is not aware of its individuality. A soul encased in the form of magnesium is unaware of its beneficial qualities, nor does it harbor a compelling desire to become an emerald.

The most awe-inspiring display that I have seen of the beauty and consciousness in minerals was in the Frasassi caves in the Apennine mountains of eastern Italy. Formed over 190 million years, each of the interconnected caves expresses the grandeur and delicacy of God's creation in unique ways. You can enjoy a short virtual tour of the Frasassi caves,* and if you visit Italy, you should be sure to see them.

## Plants

Plants have a higher degree of awareness than minerals. They respond sensitively to changes in the weather and climate, and they react more sensitively to outward stimuli, including music and even our thoughts. All life on earth depends on plants, yet even though they are essential to human health and well-being, they are not conscious of their value; plants are not self-aware – a carrot doesn't aspire to become a mango!

### Jagadish Chandra Bose

In his *Autobiography*, Yogananda pays tribute to the renowned Indian scientist Dr. Jagadish Chandra Bose. When Yogananda visited Dr. Bose in his laboratory, the scientist demonstrated his "crescograph," an instrument of his invention that greatly magnified the vital movements of plants and metals.

First, he showed Yogananda the smooth movements of a growing fern. When Bose cut a leaf with a razor, the crescograph revealed spasmodic flutters in the plant's movements, indicating that the plant was experiencing pain. When he applied chloroform to the plant, its movements were slowed, but when a stimulant was administered it resumed its normal rate of growth.

* https://www.frasassi.com/?language=EN.

Bose then repeated the experiment with a piece of tin, with the same results. Bose's research was later used in experiments with plants to demonstrate that music and even human thoughts can affect the plants' health and life cycle.

The fact that every particle in the universe is conscious, and that it can be influenced by external and internal stimuli, is one reason why "self-healing" is effective.

While minerals are fixed and immobile, plants have many moving parts. Their roots spread out in search of water and nutrients, sometimes extending their networks for miles. The plants' stems and leaves move with the rhythms of sun and wind, and their tendrils enable them to climb.

Intelligence in plants expresses as a primitive instinct for survival. There are carnivorous plants such as the Venus flytrap that attract, trap, and kill insects. The Walking Palm tree, native to some South American countries, moves itself up to sixty meters in a year.[9]

Plants have been used for healing since prehistoric times.* Although Yogananda did not detail the use of herbs for specific conditions, he talked about the vibrational qualities of fruits and vegetables and their psychological effects.†

## Animals

Having reached the most refined level of evolution as a plant, the soul migrates to the physical forms of animals, starting with the simplest single-celled microorganisms and progressing to the largest land and sea mammals. Distinguishing characteristics of animals are their capacity to move, and at the higher end of the animal evolutionary arc, to express aspects of human-like intelligence. Animals are capable of emotions such as empathy, joy, and sadness, as well as inspiring qualities of loyalty and self-sacrifice. They develop ways to communicate among their own species, and in some cases with human beings. Animals that live in close contact with humans have been observed to have unique personality traits.

---

* Archaeological evidence indicates that the use of medicinal plants dates to the Paleolithic age approximately 60,000 years ago. Written evidence of herbal remedies dates back more than 5,000 years to the Sumerians, who compiled lists of plants.

† You will find these vibrational qualities on page 345.

> In the animal world...the souls of one species of
> animals are always reborn after death into a
> higher grade of animals, until they get into the
> bodies of human beings. Dogs, horses, and
> monkeys are the highest species of animals.[10]

Recent research using magnetic imagining technology on the brains of dogs reveals that they respond emotionally to attention from human friends. Some breeds are capable of developing the intelligence of a two-year-old child, and can distinguish objects, understand words, and solve problems. If you are a dog enthusiast, watch the video link in the footnote.*

> Animals evolve more rapidly if they
> mix closely with human beings. This is
> the benefit to them of being pets.
>
> Speak kindly to animals. To encourage them
> is to hasten their soul-evolution.[11]

As intelligent and charming as animals can be, they have no sense of self-identity – they follow the instincts of their species and live the life they are given, with no desire to be anything else. At this level, evolution still goes its predestined, merry way, as the soul moves automatically to its next set of experiences. But the mechanical, automatic nature of the soul's evolution forever changes once a new actor takes the stage.

> Evolution is not a blind thrust upward from below,
> a mere incident in the struggle for survival....It is
> consciousness, inherent in all things, reaching out
> to reclaim its own. All things are divine; sooner or
> later they must realize their own divinity.[12]

*https://www.youtube.com/watch?v=tGlUZWNjxPA&ab_channel=60Minutes.

### Evolution

God is buried in the black clod of the earth.
He cried and coaxed to come out, then the black
clod's heart melted and God smiled as silver,
copper, gold, diamonds, and a million gems.
He lovingly talked to the elements and said:
"You reflect my luminosity, but lack
my fragrant tenderness."

So the elements melted by His love into clusters
of living blossoms. God played ever-fragrant
in costumes of multi-colors on the stage of petals.
He talked to the blossoms and beckoned them
to sing, and the flowers became birds of
paradise and nightingales, with living plumes
that could fly, and slender throats that
could sing. God coaxed the nightingale to let
Him sing and talk intelligently through her.

The nightingale refused, so God took the
form of an angelic man and talked and sang
knowingly, but God said to man: "My beloved
image, you cannot talk about everything and
cannot sing my song of Eternity as you should."

So man only was blessed enough to willingly
heed the loving advice of God... [then] man made
himself into a superman able to talk and sing like
God, and the superman, when he could talk and sing
like God, found himself talking in every
living and non-living speck of life, and singing
the song of omnipresent bliss through
every flute of tiny openings in all space.[13]

## Human Evolution

A human being is a part of the whole
called by us universe, a part limited in time
and space. He experiences himself, his thoughts
and feeling as something separated from the rest,
a kind of optical delusion of his consciousness.
This delusion is a kind of prison for us, restricting us
to our personal desires and to affection for a few
persons nearest to us. Our task must be to free
ourselves from this prison by widening our circle of
compassion to embrace all living creatures and the
whole of nature in its beauty.[1] —ALBERT EINSTEIN

After attaining human existence and
intelligence and free choice, we must use
them to find God.[2] —YOGANANDA

**When the soul** takes a human body, the evolutionary drama changes in fundamental ways. The individual soul no longer passively plays a set of pre-assigned roles; rather, it begins to write its own story, thanks to capacity uniquely granted to human beings: **free will.**

With free will, the individual soul becomes self-determined. Minerals and plants have no ability to choose their activities, which are regulated for them by the laws of their nature. Animals have a modicum of choice which is regulated primarily by the instinct of survival. But human beings are endowed with the ability to choose their actions freely, with the caveat that they must experience the karmic consequences of their acts. Thus, free will is inextricably linked to – and is, in fact, the cause of – the law of karma.

> We are endowed with free will and act as we like,
> thus accumulating good or bad seeds of actions
> which govern all our future lives. Having free will,
> we are the architects of our own destiny.[3]

With the emergence of free will, the human ego begins to take an active role, as it quickly realizes that it has been granted the freedom to delineate its own boundaries as a separate entity.

> This consciousness of individual existence
> cannot but be separative at first, as an
> entity beholds itself as being distinct from
> every other individual expression in infinity.
> As this sense of separateness becomes
> intensified by feelings of attachment to that
> individuality, it becomes ego-consciousness....
> Awareness at the human level becomes
> *self*-awareness; it becomes clearly
> defined as ego.[4]

When the soul enters the human level, its first task is to explore its uniqueness.

While the animals are driven by their instinctive desires to eat, find shelter, and procreate, without any yearning to be more than or different than they are, the ego drives human beings to explore fulfillments beyond the basic necessities of life. At the human level, the soul's desire to experience ever-greater happiness is freed from the constraints of instinctive behavior to explore a far more intense range of individual expression.

In the previous chapters, we have seen the ego in its role as a villain. Let there be no doubt, the ego is the instrument of cosmic delusion – Maya. But everything in creation has its dual, and the ego has a positive role to play as well. Let us give the ego its due – for the essential role it plays in helping us to learn many necessary lessons, even as we give all due respect to its power to blind and bind us.

It is one of the strange paradoxes of life that, while the ego is the greatest barrier to divine attainments, one needs a well-developed ego to long for those attainments.... As man progresses through the long spiral of incarnations, however, seeking happiness and fulfillment in one material channel after another, and repeatedly being disappointed, he begins to become painfully aware of his own personal frustration and inadequacy. Consequently he begins gradually to develop a desire to find deeper, personal, solutions. The desire to seek something deeper demands this sense of *personal* need. The ego, therefore, though in the end our enemy, is for a long time our greatest friend.[5]

Now that free will and the ego have come into play at the human level, we cannot predict how many incarnations it will take the ego to reunite with Spirit.

Spiritual evolution from this time onward becomes speeded up, or delayed, or temporarily reversed, according to the caliber of the individual's own efforts.[6]

### The four stages of the ego's evolution

Despite the soul's free will, it proceeds through four clearly defined, orderly stages during its human incarnations, as it broadens its self-definitions to include ever-wider vistas of reality. These natural stages in the progress of human awareness are the ancient spiritual basis for the caste system in India. Originally, it was universally accepted that people would naturally rise through the castes as their awareness grew increasingly refined. The castes only became a rigid system of social exclusion during the materialistic age of Kali Yuga, with its preference for rigid forms and hierarchies. The spiritual scientists of ancient times described the castes as simply the road map that the ego naturally follows as it broadens its self-definitions.

Spiritual development at the human level was
delineated in ancient times as a progressive
series of what were called *varnas*, or castes.
This progression became institutionalized,
and gradually hardened into what was, in effect,
a system of socially sanctioned injustice.
Originally, however, it was based on an
enlightened understanding of human nature;
its purpose was to encourage people to
develop towards their own divine fulfillment.
The *varnas* were not so much a system as
a teaching, based on inner revelation and on
the self-understanding of great rishis....

The beauty of the caste system, rightly understood,
is that it fixes no one in a permanent mold,
but encourages all according to their own natural
line of spiritual development. Moreover, it gives to
everyone a clear directive in those attitudes which
lead to final liberation. The ultimate purpose of
reincarnation is to refine the ego's understanding
until the ego perceives itself as a thin veil, merely,
through which the infinite light of Spirit shines.
Tearing asunder that veil, the soul emerges
at last into absolute, eternal bliss.[7]

Let us now look at how the ego evolves during each of the four stages, including the lessons it learns at each stage, how it broadens its self-identity, how it refines its desires, and how it acquires the wisdom to use the gift of free will to achieve increasingly expansive and inclusive ends.

> Theoretically, it should be possible for the soul,
> once it reaches the human level, to realize its true,
> spiritual nature fairly quickly. In practice, alas,
> the process invariably is a very long one.[8]

As we examine these stages, it will be good to remember that we are not judging individuals or groups of individuals as "superior" or "inferior," however more or less aware they may be at a particular stage of their spiritual evolution. It was only during the centuries of Kali Yuga, the lowest age in the grand cycle of earth's history, that the caste system in India devolved into an instrument of privilege, exclusion, and oppression that is distant from the vision of the sages who outlined the stages as natural stepping stones in the evolution of our consciousness toward our inner freedom.

Thus, with due respect for the limitations of language, let us understand that when we refer to the "shudra caste," the reference is not to an individual or a community of people, rather it is to the mental qualities and behaviors exhibited by the evolving ego. Every individual will express a mixture of these characteristics that will change variously as it passes through the stages of individual life from infancy to old age, and even during a single day. Being aware of these stages of the ego's development will help us avoid the pitfalls of the negative characteristics of the stages, and keep moving in the direction of ever greater expansion.

## *Shudra* STAGE

- **Self-identity:** The physical body
- **Desires:** Gratification of the physical senses
- **Willpower:** Sleeping

Yogananda tells us that "animals' souls, for further advancement, were made to reincarnate in the specially created human bodies." [9] Spiritual evolution is very different, once the soul has made the transition from an animal to a human body, thanks to the uniquely human gift of free will.

> The human body was therefore not
> solely a result of evolution from beasts,
> but was produced by an act of special
> creation by God. The animal forms
> were too crude to express full divinity;
> the human being was uniquely given a
> tremendous mental capacity – the
> 'thousand-petaled lotus of the brain –
> as well as acutely awakened
> occult centers in the spine.[10]

At the shudra stage of spiritual development, the ego identifies strongly with the physical body. The shudra is driven by the ego's desire for physical pleasure and fulfillment. The shudra is passive, apathetic, and lazy, becoming active only in the pursuit of physical satisfaction. Because the shudra mind is passive, inert, and puts out as little energy as possible to barely get by, it is vulnerable to depression and addictions of all kinds – these are common at the shudra stage.

For the shudra, no reality exists outside of his own. Meaningful relationships are out of reach, since the shudra is unaware of or uninterested in other people's realities. Lacking motivation to improve himself, the shudra is dependent on others to prod him to act. He is a burden on his family and society, insisting on being supported without desiring to make the slightest efforts to improve himself.

> The *Shudra* is the type of individual whose
> purely automatic responses brand him as a
> perennial effect in life, never a cause:
> the sort who, nowadays, spends all his free
> time in front of a television set, and accepts
> only the ideas that are given to him at
> prime time, challenging nothing except as he is,
> perhaps, programmed to challenge.[11]

During much of the shudra stage, willpower and self-determination are more or less asleep:

> Human consciousness, at its lowest level of refinement, is unwilling to reason deeply. It virtually never thinks unselfishly. And it is overwhelmed by any challenge to think creatively.... [The shudra] thinks first in terms of satisfying his physical appetites; only rarely does he show himself capable of initiative, except in his readiness to accept favors from others. His lack of creativity is a travesty of his divine potential, for he needs continual supervision in everything he does.[12]

After many lifetimes, the shudra realizes that he can obtain more of what he desires by making the effort to work to earn money. Motivated by his selfish desires, he will, almost inevitably, fall into unwholesome and sometimes nefarious activities, allowing himself to be lured into crime by the promise of worldly gain, while not realizing that he is as much the preyed-upon as the predator.

**Progress:** Shudras, being extremely passive when left to their own devices, need to be outwardly compelled to evolve. The best way to help them is to offer them gainful employment, the most suitable work for shudras being physical labor.

> To ask such a person to think creatively would be unrealistic. It is enough to ask of him that he not be totally inert; that he exert himself at least physically, and thereby develop, if only on a level of body-awareness, a measure of dignity and pride in the fact of his humanity.[13]

It is also helpful to the shudra's spiritual evolution to have contact with those more spiritually evolved than himself.

> *Shudra* types of human beings...
> can evolve more quickly if they are able
> to serve in the homes of higher types of
> human beings: *Vaishyas*, perhaps especially,
> to whose outlook on life they themselves
> may be better attuned.[14]

## *Vaishya* STAGE

- **Self-identity:** Work, possessions
- **Desires:** Wealth, power
- **Willpower:** Creative activities

The *shudra* eventually wearies of relying on others to get what he wants and grows dissatisfied with the little they are reluctantly willing to give him. Seeing that others seemingly not so different from himself possess far more than he does, motivates the *shudra* to do whatever he can to get more for himself. The desire for more eventually inspires him to activate his heretofore dormant willpower, enabling him to progress to the next stage of spiritual evolution, the *Vaishya*.

The *vaishya* stage is where the will to work is born, accompanied by the development of intelligence, creativity, desire for a family, enthusiasm for entering the stream of supply and demand, the excitement of testing one's will against the will of others, and the satisfaction of self-expression – all with an underlying motivation of personal gain.

The *vaishya* esteems himself according to the amount of money he is able to earn and the possessions he can accumulate. There is seemingly no end to his desires – to have a regular paycheck with good benefits; to have his own business; to become a millionaire, a multimillionaire, a billionaire; to own a house, a car, a mansion, more cars, a boat, a yacht, an airplane. The *vaishya* desires wealth, prestige, recognition, and power. His self-identity is circumscribed by what he has and what he does – not by who he is.

> Typically, the *Vaisya*-type nowadays
> is the sort of person who devotes all
> his energy to "making a fast buck."
> He is clever. He possesses initiative and
> an abundance of energy and ingenuity.
> All this energy and ingenuity, however, is
> devoted to "looking after number one."[15]

At the *vaishya* stage, the ego is active in dual roles: expansive and contractive. The *vaishya*'s ego-driven desires stimulate his willpower, and the *vaishya*'s ego motivates him to expand his awareness by broadening his horizons, his activities, and his relationships to satisfy his desires. Lacking this motivation, spiritual evolution would not be possible. On the other hand, the ego ensures that the *vaishya* will be emotionally attached to the things he possesses, since they define his identity, his self-esteem, and his sense of security.

While the initial stages of *vaishya* evolution are characterized by personal greed and corruption, the *vaishya* ego begins to take pride in its social role. The survival of all social units, from the nuclear family to the nation, depends on the *vaishya*'s enterprise.

**Progress:** As the *vaishya* evolves, his self-identity begins to expand beyond his own work and family to include the realities and welfare of others. Initially there will be ulterior motives – by providing better working conditions for his employees, his company's productivity and profits will increase. By joining service organizations and sponsoring local activities, his name and company brand will become more prominent. With continued evolution, more refined desires are born, such as sharing his wealth and knowledge.

> The duty of a Vaishya is to include the benefit of
> others in his own activities. Thus, he will become
> more sensitive to the needs of others, and will
> develop, in time, the nature of a Kshatriya.[16]

D id Steve Wozniak (and others) invent the first personal computer in 1976? Wrong! Was it John Blankenbaker, who introduced the Kenbak-1 Digital Computer in 1971? Wrong again! It was Adriano Olivetti, who presented the first desktop personal computer at the New York World Fair in 1965.

But we aren't here to talk about computers, or Olivetti's innovative, stylish, award-winning typewriters. Our purpose is to shine a light on one of the earliest humanists in the business world, an innovator who pioneered the principles of Human Resources and the importance of individual personal development in building a successful business.

Olivetti – founded by engineer Camillo Olivetti in 1908 – was the first nationally prominent Italian factory to produce typewriters. Olivetti was a mechanical and design genius, but it was his son Adriano who was a social visionary.[17] Adriano developed a business philosophy and a culture that were centered on the well-being of the workers. He built a residential complex next to the factory that offered small cottages of modern design for the workers, each with space for a vegetable garden. He created a factory cafeteria that served 10,000 meals a day, as well as a nursery, a kindergarten, and a summer camp for the workers' children.

Adriano Olivetti created a training center to further the workers' career advancement, a library, an art and cultural center where famous artists and scientists offered programs, a medical care facility with doctors and social workers, and an industrial psychology center for the study of work-related mental and emotional problems. His workers were the first in Italy to enjoy a five-day work week, nine-month maternity leave, and higher salaries than, for example, automobile factory workers.

Adriano Olivetti said: "The factory cannot look only at the profit index. It must distribute wealth, culture, services, democracy. I think factory for man, not man for factory."

✳   ✳   ✳

The Olivetti and other enlightened entrepreneurs are examples of highly evolved vaishyas who embody the spirit of generosity.

> True happiness is found not in possessions, but in sharing what one has with others. Thus is one's self-identity expanded, as he learns to live in, and enjoy, a greater reality. "What I give to others I give not away, for in my larger reality it remains ever mine. I am happy in the happiness of all![18]

### *Kshatriya* STAGE

* **Self-identity:** With the needs of others
* **Soul Desires:** To help others by sharing resources and knowledge
* **Willpower:** Self-discipline

Until this point in the ego's evolution, it has done useful work by helping the soul to develop a strong sense of its individual identity. Yet during its long vaishya sojourn, the soul has come to experience that more money does not bring more happiness; rather, the opposite is more often true. It begins to lose its fascination with material achievements and is ready to relinquish egotistical desires. The ego, however, tenaciously holds on to its hard-won identity and material security. The battle now commences in earnest, and the body-bound ego becomes the soul's enemy.

> At this stage of development, a person finds himself ready to stop pampering his ego, and reaches out instinctively in sympathy to help others. At this stage, then, he needs progressively to renounce self-seeking, and is urged to seek his fulfillment in helping others, or in service to some high ideal.[19]

The *kshatriya* identifies himself as part of a greater reality and no longer desires to work for personal gain, but increasingly, only to help others. No longer concerned first with his own comfort and security, he employs his hard-won strengths and resources for the benefit of the wider community, and to help the disadvantaged, the environment, and other worthy causes.

The *kshatriya* physician, for example, may decide to serve with the Red Cross or with Doctors without Borders. The *kshatriya* entrepreneur may be motivated to donate goods and services to humanitarian causes, or to medical research, or to organizations dedicated to protecting the environment. The *kshatriya* parent may choose to care for foster children or support an orphanage for abandoned children, or an agency that places parentless children in loving homes. The *kshatriya* identifies the human race as his family, and his country as the world. He is powerfully motivated to use his creativity, intelligence, and experience to help others reach their goals.

> **People at this stage of maturity develop executive qualities....In contrast to the vaishya's typical question, "What's in it for me?" the kshatriya's natural question is, "What's in it for everyone?"[20]**

Just as our spiritual evolution is reflected on the outward stage of our social interactions, a parallel, interior drama is taking place. *Kshatriyas* are motivated to apply their willpower to develop self-discipline and raise their consciousness, as a means of increasing their ability to contribute to the overall evolution of human consciousness.

> **Those who are striving to use the powers of self-control to conquer the sense proclivities and temptations are Kshatriyas or soldiers....**
> **The spiritual warrior[s] who [are] ever ready to protect the kingdom of peace and self-control from the invasion of inimical temptations which pour in through the secret pathways of the senses.[21]**

The *kshatriya* knows that the ego is a formidable foe with innumerable weapons at its disposal. The spiritual warrior uses his willpower (and, as Yogananda called it, his "Won't power") to train his troops – body mind, feelings, and senses – to say "Yes!" to influences that will increase his joy in self-expansion, and No!" to sensory indulgences that would rob his happiness by shrinking his awareness upon himself.

Even more dangerous for the *kshatriya* is the temptation to take credit for his generous actions. The ego will rush to attack the *kshatriya*'s authentic humility with flattering words spoken by television interviewers lavishing praise on the *kshatriya* for rescuing a family from a burning house; with an award as outstanding humanitarian of the year; with a nomination for a Nobel prize. Whether the *kshatriya* accepts these honors is not spiritually relevant; what matters is whether he will let the ego tempt him to accept credit for his accomplishments, or if he will inwardly offer the credit to the Power that is, in fact, their true and sole source.

If you are ready to engage the ego in battle as a spiritual *kshatriya* warrior, the chapters that follow will offer suggestions for strengthening your inner soldiers.

**Progress:** The *kshatriya* warrior's desire to serve others will, in time, mature into a deeper understanding of the kind of help that people need.

> Even the *Kshatriya* state, however, noble though it is, falls short of the perfection that is humanity's highest potential. It is a transition, only, from thing-centeredness to bliss-centeredness. The *Kshatriya*-type does what he can for the welfare of others, and for his own inner growth. Sooner or later, however, he reaches a point in his development where he discovers...that to serve people outwardly is not so important for them, nor so satisfying for himself, as to help them to find inner joy, through an expansion of awareness. He becomes, then, no longer the warrior or dedicated public servant, but the spiritual teacher: the *Brahmin*. [22]

## THE *Brahmin* STAGE

- **Self-identity:** A channel of divine will
- **Soul desire:** To serve God
- **Willpower:** Attunement to God's will

Our free will that slept in the *shudra* stage, awakened in the *vaishya* and *kshatriya* stages to advance our spiritual evolution. Now, in the Brahmin stage, the soul dedicates its free will to the task of attuning itself to the divine will, and to identifying increasingly with the Self behind the tiny ego-self. The following affirmation by Yogananda expresses the work that the soul takes up in the final stage.

*Affirmation*

I will tune my free will with the infinite will of God and my only desire shall be to do the will of Him who sent me. [23]

To attune ourselves to our highest nature requires that we cultivate a deepening contact with the inner joy of the soul.

> Those who conquer all restlessness
> by concentration and establish the
> kingdom of ever-new bliss in
> the soul are called Brahmins
> (knowers of Brahma or Spirit.) [24]

The brahmin will dedicate many lifetimes to spiritual practices, and to experiencing a variety of religious disciplines, alone or in the company of spiritually evolved teachers and seekers.

In the *Bhagavad Gita,* Krishna describes the characteristics of a brahmin.

> The inherent duties of a Brahmin (the
> highest caste) are mind control (concentration),
> sense control (by the practice of pranayama),
> self-restraint, purity, forgiveness, integrity, wisdom,
> meditation to attain Self-realization, and
> faith in a higher truth. (BHAGAVAD GITA, 18:42)

At the brahmin stage, the ego is more active than ever, doing all in its power to block the soul's efforts to find its final release. The ego's ways are devilishly devious, wily, and crafty in the extreme.

## ※ MISSION OF THE APPRENTICE DEVIL ※

The apprentice devil was relatively new to the infernal regions; thus he was surprised to be summoned by the Boss himself. "I have a job for you, young devil – something to get you started. It has come to my attention that Mr. Patel of London has been rising at four in the morning to sit for three hours in meditation before he sets off to work. This will never do! See what you can do to hinder him."

The apprentice, after congratulating himself for receiving such an easy first assignment from the Devil himself, immediately set out for London. Upon entering Mr. Patel's bedroom at dawn, he noticed a large alarm clock on a nightstand next to the bed. When the alarm began to ring loudly, Patel groped a hand from under the covers to turn it off, whereupon he rolled out of bed to exercise before meditating.

A plan rose in the little apprentice's mind. The next morning, he moved the clock out of Patel's reach and sat on the alarm bell to prevent it from ringing. And so Mr. Patel didn't awaken until ten minutes before seven, when he jumped up with a start, threw off the covers, and rushed to dress and scurry off to work.

The apprentice, his assignment completed, returned to headquarters feeling quite proud of his ploy. Entering the Boss's office, he reported his experience, "Mission accomplished!" with a satisfied smile.

"Not in the least, you little fool!" the Devil thundered. "You should have followed him to work. He was so upset about missing his meditation that he spent the rest of day thinking of God – and now we've lost him forever!"

The ego saves its greatest efforts to interfere with the brahmin's meditations, resistance to meditation being the spiritual aspirant's greatest enemy and the most powerful weapon in the ego's quiver. It is a struggle with the ego that we can expect to fight over many lives. When the ego brandishes its devilish weapons, we must be prepared to respond with our full energy and conviction.

> **The soul loves to meditate, for in contact with the Spirit lies its greatest joy. If, then, you experience mental resistance during meditation, remember that reluctance to meditate comes from the ego; it doesn't belong to the soul.[25]**

When we sit to meditate, the ego tempts the soul with restlessness. Newcomers to the Brahmin stage find the ego unrelenting in its efforts to distract them.

> **Many meditators hope to progress spiritually by going through the prescribed motions, even if their minds are engaged elsewhere. Form, unfortunately for dilettantes, is no substitute for content.[26]**

Another way the ego tempts the brahmin with restlessness is by suggesting that he can earn equal merit by busying himself with spiritual service instead of seeking refuge in the stillness of God-contact within. Selfless service remains important at the brahmin stage, and as our efforts continue, we will eventually achieve a harmonious balance between meditation and service.

"When you work for God, not self,"
Master told us one day, "that is just as good as
meditation. Then work helps your meditation,
and meditation helps your work. You need
the balance. With only meditation you
become lazy, and the senses become strong.
With only work, the mind becomes restless,
and you forget God."[27]

Outward work must be balanced on ever deeper
levels of consciousness by the stillness of inner
communion. The more deeply one meditates,
the less necessary it becomes for him to
engage in outward activities at all.[28]

The brahmin serves others primarily by sharing with them the wisdom he has acquired through his spiritual efforts. The ego loves to insinuate itself here as well, by tempting the brahmin to think proudly of others as his students or disciples. Whenever people referred to themselves or others as Yogananda's disciples, he would firmly respond: "I never speak of people as my disciples. God is the Guru: They are *His* disciples." [29]

The spiritual efforts of the Brahmin will continue for many lives. As his ego becomes refined and purified, he understands increasingly that he is, in fact, merely serving as a channel for God's grace, and that he is only able to help others on their path to the extent that God consents to help them through him.

Master once told me that one must free
at least six others before one can be
completely freed of all karmic bondage.[30]

The poet Kahlil Gibran thus described the brahmin teacher, the one who helps others to attune themselves to the Truth of their own being.

*The teacher who walks in the shadow of the temple,*
*    among his followers,*
*gives not of his wisdom*
*but rather of his faith and his lovingness.*
*If he is indeed wise*
*he does not bid you enter the house of his wisdom,*
*but rather leads you to the threshold of your own mind.* [31]

In India, there are spiritual teachers who never speak. They are known as *munis*, "silent ones." Yet aspirants are magnetically drawn to sit in their silent, yet spiritually radiant company – and if they are receptive, they go away spiritually nurtured and blessed.

He comes to recognize that teaching others
is in itself not enough, and that the best way
to uplift others is to remain always immersed in
inner bliss. Thus, his very teaching becomes,
as he develops progressively, primarily a
sharing of consciousness, more so even than
a sharing of ideas.[32]

As the soul approaches the end of the brahmin stage, meditation may become his sole form of service.

Indeed, there comes a time on the
spiritual path when the balance shifts from
outward to inward activity. The practice of
meditative techniques, important for calming
and concentrating the mind, become then
one's spiritual work. This, too, is activity, and
should be performed as outward service is, in a
spirit of loving offering to God.[33]

In the deepest states of meditation, the ego may choose to relinquish its identity with matter and assume its true identity inseparably one with the Spirit. However, even God Himself cannot force the ego to make this choice.

> God could...free us at once from the
> thralldom of earthly miseries, imperfections,
> broken hearts, and death by using His
> Almighty material force, but He would
> not do that because that would be
> taking away our independence.[34]

> God is powerless to help man unless he will
> voluntarily accept God's ever-willing help.
> God can help only those who help themselves.
> After having once given unlimited personal
> freedom to man, God cannot become an
> autocrat and prevent His independent creation
> from doing evil, for God would contradict
> Himself should He take away the freedom
> of man after having once given it to him.[35]

**Progress:** Human evolution doesn't end with the culmination of the Brahmin stage. It only ends when the ego and the supreme Spirit are finally and permanently reunited, and the former human becomes a spiritual superman, having retraced the steps of his creation to his eternal home in Cosmic Consciousness.

> The consciousness in the superman is really
> Cosmic Consciousness. He is not a victim of
> imaginary perceptions, fanciful inspirations,
> or wisdom hallucinations, but he is actually
> conscious of the unmanifested Spirit and
> also of the entire Cosmos with all its details.

A person who has become one with
omnipresent and omniscient God is aware
of the coursing of a planet trillions of
miles distant and of the flight of
a nearby sparrow at the same time.
A superman does not behold Spirit from
the body, but becomes one with Spirit
and beholds his body as well as the
body of others, and all manifestation
as existing within himself.[36]

# PART I | CHAPTER FIVE

## Ego Transformation

The spiritual path may be defined as
a process of transcending ego-consciousness
in the realization of our true Self: the soul. [1]

Ego-transcendence is the very essence of spiritual
progress.... The real delusion to be overcome is
the bondage of ego-identity. The true goal of
renunciation is to help one to rid himself of
that self-limiting identity. [2] –KRIYANANDA

**India's great epic,** the *Mahabharata,* is set against the backdrop of a pending civil war. Although the story is based on historical events, it is an allegory – a subtle tale of the inner battle that rages within each of us, between the soldiers of the Soul and the armies of the Ego.

The general of the dark forces is the veteran warrior Bhishma, who, according to Paramhansa Yogananda's spiritual interpretation, symbolizes the ego. Bhishma's story explains why the ego is so difficult to conquer. Bhishma had performed a heroic sacrifice, whereupon the gods granted him a very unusual boon: He could not be killed unless he himself decided to die. Thus Bhishma was a formidable foe, and all but invincible.

Indeed, the ego is the last delusion to disappear.
It can only be transcended by self-offering into
the Infinite. With the final surrender of the last
shreds of ego-consciousness comes an oceanic bliss,
spreading out to embrace the universe. [3]

The ego will accompany us to the end of the battle. To win the ego over to the soul's side, we must be ready for its thrusts and prepared to counter them.

While we cannot kill the ego, we can *educate* it. Through the four stages of human evolution, the soul continually tries to show the ego, through lessons and experiences appropriate to the ego's understanding at each stage, how to expand its self-identity to include realities beyond itself, and embrace those understandings, attitudes, and actions that will bring it true, lasting happiness and inner freedom – for example, the joy of selfless service and unconditional love. In the Mahabharata, the ego in the form of Bhishma resists the soul's advances mightily, while surrounding himself with a cohort of soldiers whose role is to protect him.[4]

In this chapter, we will look at the strategies the ego adopts to protect and promote itself, and how we can deploy our soul-soldiers to disarm the ego's army. We can think of the ego's ploys as harmful weeds in the garden of our soul. If we can pull the ego-weeds the moment we see them rising in the soil of our consciousness, they will lose their power to threaten the soul's beautiful trees and flowers.

## The ego's ploys

Swami Kriyananda offered the following insights and suggestions for transcending the ego.* (*I have added personal observations in italics.*)

### Craves Flattery.
*The ego thrives on praise. When compliments come our way, we need to learn to respond with humility.*

When people praise you for any reason, don't accept their praise in your heart....Thank them sincerely, instead, but then give the credit to God. Do so in words if you like, but much more importantly, give Him the credit in your heart. Tell yourself, "God is the Doer."

People may remind you, if you say that to them, "Yes, but it takes an *instrument* of God's will to do what you've done so skillfully." True enough, but what does that really mean? Do you want to pride yourself on being a good screwdriver, or

---

* Unless otherwise noted, these citations are from Kriyananda, *A New Age Renunciate Order*, and Kriyananda, *Sadhu, Beware!*

hammer?! Move on to some other subject, and be particularly careful, in your *heart,* not to accept the compliment.

If someone calls you a genius, say, "Thank you. Though I do my best, I am well aware that any good I do comes not from me, but from God. The beauty of the clouds at sunset is due only to the sun's light upon them."

Don't toy with flattery by entertaining it even lightly in your mind.... If you allow yourself to be affected, even minutely, by flattery, to that extent you will be affixing one more iron bar in the prison of your ego. And to the extent that you allow yourself to accept in your ego even the slightest energy, to that exact extent you will create more bondage for yourself. Instead, therefore, seek in every way possible to expand your energy and consciousness *away from* yourself. In other words, don't expand your self-awareness like a balloon: *Release* it from all self-*definition.*

### Basks in self-importance.

*We have seen that the ego **identifies** with matter and **desires** material satisfactions. We can also recognize the ego by another ploy: it **takes credit** for everything. The Sanskrit word for ego is ahankara, meaning "I act," – signifying "I am the Doer." Here are some suggestions for ways we can steal the ego's thunder:*

Never draw people's attention to yourself. Try to keep it centered in the topic under discussion.

When someone else gets the credit for something you've done, don't look for a way of letting people know where the credit really belongs....You will find much greater freedom in your heart if you mentally give all the credit to God.

Don't let your mind play with the thought of where and how you yourself fit into any picture…Reject sternly any thought of self-importance, self-praise, self-justification, and blame.

When people fail to credit you for something you did and did well, say nothing. In your heart, however, give all the credit to God.

When someone has a good idea that you've had already, it will help you in the practice of humility to tell yourself, "It's the *idea* that counts, not the person who had it." Reply simply, therefore, "That's a good idea. Let's give it a try."

If you see others eager to air their views, be generous to them: let them speak. Add thoughts of your own only if you see that those others might be interested in what you have to say.

In conversation, don't wait impatiently for your "chance to speak your piece." Listen respectfully, and, if possible, listen with interest. Try to make it a conversation, not a competition of monologues.

When speaking in public, think more in terms of what you share with others than of their impression of you.

Be humble, but not self-abasing; instead, see God as the true Doer of everything.

### Wants always to be right.
*The ego abhors criticism and tries to justify itself.*

When someone criticizes you, analyze yourself to see whether there may not be something in

you that needs correction. Don't answer hotly or challenging-
ly, "Oh? And what about you?!"—proceeding then to list his
shortcomings, which balance your own.

Don't be defensive, and never try to justify yourself....Simply
say, "Thank you. Maybe you are right. I will give the matter
my careful consideration." In this way you will not involve
yourself in any personal or emotional complications.

Learn to accept slights and insults calmly and impersonally....
When others heap you with insults...give back respect. Give
back even reverence if you can universalize your feelings to
that extent. After all, what is it that really matters? Truth! Is
the insult justified? Then be inwardly grateful that someone
did you the kindness of uttering it. Is it unjustified? Then wish
to see the person or persons who insulted you released from
that negative thought, which can only pull his or their consciousness downward.

If someone scolds you for something you didn't do, you may
see some good reason for letting him know that you're not
guilty. If it doesn't really matter who did it, however, you will
gain more, spiritually, if you say nothing.

If someone challenges your point of view, never let the discussion sink to a level of personal animosity.

Try to view with sympathy points of view that differ from
your own.

Don't try constantly to explain or define for others' gratification who and what you are. Let your actions, and your inner
reality, speak for you. Never try, without some good and defi-
nite reason, to justify your actions, ideas, or accomplishments.
Whatever you've done, give it mentally to God.

*On a personal note, I have found that refusing to defend or justify myself has been an important, albeit difficult, weapon for fighting the ego. When my actions or motives are judged, I try to recognize whatever truth there may be in the criticism, and be thankful for the opportunity to improve. I try, as well, neither to defend or justify myself before God, but rather to offer everything back to Him, with gratitude.*

### Wants to win.
*The ego sees every situation and relationship as a competition, with winners and losers.*

Never place yourself mentally in competition with others.

In competition against others—in sports, for instance—do your best to win, but tell yourself you are really competing against yourself, to improve your own skill. Whether you win or lose, be gracious.

### Denigrates others and their accomplishments.
*The ego wants to be the smartest, tallest person in the room, and particularly when it is not, it disparages others to make itself appear taller in others' eyes.*

Never belittle anyone. View all with respect. Release from your heart any desire you may feel to outshine others, or even to shine at all in whatever you do. Do the best you can, always, but give the fruits of your efforts to God.

Show respect for all, but don't insist that they respect you properly.

Show others appreciation not only because they will then be more likely to appreciate you, but also, and more importantly, because thereby you will expand your own sense of identity.

Give respect, even reverence (to everyone) as children of God. Never forget that all human beings are equal, in Him.

Laugh with others, but never at them.

*Another of the ego's ploys is to belittle our own worth, often while wanting to be praised for our humility.*

Humility is *not* self-abasement. To lower oneself is an indication, not of ego-transcendence, but of preoccupation with the little self. One who bows to the ground and throws dust on his head concentrates on dust and on his own head. Implicit in this attitude is a distorted kind of self-involvement: ego-centeredness. Self-involvement is, in fact, simply the negative aspect of *egotism*, or arrogance.

### Lacks generosity.
*The ego needs to feel secure in the fortress of its possessions.*

Be more aware of what you give out to others than of what you receive from them.

When people seek their self-expansion by accumulation, they succeed only in reinforcing the walls confining them.[5]

Every time you do a selfish deed you affirm, whether deliberately or not, the thought, "I am this ego, this body." The way out of that thought is to perform generous deeds, which affirm: "I am *more* than this ego and body! My welfare embraces that of others. My true Self is the Self of all!"[6]

True happiness is found not in possessions, but in sharing what one has with others. Thus is one's self-identity expanded, as he learns to live in, and enjoy, a greater reality. People who gladly share with others feel themselves bathed by a constant, inner stream of happiness. Sharing is the doorway through which the soul escapes the prison of self-preoccupation. [7]

### Wants to control situations and the behavior of others.
*Control is the ego's principal conceit. When you find it bossing you about, remember the Beatles' song: "Let It Be."*

A good rule in life is to tell yourself simply, 'What comes of itself, let it come.' [8]

Accept with unruffled mind whatever comes. I often say, 'What comes of itself, let it come.' This is just as true for the bad things in life as for the good. Only calmness will give you a sense of correct proportion. [9]

Take everything as it comes, and tell yourself that it is all coming from God. What comes of itself, let it come. Even when you feel you have to try to correct a wrong, try first to feel His inner guidance. Then when you act, do so on *His* behalf, and never with ego-inspired indignation. [10]

### The soul's soldiers

In the *Bhagavad Gita*, which is a part of the *Mahabharata*, the army of Light is said to possess fewer soldiers than the army of Ignorance. The Gita is telling us that the ego's ploys are insidious, obscure, and innumerable, while the soul's qualities are radiant, transparent, direct, and fewer in number. Patanjali, in his *Yoga Sutras*, delineates the souls' weapons as an eightfold path to enlightenment, *ashtanga yoga*. These are the eight spiritual weapons we can make use of in our struggles to disarm the ego.

### The Yamas

- *Ahimsa.* Holding no ill will for anyone.
- *Satya.* Being honest, and seeing the truth in all situations.
- *Asteya.* Not desiring that which we have not earned, and which therefore is not our own.
- *Brahmacharya.* Controlling and preserving vital energy.
- *Aparigraha.* Non-attachment to possessions, people, and thoughts.

### The Niyamas

- *Saucha.* Purity in thought, word, and deed.
- *Santosha.* Contentment: "What comes of itself, let it come."
- *Tapasya.* Self-restraint and commitment to that which is essential.
- *Swadhyaya.* Introspection.
- *Iswara pranidhana.* Devotion to God, and openness to His guidance.

**Asana.** Centeredness in activity, and stillness in meditation.

**Pranayama.** Controlling the movements of vital energy by the proper application of willpower.

**Pratyahara.** Interiorizing the mind.

**Dharana.** Concentrating the mind and calming the thoughts and emotions.

**Dhyana.** Superconscious meditation.

**Samadhi.** Merging the soul and ego in Spirit.

---

*Affirmation*

I will wake up my soul soldiers of light, honesty, self-control, and desire for good things, and wage a furious battle.[11]

## Renunciation

As long as we are passively resigned to give the ego control of our lives, our spiritual evolution will proceed at a millennial pace. In the shudra state the use of willpower is negligible, our actions being motivated by instinctual needs rather than choice.

In the vaishya stage, our free will gets dispersed in endless outward, egoic pursuits. It is only in the kshatriya state that willpower comes to the fore, as the kshatriya's primary weapon to engage the ego in mortal combat and vigorously reject its false promises.

To truly transcend the ego, we need to willfully renounce its lures and embrace the ways of the soul.

> The only valid definition of renunciation
> is the renunciation of ego-identification.
> The renunciate must offer his entire being into
> the Infinite Self. Only when complete freedom
> has been achieved from ego-limitation
> can God be realized. At that point, indeed,
> there is nothing left to be renounced! [12]

In 2009, Swami Kriyananda founded a renunciate order for the dawning age of Energy.[13] The Nayaswami Order is non-sectarian and open to all, whether single or married, and whether embracing any or no religious or spiritual affiliations, who are committed to undertake the inner work of transcending the ego and achieving Self-realization. Swami Kriyananda taught that true renunciation is more than the aspiration to overcome our desires and attachments – the goal of renunciation is to renounce the ego itself. Thus, a renunciate is one who has achieved noteworthy progress in acquiring the following virtues:

**1.** They have no, or very few, attachments or desires.

**2.** They are without anger. (Anger appears in the heart when one's desires are thwarted.)

**3.** They accept without prejudice whatever life gives them, and live by the principle, "What comes of itself, let it come."

**4.** They never seek to justify or defend themselves, but accept all judgment by others dispassionately, as experiences given them by God for their higher good.

**5.** They keep in their hearts primarily the company of God.

**6.** They are indifferent to others' opinions of them.

**7.** They work without personal motive, to please God alone.

**8.** They are impersonal in the sense of wanting nothing for themselves, but never in the sense of being indifferent to the needs of others.

**9.** They see all beings as striving toward the attainment of Satchidananda: ever-existing, ever-conscious, ever-new Bliss, no matter how presently misguided the efforts of some people may be. Thus, they feel kinship with everyone, and with all life.

**10.** They accept nothing as their own, but only as being "on loan" to them, for the benefit of others.

**11.** They view pleasure and pain equally, as opposite (or dual) expressions of eternal, divine bliss.

**12.** They have meditated daily for years.

**13.** Because they are always happy in themselves, they are impervious to insults, outer suffering, failure, defeat, or disaster. They strive to live the ideal that Paramhansa Yogananda voiced when he said, "You should be able to stand unshaken amidst the crash of breaking worlds!"

**14.** They strive to love God unceasingly, and ever more deeply, in a spirit of utter openness to be guided by His will.

While the perfect attainment of these virtues may exceed our present reach, even a modest degree of "noteworthy progress toward their attainment" will strengthen our soul's army against the ego's attempts to conquer our inner kingdom.

## *Where to start?*

Be on high alert for the insidious ways the ego tries to insert itself in your life. The ego's army is composed of guerilla fighters – shadowy figures that hide in a forest of "good" attitudes – for example: "Showing off my accomplishments so others will aspire to them." The ego's secret warriors delight in ambushing the soldiers of the soul when least expected. By bringing the guerilla fighters out into the open through honest self-observation (*swadhyaya*) we will give the soldiers of light the advantage.

Be on particularly sharp lookout for the ego's attempts to influence your thoughts – for example, by tempting you to criticize others, or denigrate your own worth. When the alarm bells sound, immediately call on the soldiers of light mentioned throughout this chapter. For example, *Ahimsa* – non-injury – may be the best soldier to counter a critical or judgmental attitude.

The soldiers of the Light eagerly await the opportunity to protect us from the ego's deceptive wiles. When you identify one of your ego-nemeses, call up a soul-soldier to fight alongside you on the front lines – and let the battle begin!

### ❋ THE SABOTEUR UNMASKED ❋

Since my undergraduate days in college, I was plagued by an overly self-critical attitude. After giving a presentation, I would criticize my efforts severely. Had I remembered everything? Was it up to my high standards? Regardless of any positive feedback, I was filled with anxieties and doubts that I carried from talk to talk, year after year.

Recently, I had an "Aha!" moment. In a sudden flash of insight, I saw that it wasn't *I* who was doing the criticizing, it was my ego at work! Suddenly I was able to detach myself and understand that the self-doubts and self-criticisms were the ego's way of keeping me self-involved. Literally from the moment I recognized this, my worries vanished and I was able to relax and enjoy my speaking assignments.

When I presented the oral part of my doctoral thesis at Oxford, I felt not a trace of the former worries. Now that I am aware of how the ego tries to infiltrate my mind, I will not let it sabotage me in this way again. *–Julia*, *Spain*

## Winning the war

We can enjoy many successes in our war against the ego's efforts to erode our happiness, if we will concentrate on winning one battle at a time. The war will be never-ending until we have won our final  freedom in egoless oneness with God. Bhishma, who represents the ego in the *Mahabharata*, cannot be killed unless he decides to die. Similarly, we cannot kill the ego until it decides to relinquish its separate identity.

How can we persuade the ego to "die"? Once the ego gets a taste of true inner joy, the sensory satisfactions it has desired will pale by comparison.

> **One who has been accustomed to**
> **drinking nectar, and then eats stale cheese,**
> **soon grows dissatisfied with it and throws**
> **the cheese away, crying for nectar again.[14]**

Meditation, practiced regularly and deeply, gives us an experience of the soul's joy. When the soul and the ego join forces in the struggle to fulfill their mutual desire for true joy, they will, in time, succeed in conquering ignorance and win the war. Meditation is the supremely effective method for reconciling the ego and the soul. This is why Yogananda called it "the great shortcut, or airplane route" [15] to divine joy, This airplane awaits us in Part II.

# Signs of Wellness and Symptoms of Disease

> Human life can be likened unto a house fitted with three windows of the body, mind, and soul... Most people have one or more of their windows of life shut and jammed for years. That is why they suffer from chronic maladies. Their rescue lies in the knowledge of the law by which they may open their windows themselves and bask once more in the all-healing Conscious Cosmic Rays.[1]
>
> Healing in general can be classified as Physical Healing, Psychological Healing of worries, fears, nervousness, etc., and Spiritual Healing of soul-ignorance.[2] —YOGANANDA

SPIRIT
MIND
BODY

*This is how we usually think of ourselves.*
Yet this perspective is fundamentally wrong!

*This image more accurately reflects our true nature*

BODY
MIND
SPIRIT

**Physical ailments** have their roots in mental and emotional imbalances that, in turn, spring from the primary spiritual disease, which as we will shortly see is the cause of all our suffering: Ignorance.

Changing the pyramid analogy into an iceberg gives us a different perspective. The evidence of disease most usually recognized and treated is the physical symptoms. Yet these are the tip of the iceberg, because the physical body represents perhaps just ten percent of our nature, while the great mass lies below. To eradicate the symptoms permanently, we need to make adjustments at the level of the root causes.

Disease results when life force is unable to flow freely throughout the body – owing to the tug-of-war between Spirit (the Soul) and Maya (the Ego). Paramhansa Yogananda's guru, Sri Yukteswar, said that all human beings suffer from a single common illness which he called "**spiritual amnesia**." In short, we have forgotten who and what we are.

**MAN *is* A SOUL, AND *has* A BODY.**
When he properly places his sense of identity,
he leaves behind all compulsive patterns.
So long as he remains confused in his
ordinary state of spiritual amnesia,
he will know the subtle fetters
of environmental law.[3]

### The source of soul disease is forgetfulness

The soul knows the boundless bliss and freedom of Spirit. In his *Yoga Sutras*, Patanjali * refers to spiritual awakening as "*smriti*" – "memory" or "remembrance." Maya's job is to tempt us to forget our true nature as joy. And when we do remember, Maya tries to tempt us to seek joy outwardly.

* More about Patanjali and the *Sutras* in Part II.

Soul diseases are produced by ignorance and cosmic delusion by which a man forgets his perfect divine nature and concentrates on his imperfect human nature.... Spiritual ignorance is the real cause of mental and physical disease. If one removes ignorance from the soul by meditation and God-contact, he has automatically removed mental and physical disease from his body.[4]

How could the soul, which is a reflection of pure Spirit, become "diseased"? It will help us to remember that the perfect Soul can only play an active role in our lives as long as we can remain consciously connected with Spirit. When our Soul connection is active, our body, mind, and soul are perfectly harmonized and healthy. But if we lose the connection, the ego finds it much easier to open gaps for Maya to hypnotize us with ignorance and paralyze our will with false hopes.

How can we know when our Soul connection is at risk? What symptoms does the disease of Soul ignorance present? Yogananda warns us to watch out for the following signs: [5]

- *The habit of putting off meditation*
- *Unwillingness to meditate altogether*
- *Restlessness; lack of soul peace*
- *Discontentment*
- *Want of poise; unbalance*
- *Disharmony, unkindness, unforgiveness*
- *Bigotry*
- *Melancholia*
- *Lack of introspection and self-analysis*

These symptoms, left unchecked, inevitably lead to inner disharmony and unwellness. Let us consider a selection of them more closely.

**Resistance to meditation.** Regular contact with the higher Self is the secret of a balanced, healthy life. Soul-contact is the foundation that maximizes the effectiveness of all of the healing tools described in this book. If we do not have daily contact with the Self, the ego will leap into the gap and take over our awareness, persuading us that we are hemmed-in by the conditions of a treacherous physical body and the uncertainties of a meaningless existence – and eventually plunging us into unhappiness, failure, depression, and disease.

In the Bhagavad Gita, God in the form of Lord Krishna says:

> Those with unsettled consciousness have no discrimination. Those who are unmeditative cannot know peace. And for those who lack peace, how is happiness possible? (BHAGAVAD GITA, 2:66)

Yogananda comments on this passage in his Gita interpretation:

> A body-identified individual lacking meditation on the soul is restless, peaceless, joyless and without discrimination. He who is without peace is without happiness too. He who has no soul-contact is without peace, happiness and the guiding light of true wisdom.[6]

In Part II, you will find suggestions for making your meditations effective as a weapon to eradicate ignorance, the root cause of disease.

**Restlessness (lack of soul peace).** All meditators to some degree experience physical and mental restlessness that try to divert their attention. A restless, unfocused, unquiet mind drifts to memories of the past and idle thoughts of the future. Yet soul peace can only be found by immersing our whole attention in the present.

Think of a windless lake in whose smooth surface the full moon is clearly reflected. When the wind sweeps over the lake, the surface no longer reflects the moon's clear image. Similarly, we can only perceive our Soul nature in the smooth mirror of stillness and inner silence. Yogananda said: "Where motion ceases, God begins." [7]

An effective approach to curing ourselves of mental restlessness is to develop a habit of engaging each task through the day with focused attention and deep concentration, while ignoring the tantalizing distractions that would scatter our attention. We will consider further tips for stilling the mind in the chapters that follow.

**Discontentment.** Wishing things were other than they are, while apparently innocuous, is actually spiritually dangerous, because it signals a rejection of life and God's hand in it, and a sign that we are out of touch with our higher Self.

When we find ourselves complaining endlessly about inconveniences great or small, or about the way we are treated, and the real or imagined slights we receive – or our lot in life generally and the injustice of it all – we can know for a certainty that we are not spiritually well, and that it is time to pause and reflect.

An important sign of spiritual progress is a growing, ever-deepening trust and faith that whatever life brings us, it is for our long-term good. The yoga scriptures name "contentment" as the queen of virtues.

**Disharmony (unkindness, unforgiveness).** A principal quality of the Soul is that it perceives itself and all creation as, in actual truth, part of the seamless fabric of Spirit. The Soul knows that all creatures are children of the Divine, doing their best to deal with their karmic inheritance. Thus the Soul is infinitely patient and free of judgment.

When we are considering an action or about to choose a path, and we suddenly feel a certain nervousness or anxiety in the heart, we should take it as a warning from the Soul.

If our behavior is creating disharmony, at home, at work, or with friends, and if we are frequently unable to find a common ground with others, we should take time to pause and evaluate the warning.

When we are offended, if we react in kind, or if we harbor a desire for revenge – "I'll get even!" – we should take it as a warning that it is time to reconnect with Spirit.

**Want of poise.** The word "poise" evokes images of champion ice skaters whose slightest movements are polished with perfect grace and executed with effortless skill. We, too, can know that we have connected with the eternal Soul when we feel perfectly poised, balanced, harmonious, and at peace within.

Another image that comes to mind is the Hatha Yoga position called *Vrikasana* (the Tree Pose). The upper body, like the trunk of a tree, is straight; the legs are planted like roots anchored deep in the earth; while the arms, like branches, extend upward to touch the heavens. In Ananda Yoga, the affirmation that accompanies *Vrikasana* is: "I am calm, I am poised!"

When we find ourselves thrown off balance by something that someone says to us or about us, or destabilized by an unexpected event, we have lost our poise and become subject to the emotional roller coaster, which takes us ever further away from our center.

The Bhagavad Gita says: "Not even the direst suffering can shake the equanimity of the wise man. He stands unshaken amidst the crash of breaking worlds."[8]

Maintain your equilibrium amidst trying circumstances, standing unshaken by violent emotions or adverse events.[9]

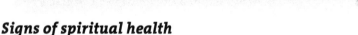

## *Signs of spiritual health*

Now that we can recognize the symptoms of spiritual disease, we can construct a profile of the qualities of people who are spiritually healthy. They –

- Regularly contact the state of inner peace and live in that awareness throughout the day

- Live in harmony with themselves, and create harmonious relationships and environments

- Are kind, generous, patient, tolerant, and serviceful

- Remain calmly centered even in difficult situations, and are able to help others in a crisis

- Welcome challenges and unexpected situations as opportunities for growth and understanding

- Associate with people of truth, integrity, and spiritual advancement

- Are aware of the consequences of their thoughts and actions, and are able to make the needed adjustments

## Mental/emotional/psychological diseases

Yogananda refers to the "mental bacteria" that infest the mind, and describes how the "mental diet" of our habitual thoughts and attitudes affects our health. These mental bacteria include:

| FEAR | GREED |
|---|---|
| ANGER | BAD HABITS |
| WORRY | TEMPTATION |
| SELFISHNESS | JEALOUSY |
| UNTRUTHFULNESS | DEPRESSION |
| REVENGEFULNESS | OBSESSIONS/ADDICTIONS |
| ABSENTMINDEDNESS | LACK OF SELF-CONTROL |

All of these mental diseases share a common element: they revolve around the ego – the one word that most succinctly defines all of them being "Selfishness."

Let's take a closer look at the three most common harmful mental bacteria.

### Fear

Yogananda considered fear one of the most damaging emotions to our mental and physical health. Fear overwhelms the mind, paralyzes the will, and shuts down the flow of life force into and throughout the body.

Debilitating fear is one of Maya's best friends. It tricks the mind into thinking that a possible event we fear is inevitable – when very often the "possibility" is revealed as improbable or an outright lie.

> A mental indulgence in fear will
> create a subconscious fear habit...
> [which] will assert itself,
> magnifying the object of our fears
> and paralyzing the will-to-fight-fear
> faculty of the conscious mind.[10]

In extreme cases, fear can be fatal.

## ☼ DON'T BLAME ME ☼

The saintly hermit had shown himself eager to help the villagers over the years, and they trusted that he would now protect them from the outbreak of smallpox in the village that had taken three victims.

They knew that the saint's powers were real, and when the villagers sought his aid, he tapped the ground with his staff three times and recited a mantra to summon the astral entity that had sent the disease into the village.

When the dark spirit appeared, the saint recognized him as a servant of Yama, the Lord of Death.

"This village is under my protection," the hermit declared. "You have no more to do here." Recognizing the saint's power, the entity agreed to do no more harm, whereupon he disappeared.

The saint assured his flock that the village was safe. Yet not a week passed before the saint found the villagers again at his door, wringing their hands, faces distorted with despair. A hundred had died from the dread disease! Why had the saint failed to keep the evil entity away?

When the hermit again summoned Yama's servant, he sheepishly declared: "Holy one, I was true to my word. I took the first three, but the others died of fear, and for that I cannot be blamed!"

In *Autobiography of a Yogi*, Yogananda tells a story with a moral that his guru Swami Sri Yukteswar told him, from his childhood.

> My mother once tried to frighten me with
> an appalling story of a ghost in a dark chamber.
> I went there immediately, and expressed my
> disappointment at having missed the ghost.
> Mother never told me another horror-tale. Moral:
> Look fear in the face and it will cease to trouble you. [11]

## Anger

Anger is just one of a spectrum of harmful emotions that may begin as a mild irritation, disappointment, or fear, and grow into rage and violence. Anger creates chemical and hormonal changes in the body that are damaging to the nervous system, and that infest the body cells with toxins and cloud the brain's ability to reason. Anger is harmful not only to ourselves but to the recipients and even to the bystanders. It pollutes our inner and outer environment.

> In anger, you burn the nerves out.
> The reason why you should not be angry
> is that it poisons the blood. Anger changes
> chemicals of the blood. Angry vibrations
> affect circulation. An angry mother can
> poison her milk that feeds her child. [12]

Why do we let ourselves be infected by anger?

Anger and its cohort arise from frustrated desire. We might be disappointed and then angry that someone is not acting as they should, not recognizing our merits, not giving us what is rightfully ours – respect, priority treatment, benefits at work.

As the following story shows, repressed anger can have serious health consequences.

Her grief at his passing was eclipsed only by her rage. She was furious – how could he leave her so unexpectedly alone to manage the ranch! How could he be so inconsiderate! The ranch was drowning in debt, her husband's life insurance policy was paltry, the children were long gone and lived far away.

How could he do this to her! Day after day the anger ate at her – there were no longer tears, only a pit of despair.

The cancer appeared six months after her husband's passing, forcing her to put the ranch in the hands of the foreman while she spent months in bed or in the hospital. There would be more treatments, and she needed time to regain her strength.

On the day she came home, the weather was sunny. When the taxi turned onto the dirt road through the extensive ranch property, she gazed in wonder at the fields, the animals, and the barn and silo, amazed to find them impeccably maintained. After speaking with the farm hands and looking over the accounts, she realized that the ranch was making a modest profit – all due to the foreman's rare abilities.

Over the ensuing months they worked together, forming a friendship and a business partnership. The cancer improved, and in time was cured. They married, and their personal and business partnership thrived.

All was well for several years, as her happiness and the profits from the ranch increased, until the fateful day when her husband failed to come home and she found that he had absconded with the money. Broken again in heart and spirit, the anger returned along with the cancer, and within months she was gone. **–Anonymous**

In our times we too often see rage on the freeway, in the air, and in our schools – always with tragically avoidable consequences. We are not living in healthy times.

## Worry

While worry is often fear's partner, it deserves its own discussion. Worries may seem less toxic than fear, yet they are more pervasive and enduring. Like fear and anger, worries trap our energy and cloud our judgment, weakening our nerves and suppressing our immune defenses. Worry is a major cause of sleep disorders and generalized stress.

Where do worries come from? They are spawned by Maya, who loves to feed our imagination with thoughts of: "What if…?" What if this happens?" "How will I manage?" "Where will I go?" "Who will take care of me?

Worry is not only debilitating, it is rarely of any practical value. Instead of bringing us solutions, it makes things worse, by inventing "reasonable" fears and "logical" justifications for our worries. Worry breeds worries without end.

How does the Ego tempt us into believing that our worries are justified? It tricks us into believing that worrying will help us resolve our problems, if we worry long and hard enough. Once ensnared in worry's labyrinth, the Ego comforts us that we've done our job and we needn't do more. Thus worry is its own reward – we feel virtuous because we worry, which shows how conscientious and sincere we are. However, our experience tells us that regardless of the Ego's self-justifications, worrying doesn't get us anywhere.

The simplest and easiest solution to the worry habit is to ignore Maya's worry broadcasts and roll up our sleeves and do something to resolve the issues we are worried about. If you're worried about losing your job, a better option would to be become so indispensable that they can't fire you. If you are worried that you might get sick in the approaching winter months, start building your immune reserves and general health by exercising and eating wisely in the warm months. Above all, realize that solutions are always at hand for the problems we are facing – we just need to know where to look for them.*

* Other worry cures are discussed in Part VI, Volume Two.

## Physical diseases

> All physical diseases originate in mental and spiritual
> inharmony. Ignorance of the laws of mental hygiene,
> and of the spiritual art of living are responsible
> for all human bodily and material suffering.
> If the mind is free from the mental bacteria of anger,
> worry, fear, etc., and the Soul is free from ignorance,
> no material disease or lack can follow.[13]

We can often trace the source of an illness to an imbalance in our energy (the astral body) and thoughts (the causal body) that, over time, caused physical imbalances and disease.

Our physical form is nourished by the astral body, which is composed, as we have seen, of "lifetrons." By practicing the methods offered in this book, we can learn to direct the vibratory lifetrons upward toward the brain to reinvigorate our mental and spiritual faculties, or downward to purify and regenerate the body's cells, tissues, organs, and nerves.

The astral lifetrons are activated – or blocked – by thoughtrons: subtle vibratory thoughts that originate in the causal body that create the blueprint or pattern for the astral body.

While medical science has made impressive progress toward eliminating many diseases, it is still rare for human beings to enjoy life-long freedom from health issues. The bodies of all people are subject to physical laws as well as the effects of karma. Even the saints are not immune from disease. St. Francis suffered from grave physical illnesses, yet he is known as a saint of joy.*

Although just the tip of the iceberg, the body is subject to innumerable diseases. The ways in which they manifest depend on our present and past history: on our karmic heredity.

---

* "Think of St. Francis, who is considered by many to be the most perfect of all Christian saints. He was a saint of joy. The Catholics today depict him as a saint of sorrow, but he had the joy to transcend the suffering he was given, and to realize that nothing is important except the divine joy of the soul. This is why Yogananda called him his patron saint." – Kriyananda, *The Light of Superconsciousness*, 62-63.

# What about Karma?

> Health and success or disease and failure
> are the fruits of our actions not only in this life
> but in many lives. When the repeated efforts of an
> intelligent person to gain health or success miscarry,
> then disease and failure had their inception
> in past incarnations.[1] –YOGANANDA

**Karma is a spiritual law,** just as gravity and motion are physical laws: our actions have consequences, even as Newton's Third Law of Motion tells us that every physical action produces a reaction.

The Bible refers to this principle:

"Be not deceived; God is not mocked: for whatsoever a man soweth, that shall he also reap." (GALATIANS 6:7)

Each of our actions and thoughts will have consequences, immediately or in the long run. We set the machinery of karma in motion, for good or ill, by the manner in which we exercise of our free will.

> All physical diseases, accidents, and mental
> or spiritual suffering are due to the law
> of cause and effect as applied to our actions
> governing this life and previous lives.[2]

Contrary to popular belief, karma has nothing to do with "sin" or divine punishment or vengeance. Karma is simply the impersonal operation of divine law on the physical, mental, and spiritual planes. Healthy habits have positive results, whether in the form of abundant physical energy and strong immunity, mental clarity and creativity, prosperity and success, or happiness and contentment. Breaking the laws of body and mind brings disease, confusion, and unhappiness.

> God never punishes or rewards you, for He has given you the power to punish or reward yourself by the use or misuse of your own reason and will. It is you who transgressed the laws of health, prosperity, and wisdom and punished yourself with sickness, poverty, and ignorance.[3]

"Karma" is simply a name for the impersonal mechanism by which the consequences of our actions are delivered. It is impersonal, because it applies to everyone equally, without exception. It is in a sense mathematical, good karma in the present life mitigating bad karma from the past.

Karma is also benevolent because it brings to our awareness the thoughts and actions which have resulted in wellbeing and happiness or in illness and suffering. By studying the results of our actions, we can avoid making mistakes in future that will have serious consequences, and engage instead in actions that will speed our spiritual evolution while avoiding karmic traps and byways.

We can think of past health karma as being a messenger. Gently at first it brings signs of discomfort – a physical pain, a distasteful argument, a disappointment – warning us to take stock and make adjustments. If these signs are repeatedly unheeded, however, they can become the harbinger of chronic disease.

> Whenever a person transgresses physically, mentally, or spiritually, a portal for a specific disease is opened, according to the nature of the transgression, to enter the body.[4]

The boomerang effect of karma, good or bad, can be delivered instantly or slightly delayed, or it may mysteriously appear as a consequence of unremembered actions in distant past lives.

We've all experienced *"instant karma"* – when, for example, we've overeaten or consumed foods that didn't agree with us, whereupon an instant message arrived in the form of a tummy ache.

Let us not forget the positive side of instant karma – the kind gesture or noble action that brings a rapid reward.

You are in a hurry to get to the bank before it closes. On your right, a line of cars is trying to enter the stream of traffic. You courteously slow to allow several cars to enter. Whether they ignore your kind gesture or signal their appreciation with a smile and a wave, several blocks later, when you try to enter a busy thoroughfare, someone lets you in, and when you reach the bank you find a free parking space in front of the door. The karmic law can be snappy, and it can deliver results with interest.

With **Delayed karma**, the consequences of our actions may need time to get sorted and organized before they are delivered – human relationships are an area where we commonly see this. If we criticize a colleague's work behind his back, we should not be surprised if, months later, the authenticity of our work is called into question and we are denied a promotion.

On the positive side, if you help a colleague by sending him useful resources anonymously, you may be surprised to find an unexpected tax refund appearing in the mail months later.

**Forgotten karma** is where a crisis, or a blessing, occurs with no apparent cause. Disabilities that appear at birth or happen as the result of illness or accidents could be due to transgressions of divine laws in past incarnations. A windfall inheritance from a distant relative could indicate a sacrifice that you made on their behalf in a past life.

## Overcoming karma

While we cannot erase our past actions, we do have some leeway to choose how we will experience the resulting karma – whether we will be passive victims of our karma, or if we will receive the message, learn the lesson, and take it as a signal that we need to correct our behavior and develop our inner strength.

The message boldly blazoned across the heavens
at the moment of birth [our astrological birth chart]
is not meant to emphasize fate – the result of past
good and evil – but to arouse man's will to escape
from his universal thralldom. What he has done,
he can undo. None other than himself was the
instigator of the causes of whatever effects are now
prevalent in his life. He can overcome any limitation,
because he created it by his own actions in the
first place, and because he has spiritual resources
which are not subject to planetary pressure. [5]

What is the final lesson of karma? This is a deep question for which I hope that all of the chapters in this book will contribute acceptable answers. The positive and negative energies that we have set in motion in countless lives will take a long time to balance in the divine ledger.

It can take a long time to pay all of our karmic debts – but it need not be so. "Knowledge is freedom," Yogananda said. The master also said that it is important to understand the Law of Karma for several reasons: [6]

- To avoid future mistakes
- To escape or minimize the results arising from errors already performed
- To be able to act rightly, independent of external influences and internal desires
- To understand how we can influence our karma and modify or reduce the intensity of its effects
- To be able to create good karma consciously and independently in harmony with divine wisdom
- To liberate ourselves from the clutches of karma by understanding it – knowledge is freedom

This book will give you spiritual resources to counteract your past karma to a significant degree and set new karmic patterns in motion that will help you eliminate or entirely avoid the karmic consequences of unwise actions in the past. The following story tells how Iris used one of these methods in the face of an untreatable disease.

According to the doctors, I should not have lived to an advanced age. Yet here I am, well into my seventies. I was born with a chronic disease – which makes no sense, unless we take account of the law of karma. It is a mucosal disease that leaves me completely defenseless against viruses and bacteria that invade my sinuses and has required thirteen operations. Without regular antibiotics, I probably would not be alive.

Lurching from one bacterial infection to the next, I began to seek other ways. When my search led me to Yogananda's book *Scientific Healing Affirmations*, I began to practice the affirmations during daily walks in the woods with my dogs. I experimented with different affirmations and finally found one that suited me well:

*O Father, Thine unlimited and all healing power is in me.*
*Manifest Thy light through the darkness of my ignorance,*
*Wherever this healing light is present there is perfection.*
*Therefore perfection is in me.*

When I repeat the affirmation, I feel protected. For the past eighteen years I have used it every evening before sleeping, when I thank God for the day He has given me. It also seems to have helped my dogs, who lived to be sixteen and eighteen. –**Iris**, *Netherlands*

❋   ❋   ❋

An especially powerful tool for mitigating the effects of our karma is meditation, which is the subject of Part II.

**All effects or seeds of our past actions**
**(Karma) can be destroyed by roasting**
**in the fire of meditation, concentration,**
**[and] the light of superconsciousness.**[7]

- The soul is individualized Spirit. The ego is the soul, identified with the body.

- The conflict between the soul's identification with Spirit and the ego's identification with matter is the source of all disharmony and disease. This conflict is known as "ignorance" and is the root cause of disease at all levels of our life: spiritual, mental, and physical.

- Every atom in creation is endowed with a consciousness that becomes increasingly self-aware as it progresses through the stages of mineral, plant, animal, and human evolution.

- The characteristic that uniquely distinguishes human evolution is free will: the ability to choose our thoughts and actions.

- In the Shudra stage of spiritual evolution, free will sleeps.

- The individual of Vaishya consciousness uses his free will for personal gain.

- The Kshatriya uses his free will for altruistic endeavors, to develop self-discipline, and to transcend the ego through selfless service.

- The Brahmin relinquishes the ego's limited self-identity by deep meditation, in which he realizes his true identity in oneness with Cosmic Consciousness.

- When we use our free will to violate the laws of health, illness ensues.

- Some illnesses are the result of transgressions in past lives that have waited to come to fruition in this life, when the circumstances were right.

- We can mitigate or even avoid the karma of poor health by creating good strong health habits in this life.

# NOTES ｜ PART ONE

## Chapter One

1 Yogananda, "Meditations and Affirmations," *East-West*, April 1932; and *Inner Culture*, October–December 1941.
2 "Chinese Creation Myths," Wikipedia, https://en.wikipedia.org/wiki/Chinese_ creation_myths.
3 Kriyananda, *Keys to the Bhagavad Gita.*
4 Kriyananda, *God Is for Everyone*, 49.
5 Yogananda, *Advanced Course on Practical Metaphysics*, Lesson 2.
6 Yogananda, "Imperishable Soul," Spiritual Interpretation of the Bhagavad Gita," *Inner Culture*, August 1937.
7 Yogananda, "Recipes," *East-West*, November–December 1928.
8 Kriyananda, "Good Health," *Affirmations for Self-Healing*, 43.
9 Yogananda, *Autobiography of a Yogi*, 263.
10 Yogananda, "Meditations and Affirmations," *East-West*, September 1932.

## Chapter Two

1 Yogananda, *Autobiography of a Yogi*, 401.
2 Yogananda, *Essence of Self-Realization*, 6:1.
3 Yogananda, *Autobiography of a Yogi*, 410-411.
4 Yogananda, "Second Coming of Christ," *Inner Culture*, September 1938.
5 Yogananda, "Curing According to Temperament," *Scientific Healing Affirmations.*
6 Yogananda, *Autobiography of a Yogi*, 402.
7 Yogananda, 402.
8 Yogananda, 403.
9 Yogananda, "Second Coming of Christ," *East-West*, March 1933
10 Yogananda, *Autobiography of a Yogi*, 401.
11 Kriyananda, *Awaken to Superconsciousness*, 140.
12 Kriyananda, *How To Be a True Channel*, 34.
13 Yogananda, "Obtaining Divine Healing," *Inner Culture*, October 1940.

## Chapter Three

1 Kriyananda, *The Hindu Way of Awakening*, 98.
2 Yogananda, *Praecepta Lessons*, Vol. 5:109.
3 Kriyananda, *Conversations with Yogananda* No. 2.
4 Kriyananda, *Conversations with Yogananda* No. 91. See also *Conversations* No. 263 and No. 340.
5 Yogananda, "Second Coming of Christ," *East-West,* October 1932.
6 Yogananda, *Advanced New Super Cosmic Science Course*, Lesson 4.
7 Kriyananda, *The Art and Science of Raja Yoga*, 432.
8 Kriyananda, *The Hindu Way of Awakening*, 250.
9 The walking palm grows with its trunk balanced upright on a tepee-like frame of roots of which only the ends are in the ground. The roots grow in the direction of travel, where they bite into the ground and hitch the whole plant forward. "The Walking Palm," Nature and Culture Intenational, September 28, 2020, https://www.natureandculture.org/field-notes/walking-palm/.
10 Yogananda, *Advanced New Super Cosmic Science Course*, Lesson 4.
11 Kriyananda, *The Essence of the Bhagavad Gita*, 95; and *Do It Now!,* April 18
12 Kriyananda, *The Art and Science of Raja Yoga*, 431.
13 Yogananda, *Advanced New Super Cosmic Science Course*, Lesson 4.

## Chapter Four

1 Einstein, "The Einstein Papers: A Man of Many Parts," *The New York Times*, March 29, 1972, https://lnkd.in/gWV2x9VW.
2 Yogananda, "Is Life Real?" *Inner Culture*, January 1941.
3 Yogananda, "Second Coming of Christ," *Inner Culture*, January 1940.
4 Kriyananda, *The Hindu Way of Awakening*, 196, 251.
5 Kriyananda, *The Art and Science of Raja Yoga*, 433-434.
6 Kriyananda, *The New Path*, 313.
7 Kriyananda, *The Hindu Way of Awakening*, 252, 270.
8 Kriyananda, *The Art and Science of Raja Yoga*,, 432.
9 Yogananda, *Advanced New Super Cosmic Science Course*, Lesson 4. "A solution of the dispute between the evolutionist and the special creationist is reached by a medium view in the following way: The scientist is right when he declares that all animal bodies are inter-related, such as baboons and horses, and that they came from the lemur, the lemur from the fish family. But since the scientist cannot find the missing link, he must admit the special creation of man, but then he might ask: 'How is it that there are animal characteristics in man?' The answer is that the animals' souls, for further advancement, were made to reincarnate in the specially created human bodies, beginning with Adam and Eve."
10 Yogananda, *Autobiography of a Yogi*, 171.
11 Kriyananda, *Out of the Labyrinth*, 155.
12 Kriyananda, *Hindu Way of Awakening*, 257-259.
13 Kriyananda, *Out of the Labyrinth*, 155.
14 Kriyananda, *The Essence of the Bhagavad Gita*, 95.
15 Kriyananda, *Out of the Labyrinth*, 156.
16 Kriyananda, *The Essence of the Bhagavad Gita* (18:44), 552.
17 "Adriano Olivetti," Wikipedia, https://en.wikipedia.org/wiki/Adriano_Olivetti.
18 Kriyananda, "Sharing," *Affirmations for Self-Healing*, 28.
19 Kriyananda, *Out of the Labyrinth*, 157.
20 Kriyananda, *The Hindu Way of Awakening*, 261.
21 Yogananda, "The Four Natural Divisions of Society," *Bhagavad Gita Interpretations* 2:31-32, *Inner Culture*, February and March 1938.
22 Kriyananda, *Out of the Labyrinth*, 157.
23 Yogananda, "To Develop Will," *Metaphysical Meditations*, 102.
24 Yogananda, "The Four Natural Divisions of Society," *Spiritual Interpretation of the Bhagavad Gita, Inner Culture*, February 1938.
25 Yogananda, *The Essence of Self-Realization* 18:1.
26 Kriyananda, *Awaken to Superconsciousness*, 198.
27 Kriyananda, *The New Path*, 275.
28 Kriyananda, "What is Right Action?", Week 21, *Rays of the Same Light*, Vol. 2, 56.
29 Kriyananda, "Guru," *Letters to Truthseekers*, 78.
30 Gibran, Kahlil, "On Teaching," *The Prophet*, https://standardebooks.org/ebooks/khalil-gibran/the-prophet/text/on-teaching.
31 Kriyananda, *Out of the Labyrinth*, 158.
32 Kriyananda, *Rays of the Same Light*, Week 21, Vol. 2, 56.
33 Yogananda, "Second Coming of Christ," *East-West*, August 1932.
34 Yogananda, "Dreams of God," *Whispers from Eternity*, 205.
35 Yogananda, "The Song of the Spirit," *Interpretation of the Bhagavad Gita, East-West*, August 1932, 23.

## Chapter Five

1 Kriyananda, *Awaken to Superconsciousness*, 204.
2 Kriyananda, *A New Age Renunciate Order*, 68, 4.
3 Kriyananda, 12.
4 Endnote: "All of you, therefore, placed in your proper stations, do (everything you can to) protect Bhishma. (Bhagavad Gita 1:11). Bhishma, though "guarding" his army, must also be guarded in turn by its leaders. For the consciousness of having a separate ego-identity, as man's central reality, both springs to the defense of its delusions and has a need to be buttressed, in turn, by constant reminders of its dependence on personal involvement in outwardness." –Yogananda, *The Bhagavad Gita According to Paramhansa Yogananda*, 8.
5 Kriyananda, *Cities of Light: A Plan for this Age*, 21.
6 Kriyananda, *The Art and Science of Raja Yoga*, 190-191.
7 Kriyananda, "Sharing," *Affirmations for Self-Healing*, 28.
8 Yogananda, *The Essence of Self-Realization*, 10:9.
9 Kriyananda, *Conversations with Yogananda* No. 146.
10 Kriyananda, 391.
11 Yogananda, "Meditations and Affirmations," *Inner Culture*, July–September 1942.
12 Kriyananda, *Sadhu, Beware!*, 11.
13 Swami Kriyananda, "A Renunciate Order for the New Age," https://www.nayaswami.org/; https://anandaeurope.org/nayaswami-order/https://anandamonastery.org/renunciate-order-for-a-new-age/.
14 Kriyananda, *Conversations with Yogananda* No. 90.
15 Yogananda, *Praecepta Lessons*, Vol. 5:103/2.

## Chapter Six

1 Yogananda, "Vibratory Healing," *Inner Culture*, September 1936.
2 Yogananda, September 1936.
3 Yogananda, *Autobiography of a Yogi*, 161-163.
4 Yogananda, "Second Coming of Christ," *Inner Culture*, September 1938.
5 Yogananda, "Unique Methods of Spiritual Healing," *New Super Cosmic Science Course*, Lesson 2.
6 Yogananda, "The Secret of Inward Peace," *Spiritual Interpretation of the Bhagavad Gita*, 2:66, *Inner Culture*, January 1941.
7 Yogananda, "Meditations & Affirmations," *Inner Culture*, October 1939.
8 Yogananda, "Second Coming of Christ," *Inner Culture*, November 1936.
9 Yogananda, "To Prevent Spiritual Disease," *Scientific Healing Affirmation*.
10 Yogananda, *Super Advanced Course No. 1*, Lesson 9.
11 Yogananda, *Autobiography of a Yogi*, 105.
12 Yogananda, "Overcoming Nervousness," *East-West*, July–August 1927.
13 Yogananda, "Classification of Healing," *Scientific Healing Affirmations*, 20.

## Chapter Seven

1 Yogananda, *Super Advanced Course No. 1*, Lesson 8.
2 Yogananda, *Praecepta Lessons*, Vol. 4:104/2.
3 Yogananda, "On Reward and Punishment," *Inner Culture*, October–December 1942.
4 Yogananda, "Second Coming of Christ," *Inner Culture*, April 1935.
5 Yogananda, *Autobiography of a Yogi*, 163.
6 Yogananda, *Advanced Course on Practical Metaphysics*, Lesson 6.
7 Yogananda, Lesson 6.

**PART II**

# MEDITATION THERAPY

Ignorance is the mother of all
physical, mental, and spiritual diseases.
Abolish ignorance by contacting God
and forthwith body, mind, and soul
will be healed of all maladies.[2]

—YOGANANDA

When I started meditating, which was decades ago, I discovered that there were two of me who were sharing this body – a clueless person who was aimlessly wandering the earth, and an ageless wise soul. I'm not sure which of my twin selves was able to make me a high-powered executive manager – but I excelled in the role, and felt exalted by my boundless energy.

But when the oncologist announced that I had several types of cancer, it all came crashing down – I would need a double mastectomy, surgical removal of lymph nodes, and follow-up chemo and radiation.

My first challenge was to avoid falling into despair – and it was my meditation practice that gave me the inner serenity to accept the situation.

I was ready for the operation, but the hospital would not be available for another two months. I used the time to deepen my meditation and to gather the inner strength to face the surgery and the aftermath.

As it turned out, the aftermath was the greater challenge. Two days after I returned home after surgery, I was back in intensive care with deep vein thrombosis. And a month later I was back again for a hysterectomy. The high-energy body that I had thought of as my friend was betraying me, forcing me to look elsewhere for my support.

Even though I had never felt worse, I had also never felt so blissful. I began to hear the sound of Aum almost continuously, sometimes very quietly, other times so loudly that at first I didn't recognize it – I thought a helicopter was landing outside the house. I felt God's presence constantly and I felt comforted by Him every day and deeply loved.

After seven months of therapy, it was time to return to work, but my body and brain were far from what they had been. I was no longer able to power my way through life.

What was I to do? I was the clueless twin once again, and I had to let go of my self-image as a high-powered executive and allow God to take over. In meditation I listened for His guidance and surrendered my ego to His will.

Once I let Him take charge, He set me on a path to a completely different way of living. As a cosmetologist, I now nurture people instead of directing them. I have more time for my spiritual life and for giving love and support to my husband and the many friends who helped me through the long ordeal. In times of inner stillness I feel bliss, and my inner wise woman knows that God is gently guiding me to my true home in His Infinite Oneness. –**Leslie**, *Nevada City, California*

PART II    CHAPTER ONE

# Self-realization

Self-realization is the knowing in all parts of
body, mind, and soul that you are now in possession
of the kingdom of God; that you do not have to
pray that it come to you; that God's omnipresence
is your omnipresence; and that all that you
need to do is improve your knowing. [1]

–YOGANANDA

**When the great explorers** John Cabot, Christopher Columbus, and Hernán Cortés set sail in the fifteenth century, they launched an Age of Discovery that would initiate a vast expansion in humanity's view of the world, forcing us to look beyond our former image of the earth as flat and with a single land mass, to embrace new continents, new cultures, and new concepts.

Meanwhile, Kepler, Copernicus, and Galileo were raising their gaze above earth's land and seas to explore the planets and the vast universe that tomorrow's discoverers will continue to explore.

Modern exploration in the field of health is notable not so much for its discoveries, as the re-discovery of how people in ancient times were able to lead a balanced life in harmony with themselves, with others, and with the indwelling Spirit. They drew their greatest fulfillment from a direct knowledge of the Self – as Yogananda calls it, from Self-realization.

Meditation is the supreme science of Self-realization mentioned in the ancient Vedas, the *Yoga Sutras* of Patanjali, the *Bhagavad Gita*, and in numerous Upanishads and Puranas: the scriptures of Sanatan Dharma.*

In the following passages the Bhagavad Gita describes the meditative state.

* Sanatan Dharma means that truth which is eternal, and which is expressed in varying ways in all the great religions of the world. See the Glossary for more details.

Free from the hopes engendered by desire, and untouched by any craving for possession, the waves of feeling in his heart controlled by yoga concentration, the yogi, retiring alone to a quiet place, should try to unite his little self with the Supreme Self....

The state of complete inner tranquility, which is attained by yoga meditation, wherein the little self (the ego) perceives itself as the Self, enjoys itself as the Self.

[That] state...once attained, is considered the treasure beyond all other treasures: In that state alone does the yogi become immune to grief even in the face of the greatest tragedy.
(BHAGAVAD GITA 6:10, 20, 22) [2]

<hr/>

### ❈ MY MEDITATION ANCHOR ❈

Here where I live in the bustling modern city of Milan, Italy, it is not so easy to remain centered – I am constantly bombarded by distracting sights and sounds and pulled into frenetic rhythms that make me lose myself in an illusory world.

My anchor is meditation. As my breath slows I return to a calm, regular rhythm that carries me to my center, where I feel strong, stable, and protected.

In that state I find myself able to listen to the sounds in my environment with a healthy detachment that enables me to stay open and receptive. Meditation brings me to a deep, forgotten part of myself where intuition accompanies the steps of the day and connects me to meaningful thoughts, words, and encounters.

I simply cannot do without meditation! It transforms my days and the quality of my sleep, granting me the gift of a life that is filled with joy and gratitude. –*Cecilia*, *Milan*

# Health Benefits

※ A SAFE HAVEN ※

Before a meditation practice came into my life I lived under a constant black cloud. If I could call it living...my mind was filled with a certainty that something was about to go wrong, that bad luck was my lot, and that my future would be bleak. Sadness was my norm, and I would bask in my negative moods.

Meditation practice awakened me and helped me emerge from my mental tunnel. When I meditate I find my perspective changing – my negative mindset begins to ebb, and in time, the vicious cycle of sadness and oppressive thoughts vanishes like soap bubbles, giving way to feelings of peace, relaxation, and well-being.

Depression doesn't vanish overnight, especially if it is chronic, but we can remind ourselves when it rears its head that there is a way out. Through my meditation practice I have realized that the solution is inside me, and that my inner Self is a safe and shining haven. –*Daniella*, *Milan*

**Research on the** physiological effects of meditation tells us that as little as twenty minutes of daily practice improves physical and mental health and reduces the frequency and recurrence of illness. A growing number of medical and holistic health practitioners now recommend meditation as part of a daily health regime. [1]

Research by Dr. Jon Kabat-Zinn [2] and others has shown that just six weeks of regular meditation can deliver at least some of the following benefits:

- Accelerates post-operative healing and reduces the duration of post-surgery hospitalization.

- Decreases the frequency and pain level of headaches.
- Decreases respiratory rate.
- Increases blood flow and slows heart rate.
- Lowers blood pressure in people whose levels are normal to moderately hypertensive.
- Increases exercise tolerance in heart patients.
- Reduces anxiety attacks by lowering blood lactate levels.
- Leads to deeper relaxation.
- Low levels of serotonin are associated with depression, obesity, insomnia, and headaches. Meditation increases serotonin production, positively affecting mood and behavior.
- Helps alleviate chronic diseases such as allergies and arthritis.
- Reduces the symptoms of pre-menstrual syndrome (PMS).
- Strengthens the immune system and increases the number of T-cells that defend the body against bacteria and cancer cells.
- Alleviates stress and stress-related disorders such as insomnia and heart disease.
- Improves the quality of sleep.

## Mental health

Stress is a pandemic malady in our times. It affects people of all ages, cultures, and geographic locations. It is difficult to find inner peace when the world is seething with turmoil and uncertainty about the future.

> The world was sadder and more stressed out in 2021 than ever before, according to a recent *Gallup poll*, which found that four in 10 adults worldwide said they experienced a lot of worry or stress.[3]

When we encounter unexpected or difficult situations we all experience stress to some degree. If we allow these situations to overwhelm us with fears and anxieties, we put ourselves in danger of becoming seriously ill.

The long-term activation of the stress response system and the overexposure to cortisol and other stress hormones that come with it can disrupt almost all of your body's processes. This can put you at increased risk for a variety of physical and mental health problems, including anxiety, depression, digestive issues, headaches, muscle tension and pain, heart disease, heart attack, high blood pressure, stroke, sleep problems, weight gain, and memory and concentration impairment.[4]

## ❊ THE SHOCKING BILL ❊

I knew better than to check the mail before my evening meditation, but this evening my curiosity got the better of me. As I scanned my electric bill for the month, I catapulted from calmness to panic – it was three times the normal bill and I didn't have the money to pay it.

As I sat to meditate, I was certain that obsessive thoughts about the electric bill would haunt me, so I did some extra breathing exercises and prayed for help to resolve the situation, then I began to meditate. As the meditation progressed and my mind expanded, the problem began to shrink until it disappeared, replaced by a feeling that I was not alone, and that something larger than my anxious ego was taking care of me.

The next morning, after another peaceful meditation, I called the phone company and calmly explained the situation, speaking from my heart with the representative. She immediately looked into the situation and explained that it was a mistake, and there was nothing to worry about.

I realized again how the mind magnifies our fears and anxieties, and that when we open ourselves to the light of truth, the fog of emotions disappears and the sunny skies return. –**Gloria**, *Gualdo Tadino, Italy*

❊　　❊　　❊

Many of our anxieties are self-generated. Fears that are unrelated to our actual situation can arise from the ego's concern for our physical survival and its desire to control the circumstances of our lives.

Y ou could say that I was a hypochondriac – I fit the description in every way. I was continually fearful of getting sick although the doctors told me that I was perfectly healthy. I would become convinced that I had a certain disease, and when the symptoms weren't forthcoming I was convinced that I had another one.

These fears made me continuously anxious. I had frequent panic attacks, and it got to the point where I couldn't function normally. I was utterly paralyzed by my fears, unable to study, or go to work or sleep. My life was not a happy one.

And then I came upon Paramhansa Yogananda's teachings quite by chance, and I started to meditate, whereupon my situation changed right away.

Whenever I felt relaxed from my meditations, I became aware that the cause of my anxieties was that I was afraid of losing control of my life. When these irrational fears now try to bubble up, I focus at the spiritual eye and open my heart, while affirming that the fear is an illusion, and I ask God to guide me past the fear to the Truth of my existence. After a few minutes, I feel calm, and my mind is no longer spinning around its former anxieties, but attuned to God's love.

It truly is a miracle! I am free of my former irrational fears, knowing that I am in God's hands. My motivation and enthusiasm for life have returned, I'm sleeping well, and the time I formerly wasted researching imaginary diseases I can now dedicate to my studies in Ayurveda and volunteer service.

I am grateful for the suffering that brought me to meditation, to my spiritual path, and to the liberating joy of inner freedom. *–Tessy, Netherlands*

Meditation practice is one of the most effective means of calming the stress response. As the rhythms of breathing and heartbeat slow, runaway thoughts and emotions come under our control.

According to neuroscience research, mindfulness [meditation] practices dampen activity in our amygdala and increase the connections between the amygdala and prefrontal cortex. Both of these parts of the brain help us to be less reactive to stressors and to recover better from stress when we experience it.[5]

Even a little bit of regular meditation quickly brings results.

> By knowing God through deep and frequent meditation, you will lose all your fears and troubles.[6]
>
> If anyone, even twice, during the earliest hour of dawn and in the depth of night, worships God in the church of meditation for fifteen minutes to one hour, he will find that the Spiritual habits of peace will predominate over his worry-producing material habits.[7]

## ❊ WE BOTH SURVIVED ❊

My son had a psychotic crisis that led him to consider suicide. We were able to find a psychiatrist and a psychotherapist in the nick of time, and the therapy led him to a complete recovery.

For me, this period was stressful, unnerving, and filled with anxiety for his survival. It was only by meditating every day that I was able to reach a state of inner peace where I experienced unconditional love for my son and found a way to support him through his trials. Meditation saved me – and my son as well. –*Maria Antonietta*, *Rome*

## Concentration, Clarity, and Creativity

Concentration is a built-in function of the brain. Like other brain functions, it can become dormant through disuse, or weakened by misuse – for example, from a habit of trying to focus in too many directions at once. A fundamental goal of all meditation techniques is to strengthen the mind's ability to focus.

The ability to concentrate deeply is essential for success in every area of our lives.

> Concentration it is that awakens our powers
> and channels them, dissolving obstacles
> in our path, literally attracting opportunities,
> insights, and inspirations. In many ways,
> subtle as well as obvious, concentration is
> the single most important key to success.[9]

Our power to concentrate can be weakened by many factors, including raw emotions. Brain researchers have discovered that raw emotions and mental concentration are localized in two separate, mutually exclusive areas of the brain. In practical terms, what this means is that when our emotions are out of control we are unable to concentrate deeply, and if we can concentrate deeply we will find our emotions becoming calmer and less able to dominate our awareness.

This is the physiological reason for the practice of giving people who have received emotionally shattering news some simple, practical tasks that will require them to concentrate. This is not merely a way to distract them from their need to confront reality – it is helping them to achieve a state of calmness and emotional detachment and objectivity in which they will be better equipped to deal with the trauma.

In 2002, scientists at Duke University used brain scans to verify that raw emotions interfere with concentration, and that mental focus and raw emotions exist in a mutually exclusive relationship. That is, not only does emotion distort our ability to focus, but deliberately focusing attention is an effective way to calm and "neutralize" emotions. As the Duke news release put it, "Surprisingly, an increase in one type of function is accompanied by a noticeable decrease in the other." [10]

When the mind is calmly focused, it is able to perceive situations far more clearly, from a broader perspective, and it is able to find solutions to problems as they arise.

### ✳ AN INTUITIVE UNDERSTANDING ✳

Within a period of only ten days our mother had changed from an energetic woman who was in full control of her life, to displaying slight lapses of memory, to becoming aggressive and suffering a violent psychotic episode.

We called for assistance, and Mother was taken to the hospital where she was diagnosed with advanced Alzheimer's disease. It seemed that she would require full-time care in a specialized facility.

The doctors told us that Mother would not return to a normal state of mind, and that keeping her at home would not be helpful for her, or easy for the rest of us. Our father agreed that we should look for a good place, and in the meantime she remained in the hospital.

Everyone was frantic, racing in all directions without knowing where to go, their stress levels way beyond manageable. While my entire family rushed around in search of an affordable facility, I sought answers in meditation. Before I joined the search for an appropriate place for our mother, I wanted to feel inwardly that it would be right for her soul. Whenever I feel carried away by anxieties and uncertainty, I have a short "meditation snack" to bring myself back to inner calmness and find the right, intuitive solution.

The outward investigations were hitting roadblocks – the care facilities had long waiting lists – a minimum of a year – and they were vastly expensive, far beyond our means, even if we could find an opening.

A social worker called me with good news – there was an opening in an excellent facility just ten kilometers from our home. Logically, it seemed like a good solution, but I wanted to know that it was the right one. Much to my family's displeasure, I decided to go for a weekend meditation retreat to look for inner guidance.

By Sunday evening, when I returned, the storm of the family's emotions had become a hurricane, with everyone saying that we must get Mother to the facility as soon as possible. When I meditated on Monday morning, I felt that I should see her before I visited the care facility.

She was perfectly calm and lucid. She recognized me and was completely aware of her surroundings and the situation. She wanted to go home as soon as possible. Father was relieved. We made arrangements for her to be dismissed the following day.

It was clear that Mother would need assistance at home. Where could we find the right person for her? I had another "meditation snack" before I left for a lunch date with a friend. During our conversation, she told me about an excellent caretaker who was looking for work. She turned out to be perfect! – there was no need to look further. My mother is very happy with this kind woman from Sri Lanka whose smile and shining eyes remind us that when we put our lives in God's hands, He takes care of every detail. –*Silvia*, *Cortona, Italy*

While the ego needs to surround itself with material possessions in order to feel secure, the soul seeks its security and fulfillment in expressing its inherent creative nature. In a meditative state, doorways to creative inspiration can open wide.

We knew exactly how we wanted the interior of our house to look, except for the bathroom. I am an artist, and I wanted to create something special for it, but no clear image came to mind. When this happens in my creative work, I've formed a habit of stopping and going into a calm meditative state. It is magical – in that state, curtains open to my inner vision, and I can see a clear image of what I want to create.

One day, when we were getting ready to finalize the designs for the rest of the house, the curtains opened in meditation to reveal a sculptured mirror two meters long, with intricate work in white, gold, and copper that lined the mirror like a frame. Whenever my creations come from the magic meditation space, they fill me with energy and enthusiasm. –*Cristina*, *Porziano, Italy*

## Spiritual health

The ego delights in pleasures and possessions; the soul delights in meditation.

> "The soul loves to meditate, for in contact with the Spirit lies its greatest joy. If, then, you experience mental resistance during meditation, remember that reluctance to meditate comes from the ego; it doesn't belong to the soul." [11]

When meditation becomes regular part of our daily routine, we experience a deep, pleasurable satisfaction that exceeds all others.

The ultimate benefit of meditation is that it cures the root cause of disease – Ignorance – by reuniting the ego and soul. By regularly experiencing the higher states of meditation, the ego becomes persuaded of its true identity.

> If one removes ignorance from the soul
> by meditation and God-contact,
> he has automatically removed mental
> and physical disease from his body.[12]

A regular meditation practice is the best investment we can make for our health. We can greatly enhance the effectiveness of every healing practice in this book by doing it in a state of meditative calmness.

# Meditation Metaphysics

> [By] meditation [we] call into operation
> the unfailing, unlimited divine healing power
> for healing not only the body and mind
> but the soul.[1] —YOGANANDA

**Before the dawn** of Creation, before duality created the appearance of separation, the soul and ego were united in Spirit. The memory of that unified state is part of our "metaphysical DNA."

> Patanjali, the ancient authority on yoga,
> described spiritual awakening as *smriti*.
> Smriti means "memory." The mind has only to
> remove the obscuring fog of false self-identities:
> identities such as, "I am a businessman; I am rich;
> I am a man, a woman, an American, a Frenchman;
> I am old, young, victorious in life, defeated by life."
> These waves of outward involvement need to
> be stilled. Once they become calm, one's
> eternal reality is *remembered* at last.[2]

As we journey through the four stages of human evolution,* we assume different identities and seek different fulfillments. The *shudra's* identity and desires are related to his physical body. The *vaishya's* desires are related to his work and the pleasure he hopes to find from his wealth, possessions and status. The *kshatriya* identifies himself and seeks satisfaction in helping others. The *brahmin* sees himself as a channel for a higher power, and finds his fulfillment in doing only God's will.

---

* See Chapter Four in Part I for a discussion of the stages of human evolution

Spiritual awakening is not confined only to the latter stages of our journey to ever-broader awareness; it happens gradually throughout the stages, as a growing recognition that our self-identities are transitory, and their pleasures are fleeting. In meditation, the waves of restless desires, generated by our search for fulfillment in transient objects and pleasures, are stilled at last. In stillness the body reflects the perfection of the soul, and in deep meditation the ego recognizes its true identity.

Once the soul and ego are reunited, health and harmony reign.

### ✳ LORD, COME INTO THIS BROKEN TEMPLE* ✳

The man was dying of diabetes – the doctors gave him only three months to live. He decided, 'If I only have three months left, let me spend them seeking God.'

Gradually, he disciplined himself to sit in meditation for longer periods. All the while, he prayed, "Lord, come into this broken temple."

Three months passed, and he was still alive. Then a year passed. Continuing his practice, he gradually lengthened his meditation to eighteen hours a day.

After three years, a great Light filled his being and he was caught up in ecstasy. Upon returning from that divine state, he found that his body was healed.

"'Lord,'" he prayed, "I didn't ask for a healing. All I asked was that You come to me."

The Lord replied, "Where My light is, there no darkness can dwell."

The saint then wrote in the sand with a finger, "And on this day the Lord came into my broken temple and made it whole!"

Patanjali describes the goal of meditation in his *Yoga Sutras*, the definitive text on the science of Raja Yoga:†

* Told by Yogananda and recounted by Swami Kriyananda in his book, *The Essence of Self Realization* 7:28.

† The Yoga Sutras were compiled by the enlightened sage Patanjali roughly two thousand years ago. The central themes of the Sutras are the practice of meditation and the goal of Self-realization.

## "Yogas chitta vritti nirodh."

The meaning is: "Yoga" (the reunion of soul and ego) is experienced by neutralizing (nirodh) the waves (vrittis) of ego-generated emotional feeling (chitta).

The single word "neutralize" expresses the purpose of meditation – to calm the mind and feelings to a point of perfect stillness. In that stillness, the experience of joy naturally unfolds.

Do away with the motion for the sake
of meditation. The way to God is motionless....
Where motions cease, God begins.[3]

Supreme blessedness...comes to that yogi
who has completely calmed his mind."[4]

By concentrating on the inner light...
or upon any other divine reality that one
actually perceives when the mind is calm,
one gradually takes on the qualities of that
inner reality. The mind loses its ego identification,
and begins to merge in the great ocean of
consciousness of which it is a part.[5]

### Ashtanga Yoga: Achieving stillness

Patanjali describes the classic path of Raja Yoga, which proceeds in eight stages toward the goal of inner stillness and the experience of perfect bliss. Ashtanga (Eightfold) Yoga was mentioned in Part I; now we will revisit the eight stages of yoga in the context of meditation practice.

**The Yamas and Niyamas,** sometimes referred to as the "ten commandments of yoga," offer us guidelines for gaining control of the direction in which our energy flows.

> Their essential purpose is to permit the milk
> of inner peace to be gathered in the pail of the
> mind by plugging holes that have been caused
> by restlessness, wrong attachments, desires, and
> various forms of inharmonious living.[6]

**Asana** requires that the body be able to sit motionless to provide a stable platform for meditation. Guidelines for achieving physical stillness are discussed in Chapter Four.

> The ability to hold the body still [is] a
> prerequisite for deep meditation. Any
> comfortable posture will do, as long as the
> spine is kept erect and the body relaxed.[7]

**Pranayama** means to gain control of energy (prana) and regulate its movement in the astral body.

> [It is] a state in which the energy in the
> body is harmonized to the point where its
> flow is reversed—no longer outward toward
> the senses, but inward toward the Divine Self....
> Only when all the energy in the body can be
> directed toward this Self can one's awareness
> be intense enough to penetrate the veils of
> delusion and enter superconsciousness.[8]

**Pratyahara** is the ability to withdraw the mind from the senses and outward activities, in order to focus it wholly in the Self.

> Once the energy has been redirected towards its
> source in the brain, one must then interiorize one's
> consciousness, so that his thoughts, too, will not

wander in endless by-paths of restlessness and delusion, but will be focused one-pointedly on the deeper mysteries of the indwelling soul.[9]

**Dharana,** the subject of Chapter Five, is the stage in which the interiorized mind is brought to a single point through yoga techniques of concentration.

Concentration implies, first, an ability to release one's mental and emotional energies from all other interests and involvements, and second, an ability to focus them on a single object or state of awareness.[10]

**Dhyana,** discussed in Chapter Six, is the stage in which the meditator becomes absorbed in experiences of superconsciousness.*

*Dhyana* signifies that stage when the mind, calm and fully receptive, loses itself in the light (or in some other divine attribute) and finds its ego-consciousness dissolving in that light.[11]

**Samadhi** is the experience of ecstasy, of complete Oneness in which the soul and ego are reunited.

[The experience of samadhi is] when the soul, losing body-identity altogether, merges in the greater reality of which the body and everything else in creation is only a manifestation....It is cosmic consciousness, the state where the soul perceives itself as truly "center everywhere, circumference nowhere.[12]

---

* Superconscious experiences are detailed further in Chapter Six. The superconscious dimension of the mind is explained in Part VI, Volume Two.

## Samadhi
*From the poem by Paramhansa Yogananda\**

*Smoldering joy, oft-puffed by meditation*
*Blinding my tearful eyes,*
*Burst into immortal flames of bliss,*
*Consumed my tears, my frame, my all.*
*Thou art I, I am Thou,*
*Knowing, Knower, Known, as One.*
*Myself, in everything, enters the Great Myself.*
*Gone forever, fitful, flickering shadows of mortal memory.*
*Spotless is my mental sky, below, ahead, and high above.*
*Eternity and I, one united ray.*

---

\* Yogananda, *Whispers from Eternity*, 172. You will find the complete poem in the Appendices. Paramhansa Yogananda told the monks, "Memorize my poem, *Samadhi*, and repeat it daily. It will help to awaken within you that lost memory of what you are in reality: sons of Infinity." –Kriyananda, *The Essence of Self-Realization* 18:16.

# PART II    CHAPTER FOUR

## The Meditation Journey

Here is My promise: Yoga, though difficult
for the ungoverned mind to attain, can be reached
through proper methods if one strives
(earnestly) to achieve self-control.

(BHAGAVAD GITA 6:36)

**Meditation is a journey.** Much like a vacation in exotic lands, we must make careful preparations before we set out on the adventure. We will need reliable transport to reach our destination. And, having arrived, we will enjoy the unfamiliar delights of this wondrous new place.

*Preparation:* The details we need attend to before we start out on our meditative journey.

*Technique:* This is the "getting there" phase of the journey, using a specific technique that serves as a vehicle to get to the destination. While the term "meditation" is commonly used to refer to this stage of the journey, it more properly refers to the following stage.

*Silent meditation:* Once we have arrived at our destination (a state of inner stillness), the technique-vehicle we used to get there is no longer necessary. We will want to enjoy this state for as long as possible.

*Coming back:* Cherished memories will accompany us on the return journey, along with a desire to return very soon to the land of superconsciousness.

*Transition:* We cross the bridge between our dawn meditation and our daily activities, and between our evening meditation and sleep.

## Preparation

**Where to meditate.** Every place has a particular atmosphere about it, and is suitable for certain activities: train stations for bustling; restaurants for eating and socializing; gyms for physical exertion; and quiet places for meditation.

You will want to create a space in your home where you can begin and end your day undisturbed. You could repurpose a closet or storage area, or an attic, loft, or basement nook – or you can screen off a corner of your bedroom. It should be a space that is wholly dedicated to meditation and other spiritual activities.

> If you can set aside a room in
> your home as a little chapel and use it
> only for meditation, you will find in
> the course of only a few months that
> it will develop an atmosphere of peace
> which will help you to go deep
> when you sit to meditate. [1]

**How to sit.** They way we sit for meditation requires special attention. We want to have a steady and relaxed posture so that, as the meditation journey proceeds, we no longer need to pay attention to the body.

The seat needs to be appropriate to our physical needs. A cushion of the right height and thickness may be ideal if we want to meditate on the floor. We may select a chair of comfortable height with a flat seat and no armrests, or a kneeling bench – again, of the right height so that we can sit comfortably without putting too much weight on the knees. Experiment until you find what works best for you.

Whether you sit on the floor, in a chair, or on a kneeling bench, the primary criterion is that the spine be straight. The spine is the channel through which life force flows to all parts of the body and senses. The goal of meditation is to withdraw the life force into the spine and direct it upward to the brain.

> A bent spine during meditation offers
> real resistance to the process of reversing
> the life currents. A bent spine throws
> the vertebra out of alignment and
> pinches the nerves, making it impossible
> for the Life Force to reverse its direction
> and flow through towards the
> Spiritual Eye and the medulla.[2]

Strong back muscles can help keep the spine straight in meditation – too often these muscles are weakened by poor postural habits. To strengthen them, make a conscious effort to keep the spine upright, at least at brief intervals during the day. You could place your laptop on a desk or table instead of on your lap, preferably on a raised stand. While walking and eating, hold your chest up and shoulders back and relaxed downward, and try to sit upright when you drive. The Life Force Energization Exercises (see Part IV) and the postures of hatha yoga can strengthen the back muscles over time.

### A Secret of Meditation

> The secret of meditation is to sit upright
> with a straight spine. Holding your body
> perfectly still, gradually free yourself from
> the compulsion to move. Feel that your
> strength emanates from your spine rather
> than from the muscles of your body.[3]

What if your efforts to sit perfectly continue to create physical and mental tension? As with all new habits, it helps to take a step-by-step approach. For example, during the first three minutes of your practice, you might make a special effort to sit upright and perfectly still. When you find that you are able to do this comfortably, add a minute, and so on. Make an effort to keep the mind focused and steady, even when the body needs to move.

Place your hands palms upward on
the thighs, at the junction of the abdomen.
Keep your elbows back, your shoulder blades
drawn slightly together, your chest up—
all the while emphasizing relaxation;
don't be tense. Hold the chin slightly back,
parallel to the ground. Look upward,
and close your eyes.[4]

**The position of the eyes** can help the life force flow upward toward
the centers of higher awareness in the spine and brain.

The direction of one's gaze is an indication of
one's state of consciousness. It also helps to
*induce* the state of consciousness one desires.
A downward gaze is associated with the
subconscious, and tends to induce
subconsciousness. Gazing straight ahead
is not only associated with wakefulness,
but helps one to be "awake and ready"
if he feels himself growing sleepy.
And an upward gaze is associated
with superconsciousness.[5]

While looking gently upward, as if gazing at a distant mountain peak,
hold your relaxed gaze as steadily as possible at the spiritual eye,* at a
point midway between the eyebrows, with eyes closed or partially open.

Holding the spine, neck, and head firmly erect
and motionless, let the yogi focus his gaze at

* The spiritual eye is: "The point midway between the eyebrows. [It] is described as
the seat of the intellect, of will power, and—in superconsciousness—of ecstasy and
spiritual vision. –Kriyananda, *The Hindu Way of Awakening*, 110-111.

> the starting point of the nose (*nasikagram*)
> between the two eyebrows; and let him not
> gaze elsewhere, but keep his gaze calmly
> one-pointed. (*Bhagavad Gita* 6:13)

***Energize.*** If you meditate when you are tired, you'll be much more likely to fall into subconsciousness or sleep. This is called a nap – not meditation. Before starting your meditation, it can help to do some energetic movement, but not too outward or restless. The Life Force Energization Exercises and the Life Force Full Body Recharge (see Part IV) are ideal for this. They are recommended as a quick, effective way to awaken energy for meditation. The Superconscious Living Exercises in Part VIII of Volume Two are another way to energize the body and simultaneously elevate the mind.

***Relaxation.*** Physical and mental tension is a major obstacle to meditation, as it prevents us from interiorizing our energy and attention.

> Relax when you meditate.
> Don't strain....Meditation comes only by
> deeper and deeper relaxation—
> physical, emotional, mental,
> and spiritual.[6]

Once the body and mind are energized, the next step is to make sure the muscles are relaxed. Yoga postures are ideal for releasing tension to prepare for meditation. Kriyananda's Ananda Yoga lessons offer an approach to the yoga postures that helps release mental and emotional tensions and affirm higher states of awareness by accompanying each posture with an appropriate affirmation.[7] Yogananda's Life Force Energization Exercises are extremely effective for vitalizing and relaxing the body.

Unrelieved tension blocks the flow of nourishing life force, and can lead to illness. The following exercises are helpful to prepare the body for meditation, and will keep the body and mind relaxed, alert, and healthy when practiced several times a day.

# Relaxation exercises to relieve physical tensions

**Phase one:** First, breathe in through the nostrils with a long, slightly forceful inhalation.

Gradually contract all of the muscles in the body until they are vibrating strongly.

Exhale with a long breath through the mouth, while gradually releasing any tension in the body.

Repeat the inhalation and exhalation three to twelve times, until you feel that all tension has been released.

**Phase two:** Slightly tense, then completely relax the following body parts:

- Both feet • both calves • both thighs • both buttocks
- the stomach and abdominal muscles • both hands
- both arms • both sides of the chest • both shoulders
- the neck • and finally, the muscles of the face

**Phase Three:** Repeat the first phase one or more times.

## Inner Space

Think of your body as surrounded by space—space in all directions spreading out to infinity.

Now think of your feet, and visualize this space gradually seeping through the pores of the skin into your feet, until your feet become space.

Visualize this space as gradually coming up into the calves, thighs, hips, the abdomen and stomach, the hands, forearms, upper arms, shoulders, chest, the back of the neck, sides of the neck, the throat, jaw, tongue, lips, cheeks, eyes, and brain.

In feeling space in your brain, release from your mind all regrets about the past, all worries about the future.

Rest in the infinite ocean of the eternal Present.[8]

If you suffer from chronic tension in your neck, shoulders, and/ or back, you may need to supplement these practices by consulting a physiotherapist.

> In massage, osteopathic treatment, adjustment of the vertebrae, Yoga postures... we can remove or relieve the congestion in the nerves or vertebrae and permit the free flow of Life Energy.[9]
>
> Spinal adjustments and massages are effective... for the adjustment of the spine releases obstructed life-force which can bring about a quicker and surer healing of physical diseases than anything else.[10]

After relaxing the body as described above, the following breathing exercises will help you relieve any remaining mental and emotional tension.

**Mental relaxation.** The breath is intimately connected with the mind. When we experience fear, anger, or other negative emotions, the breath becomes irregular. When we are relaxed, our breathing becomes slow and regular.

> An intimate connection exists between the mind and the breath. This interesting truth can be turned to good advantage, for as the mind influences the breath, so also the breath influences the mind. Harmful emotional states can be overcome to a large extent by deliberate, deep, harmonious breathing.[11]

It is very helpful to start your meditation with exercises to harmonize your breathing. The following exercises can also help you calm your emotions in difficult situations, or when you are experiencing internal turmoil, such as panic attacks.

### Exercise to defuse emotions

> Whenever you feel anxious or fearful about anything, or distressed over the way someone has treated you, or upset for any reason, inhale and tense the body. Bring your emotions to a focus in the body with that act of tension. Hold the tension briefly, vibrating your emotions along with the body. Throw the breath out, and, keeping the breath exhaled as long as you can do so comfortably, enjoy the feeling of inner peace. Remain for a time without thought.[12]

### Breathing exercise before meditation

> When you sit to meditate, begin by tensing the whole body, then throw the breath out and relax. Repeat two or three times.
>
> Now inhale, counting mentally to 12; hold the breath, counting to 12; and exhale, counting to 12…. The count can be 8-8-8, 10-10-10, 12-12-12, or whatever you feel comfortable with….
>
> Gradually, *if you can do so comfortably*, increase this count to 20-20-20, but keep the count equal for all three phases of breathing. Repeat this breathing exercise six to 12 times.
>
> Your whole body should now be completely relaxed, and your mind ready for meditation.[13]

If you find that a count of 8-8-8 is too long for comfort at the start, use whatever count you can manage comfortably, perhaps 4-4-4. Make sure you are using the diaphragm to breathe as deeply as possible.

You will find other pranayama exercises in Chapter Three of Part III. Before meditating, you may find it helpful to spend a few minutes or longer on these breathing exercises. As with any breathing exercises, feel free to use them throughout the day to bring your attention back to a calm, inner center.

**Receptivity.** Meditation is an experience, not an achievement. It is the soul's natural, preferred state. Meditative states happen naturally when the body and mind are still and the heart is open. If our life experiences have prompted us to build protective walls around our heart, and if we are not able to enter into loving relationships, we may be unable to recognize opportunities to give and receive love. A potential loving friend could be living next door, and we will not be able to recognize the love that is calling us. In the safety of meditation, we can gradually learn to open the heart to receive the divine love that is beckoning us through our soul, and through the call of human friendship.

Before we start our meditation, it is very helpful to remember that an essential quality for success in meditation is receptivity. We will want to learn to relax any habitual emotional barriers around the heart. An effective practice for achieving a relaxed, open and receptive state of mind is offering sincere, spontaneous prayers from the heart – a subject that we will discuss in detail in Part IX of Volume Two. Another effective way to open the heart is by singing, especially devotional songs, as will be discussed in Part XII of Volume Three.

> Spiritual vibrations also permeate things that
> are insubstantial, such as prayers that have
> been uttered, and chants that have been sung,
> by great saints or by devout worshipers for
> many years. If, at the beginning of your meditation,
> you repeat such prayers or chants, you will find
> that they have the power to lift you into
> a state of inner communion. "Chanting,"
> Yogananda used to say, "is half the battle." [14]

### Exercises to open the heart

#### The heart flower

Feel in meditation that your heart center (situated in the spine opposite the heart) is like a flower with its petals turned downward. Mentally turn these petals upward so that they point toward the brain. Feel rays of energy flowing up from the heart toward the point between the eyebrows. Awaken love in the heart, and channel all this love upwards.[15]

## Sphere of light

Focus your attention on the *anahata chakra*, located in the area behind the physical heart. Draw your shoulder blades together several times by tensing and relaxing the area of the back behind the heart. Visualize a great sphere of light expanding outward from the area of your heart. Feel this sphere encompassing everything around you—your house, neighborhood, country, the world, and all of space. Try to feel that everyone and everything is bathed in this light. Sit quietly and keeping your body relaxed, try to feel an actual sensation of warmth or energy in the anahata chakra.[16]

PART II CHAPTER FIVE

# Concentration

### THE EYE OF THE BIRD

*From the Indian epic, the Mahabharata*

His princely students had made good progress, and it was time to test their abilities at archery. Dronacharya gathered his pupils in an open field and drew their attention to a small image of a bird that he had hung in a distant tree. He then challenged them to send an arrow through the bird's eye.

One by one, he called them forward, but before giving them permission to shoot he asked: "What do you see?"

The students answered:

"I see you, revered teacher."

"I see the field and the distant tree."

"I see the other students awaiting their chance."

"I see the bird in the tree."

"I see the branches and leaves surrounding the bird."

One by one they let fly their arrows, and as the teacher expected, none hit the target.

Finally he called his most skilled pupil, the noble Arjuna. When he inquired what Arjuna saw before him, Arjuna replied: "I see the eye of the bird." Drona then asked, "What else do you see?" "Nothing," Arjuna said. "I see only the eye of the bird." Confident of the outcome, Drona was unsurprised when Arjuna's arrow hit the mark.

**An essential step** on our journey to Self-realization is to gain control of the restless mind. By its nature, the mind easily becomes lost in a whirlpool of thoughts, desires, memories, and plans. The unfocused mind leads us down bypaths that will not bring us to our destination.

### A Secret of Meditation

The secret of meditation is setting
resolutely aside every plan, every
project, and focusing on the moment.
(The world will still be there after
you finish your meditation.) [1]

To remedy a habit of letting our thoughts become distracted from our higher purpose, we can engage them in breathing exercises, as discussed in the last chapter, and then learn to focus our attention on one thing at a time.

Various meditative traditions suggest a variety of objects that we can use to train the mind to focus: a candle, a mandala, an image of a holy person, an icon. In the Dominican monastery at the church of Saint Mark in Florence, the renowned painter and monk Fra Angelico decorated each of the monk's cells with a fresco of an event from Jesus' life. These scenes, one surmises, served to give the monks a focal point for their prayers.

### A Secret of Meditation

Visualize your breath as a flow of energy
in the spine, upward with inhalation,
and downward with exhalation,
until the flow seems a mighty river....
rising in joyful aspiration toward
the point between the eyebrows. [2]

A technique common to many traditions, and the one that Yogananda adopted, is to focus our attention on the natural movement of the breath. Practical because the breath is always at hand, this technique quickly works to concentrate the mind.

You can use this practice as a "warm-up" before the meditation technique you already use, or as a meditative practice in itself.

## Concentration on the natural flow of breath

Inhale deeply, and then slowly exhale. Wait for the breath to come in of its own accord, and watch its flow.

As the breath flows out naturally, again observe the movement. This is not a breathing exercise. Don't inhale and exhale deliberately. Simply watch the breath.

Don't watch your body breathing. Notice the breath itself.

Be particularly aware of the rest points between the breaths. Enjoy the peace, and the feeling of inward release and freedom that you feel when your body is without breath.

Practice this technique as long as you feel to.[3]

*Go deeper now*: Feel yourself breathing in the spine: up with every inhalation, down with every exhalation. Let the movement begin in the region of the heart, starting at a point slightly below it and extending slightly above.

Lengthen the flow gradually, beginning lower in the spine and ending higher up.

At last, take a slow, deep breath through the nostrils, beginning at the base of the spine and ending at the point between the eyebrows. Hold the breath at that point as long as it is comfortable to do so. This time, with your exhalation, feel your breath and consciousness soaring out through the forehead, taking you with them into infinite space.[4]

## *Focus at the spiritual eye*

The frontal lobes are the brain's primary memory storage bank. They are also the area where higher executive functions are localized, such as the ability to form long-range plans and carry them to completion, and the ability to organize, to initiate actions, and solve problems. The Spiritual Eye* that is seen in deep meditation is an inner portal

* In the Appendices for this Part you will find an article by Yogananda, "The Metaphysical Cosmos," in which he refers to the Spiritual Eye as the Astral Eye, the Cosmic Eye, and the Christ Eye.

between the material and astral worlds. It is located at a point in the forehead, approximately midway between the eyebrows The spiritual eye is the doorway to higher states of consciousness.

> When anybody concentrates at the point
> between the eyebrows with eyes closed,
> he sees a light which has a white star in the
> middle, encased within a sphere of blue light
> which is encircled by a golden ring of light.[5]

Focusing with calm relaxation at the spiritual eye will, in time, open a portal to superconsciousness. You can end your meditation by watching the breath at that point, with calm, steady attention and uplifted, relaxed gaze.

> Concentrate at the point between the
> eyebrows....When you concentrate at this point,
> try to do so without any mental or physical
> tension. We simply want to make the Spiritual
> Eye the one-pointed focus of our attention.
> When our awareness returns to the habitual
> patterns of thinking, reviewing, and planning
> that are the activities of the conscious mind,
> gently and repeatedly return your attention
> to the point between the eyebrows.[6]

Meditation is, in a sense, like climbing a mountain. After we've done the hard work and we've arrived at the summit, we can relax and enjoy the view. When your attention is calmly concentrated at the spiritual eye, you can release conscious thoughts and concerns and experience the state of superconciousness. This is when the actual meditative phase of the practice begins.

# PART II   CHAPTER SIX

## Meditation Experiences

> Once the mind is interiorized....
> it receives the first clear intimations of the
> ecstasies that await it in superconsciousenss....
> Inner sounds and lights, tear-inducing love
> and joy, healing peace—all of these
> and more are enjoyed by many meditators
> from the very beginning.[1]
> —KRIYANANDA

**The destination of meditation** is superconsciousness, a land where you can explore the sights, sounds, and higher wisdom of the soul. Superconscious experiences in meditation are like visiting a beautiful city, such as Paris. The longer you stay, the more you are able to experience. Were you to visit for just a few hours between flights, you might have time to walk along the river Seine. Were you to stay for a weekend—a two-day visit to the Louvre. On a longer visit, you could take in the Orsay Museum, Notre Dame, Montmartre, and Monet's *Water Lilies* at the Orangerie. If you're able to make friends with some *Parisiens*, many other doors will open.

The destination of our meditation journey is superconsciousness.* The Indian scriptures mention eight principal landmarks in the land of superconsciousness: peace, calmness, love, wisdom, sound, light, power, and joy. It is in superconsciousness that the soul and ego are reunited – perhaps at first only for brief moments. But once the ego has experienced the soul-satisfying pleasures of its higher nature, the craving will grow to experience that land more often, and to linger there for longer periods.

* You will learn more about superconsciousness in Part VI, Volume Two.

**Superconscious Experiences** [2]

**Peace** is an early meditative experience. Peace, like a weightless waterfall, cleanses the mind of all anxiety and care, bestowing heavenly relief.

**Calmness** is another divine experience... more powerful than that of Peace. Calmness gives the devotee power to overcome all the obstacles in his life. Even in human affairs, the person who can remain calm under all circumstances is invincible.

**Love...** not personal love, but Love infinite. Those who live in ego-consciousness think of impersonal love as cold and abstract. But divine love is all-absorbing, and infinitely comforting. It is impersonal only in the sense that it is utterly untainted by selfish desire. The unity one finds in divine love is possible only to the soul. It cannot be experienced by the ego.

**Wisdom** is intuitive insight, not intellectual understanding.... Divine perception is always from within. From within alone can a thing be understood in its true essence.

**Sound.** To experience God as Sound is to commune with the Holy Ghost, or *Aum,* the Cosmic Vibration. When you are immersed in *Aum,* nothing can touch you. *Aum* raises the mind above the delusions of human existence, into the pure skies of divine consciousness.

**Power...** is that aspect of God which creates and runs the universe. Imagine what power it took to bring the galaxies into existence! .... you will never find God until you are very strong in yourself.

**Joy/Bliss.** Bliss cannot even be *attained...* The soul simply realizes that bliss is, eternally, its own nature. For bliss simply *is.* It is what remains after everything else disappears. Bliss is the eternal, forever unchanging reality which underlies the whole universe. All things, including all other aspects of God, are contained in Conscious Bliss. They merge into, and become, eternal, Conscious Bliss. [3]

**Light...** brings calmness to the mind, purifying it and giving it clarity. The more deeply one contemplates the inner light, the more one perceives all things as made of that light. We are made of light. Healing in the future will come more and more by using rays. [4]

## Meditations on light

Concentrate at the point between the eyebrows. Visualize there a tunnel of golden light.

Mentally enter that tunnel, and feel yourself surrounded by a glorious sense of happiness and freedom. As you move through the tunnel, feel yourself bathed by the light until all worldly thoughts disappear.

After soaring through the tunnel as long as you feel to so do, visualize before you a curtain of deep violet-blue light. Pass through that curtain into another tunnel of deep, violet-blue light. Feel the light surrounding you. Slowly, the tunnel walls disappear in blue light. Expand your consciousness into that light—into infinite freedom and bliss. Now there is no tunnel. There is only the all-encompassing blueness and bliss of infinity.

At last, visualize before you a silvery-white, five-pointed star of light. Mentally spread out your arms and legs, assuming with your body the shape of that star. Give yourself to it in body, mind, and soul as you surrender every thought, every feeling to absolute, Self-existing Bliss.

Bliss cascades gently over you, like a waterfall of mist, filling your heart with ineffable peace.

Whether or not you behold the Spiritual Eye, by meditating at that point your consciousness will gradually rise until at last it passes the portals of human awareness and enters the state of ecstasy, or superconsciousness. [5]

Visualize your consciousness expanding like a blue light, encompassing all space. Imagine the stars and galaxies shining like the lights of a distant city within the infinitude of your being.

Meditate on your vastness within.[6]

## A Secret of Meditation

Visualize God in one of His eternal aspects –
as infinite light, cosmic sound, eternal peace,
love, or joy; seek to unite yourself with Him in
that aspect....affirming that you already are
those high truths to which you aspire.[7]

## *The journey back*

As our meditation journey has a beginning, so it also has a conclusion. To end your meditation, bring your mind back to the flow of breath through your nose, then to its flow in your spine, and finally to its pulsation in all the cells of your body. Take in a long inhalation through the nose, then gently tense the whole body, and then relax deeply while exhaling through the mouth. Take another long inhalation, tense more strongly, and exhale a bit more forcefully through the mouth. Now move the various parts of the body, bringing energy back to your head, trunk, and extremities.

### *Reflections*

- At the conclusion of your morning meditation, look ahead to the day's activities and visualize yourself calmly and joyfully engaging in them, centered in higher awareness. Ask for guidance for these activities, and pray to be open to receive, learn from, and take full advantage of the opportunities they offer.

- After your evening meditation, recall the day's activities, and reflect on their blessings and express your gratitude.

Many people leave their meditation practice at this point, yet there is so much more that we can accomplish, especially in the areas of self-healing, and of contributing to the health and upliftment of others. These will be the subjects of later chapters.

### *"Meditation snacks"*

Inner peace is like a cellphone battery – it needs recharging. To keep yourself calm and centered, and to prevent inner emotional upheavals, practice the following one-minute "meditation snack" at mid-morning and mid-afternoon, or once every hour if you wish. (I've set my smart watch to give me an hourly reminder.)

## A Touch of Light

- With a slow, and slightly forceful inhalation, gradually tense all of the muscles in the body until the whole body is vibrating; then relax gradually with a long exhalation. Do this three times with a slight pause between cycles.

- Focus your inward gaze at the spiritual eye and observe the natural flow of breath there for about 30 seconds.

- Give yourself a *"Touch of Light."* Place the index finger of your right hand at the spiritual eye and silently affirm: "I am calm, I am poised, I am centered within myself."

### A Secret of Meditation

The more you meditate, the more
you will want to meditate.[8]

# Self-Healing in Meditation

✷ MY INNER REALM ✷

No one believed me—how could a small child have such debilitating headaches? As far back as I can remember, they were severe and unrelenting. Only when I was twenty were they finally diagnosed as chronic migraines.

Nothing that I tried could relieve them – until I started to meditate. When an attack came upon me, I would practice the basic technique of observing the breath while imagining that with every exhalation I was releasing the pain. On one occasion, I was able to travel intuitively inside my body to the point of intense pain. Mentally, I squeezed that point, and the pain instantly disappeared!

It was then that I heard a hum so loud that I thought someone was drilling outside my window. With inner vision, I "saw" a sage-green colored wheel with petals extending outward in all directions, moving in synchrony with the loud hum. It was the heart chakra – the *Anahata*.

In my daily meditation and breathing practices, I am gradually oxygenating the blood and purifying my body and mind. As my fraught nervous system learns to calm itself and to remain relaxed through life's turbulences, the frequency of my migraines has been dramatically reduced.

My regular meditation practice has enabled me to watch my mind as a silent witness, as I become aware of my subconscious tendencies and overcome lifelong habits that are not serving me well. It is only through the deep peace that I experience in meditation that I am finding a cure for my migraines. The cure lies within, even as the vast realm of wisdom lies within me. –*Abhilasha*, *Switzerland*

**The best time** of all to practice self-healing techniques is at the conclusion of the silent part of your meditation. In that state of concentration and calmness, you will be able to direct the divine power of the life force to reestablish physical and mental balance throughout your being.

> When [you experience] the ever-increasing,
> ever-new joy contact of God in silence, then all
> things, including health, abundance, and wisdom
> will be added unto you. The soul, mind, and body
> will be perceived as the perfect manifestation
> of God Himself. It is after such realization that
> the body can remain permanently healed.[1]

> Offer every problem up for resolution to
> the peace within; allowing that peace to
> infuse your outward activities.[2]

You can use your hands as instruments for life force to heal yourself and to transmit healing vibrations to others.

> There is no power greater than the Life Force
> flowing through the hands, provided it is
> made strong by an indomitable will.[3]

### Channel healing to yourself

- Rub your hands together briskly and strongly until you feel heat in the palms.
- Place your palms on a part of your body that needs healing,
- With an inhalation, draw the life force into your body, then transmit the life force through your hands to the part in need of healing.
- As you exhale, visualize the intelligent healing life force flooding the area where you have placed your hands, and

correcting anything that needs to be adjusted as you gently
massage the region to distribute the life force over a wider
area.

- Repeat this healing exercise several times, including different locations as needed.

- To heal mental or emotional imbalances, place your energized hand on your forehead and visualize healing light
filling your brain.

By using this technique at the end of each meditation, you can
alleviate acute symptoms and, in time, you may see an improvement
in chronic conditions as well.

## Channel healing to others

You can use your energized hands to transmit healing vibrations to others and to the environment in which they live.

- Visualize the individuals to whom you wish to channel
healing energy, seeing them in their perfect, already-healed
forms.

- Hold your hands overhead, while allowing the waves of life
force to flow through them.

- Direct the waves of healing energy to their spiritual eye,
while seeing it flow through their brain and into their body.

The Life Force is intelligent – it will know what needs to be
done, once it is activated in the person receiving the energy.

## A secret of meditation

The secret of meditation is to radiate blessings
from your heart outward to all the world.[4]

### Other healing techniques

Finish your meditation routine with at least one of these techniques, which you will find in the following Parts:

- Any of the Life Force healing exercises in Chapter Three of Part IV;

- An affirmation, with methods in Part VIII of Volume Two;

- Work on eliminating a bad habit groove, as described in Part VII of Volume Two.

- Pray for yourself and others while using the techniques in Chapter Five of Part IX in Volume Two.

- Ask for inner guidance regarding a health situation or any life situation. See Chapter Four in Part IX of Volume Two.

### A bridge to daily life

Make sure that your first actions after meditating are done with your awareness focused inwardly. Hold on to the peace of meditation for as long as you are able.

> After meditation, don't strip your mental
> gears by plunging hastily into outer activity.
> Try to carry the meditative peace into
> everything you do. To develop this habit,
> it may help to begin with outward activities
> that don't involve your mind too much.
> While doing them, chant inwardly to God.
> The walking meditation is an excellent practice
> for bridging the gap between meditative peace
> and outward busyness. If you can't devote
> time to walking calmly after meditation,
> try doing things slowly for a bit, consciously
> bringing peace and energy into your
> muscles and bodily movements.[5]

Today I shall establish the joy
of meditation in the temple of
each thought that I have.[6]

The light of God's perfect health shines
in all the dark nooks of my bodily illness....
In all my body cells God's healing light
is shining. They are entirely well,
for His perfection is in them.[7]

Heavenly Father, Thou are present
in every atom, every cell, every corpuscle,
in every particle of nerve, brain, and tissue.
I am well, for Thou art present in
all my body parts.[8]

The perfect light of God is
perfectly present in all my body parts.
Wherever that healing light is manifest,
there is perfection. I am well,
for perfection is in me.[9]

# Kriya Meditation

> Practice of this technique enables man
> to recover control of his inner life force and thus
> realize his oneness with the cosmic life force.[1]
> —YOGANANDA*

### ✺ THE DAY I DIDN'T DIE ✺

I was home alone, sick in bed with Covid, thinking that I could fight my way back to health on my own. Then one evening, all of a sudden I could no longer breathe! – my lungs weren't working, and there was no breath even to make a phone call.

Certain that I was dying, I reached for my Kriya beads so that I could die while meditating. With difficulty I sat up, visualized my Master with great devotion, and with all my energy I started to practice one Kriya.

What happened then is hard to describe. I felt as though I was fainting while falling upward – there was a slight pain at first, then a tepid sweetness. There was air around me, a barely perceptible sound of bells, a boundless beauty that blazed within me, and a loving, healing presence that was welcoming me home to my most authentic origin. I don't know how long I stayed in that state of grace: it could have been an instant or an eternity. When I returned, I found myself sitting in my meditation posture and my lungs were working perfectly.

I practice Kriya with deeper faith now, knowing that there is an intelligence that sustains me. Will I have that experience again? Even if I do not, those moments were worthy to be remembered for a lifetime. –**Daniela**, *Verona*

**Possibly the most ancient** of all meditation techniques, Kriya Yoga was reintroduced in modern times in the late nineteenth century by Mahavatar Babaji, whereupon the Kriya knowledge was passed from generation to generation of saintly yogis. Paramhansa Yogananda brought Kriya to the Western world in the early 1900s. He wrote about it extensively in his *Autobiography of a Yogi* and he taught it to hundreds of thousands of aspirants.

The Kriya technique is a scientific method that uses concentration, willpower, and devotion, combined with a specific breathing pattern, to magnetically withdraw the life force from the physical body and focus it in the astral spine (the *sushumna*). Seeds of past and present ego-motivated actions (*karma*) that have been lodged in the sushumna and the chakras, are drawn up to the spiritual eye where, through deep and dedicated practice, they become neutralized, fulfilling Patanjali's definition of yoga: *Yogas chitta vritti nirodh.* ("Yoga is the neutralization of the vortices of emotional feeling.") Through the practice of Kriya, the ego recognizes its true Self and relinquishes its separate identity.

> *Kriya*, controlling the mind *directly*
> through the life force, is the easiest,
> most effective, and most scientific
> avenue of approach to the Infinite.[2]

> It teaches the seeker how to withdraw his
> energy into the spine, and then to direct it
> up the spine to the brain. By following
> this inner route...one can achieve
> realization much more quickly."[3]

Due to Kriya's ability to neutralize the seeds of past karma that are responsible for disease and disharmony, it is one of the most powerful spiritual tools for healing available anywhere today. While the Kriya technique is only given during an initiation ceremony by authorized *Kriyacharyas,* the pathway to initiation is open to all sincere seekers.

> [Yogananda] often said that Kriya Yoga
> strengthens one in whatever path—
> whether devotion, discrimination, or service;
> Hindu, Christian, Moslem, or Judaic—
> one is inclined by temperament,
> or by upbringing, to follow.[4]

Yogananda dedicated an entire chapter of his autobiography to the science of Kriya, even as Swami Kriyananda included a chapter on Kriya in *his* autobiography, *The New Path: My Life With Paramhansa Yogananda.* You can find information about Kriya in the Endnotes of this chapter. [5]

### *For those who practice Kriya*

You can use your Kriya practice to great effect for self-healing. Pray to the Kriya masters about your situation, and ask them to channel their grace through your Kriya practice. As you bring the rising current up to the spiritual eye, feel that you are offering and releasing there the karmic seeds associated with your difficulty. With the descending current, feel a warm, purifying ray of grace that starts at the spiritual eye and radiates healing power first through the brain, where samskars of past karma are imbedded in the brain cells, then down the spine.

> In deep meditation the energy
> accumulates in the brain .... withdraws
> the life force from the muscles and nerves,
> and concentrates [it] in the brain cells
> where the evil mental habits are grooved ....
> seeking out the evil habits and
> cauterizing them.[6]

The practice of Kriya Yoga...helps to free one
of the samskars (subtle tendencies) that block
the upward flow of Kundalini. These samkars –
the "seeds" of karma, as they are called –
are the result of repeated actions (karmas)
of the past - not only of this life, but of
many past incarnations. Each samskar
constitutes a subtle vortex of energy.
There are countless such vortices in the spine.
Until the energy in them has been released to
flow upward, Kundalini's upward movement
will be slow, her progress impeded.
In fact, Kundalini in her upward surge gradually
"roasts" these karmic seeds of samskars.
Once "roasted" they can never again
sprout into outward actions.[7]

*The Kriya Yoga master* ᴄ*Mahavatar* ᴃ*abaji promised:*

"Even a little bit of the practice of this
religion [meditation] will save you from
dire fears and colossal sufferings."[8]

## Sage Advice

*Suggestions for your*
MEDITATION PRACTICE
*from Swami Kriyananda* [1]

- **Be regular** in your hours and practices of meditation. It is a good practice to meditate at the same hours every day. Routine conditions the mind. You'll find yourself *wanting* to meditate whenever those hours return. It will be much easier, then, to set all distractions aside.

- **Keep the body relaxed**, upright and as still as possible. Avoid restless movements.

  [*Author's note*] Whenever the body gets tense, take a double inhalation through the nose—a short, followed immediately by a longer inhalation—strongly tense and briefly hold all the muscles, and then exhale through the mouth with a double exhalation. Repeat several times until you feel more relaxed. Relaxation is a key to successful meditation.

- **Try to meditate** at least half an hour twice a day—in the morning after you get up, and in the evening before going to bed. You'll come to enjoy meditating, in time. Then you'll find yourself meditating longer because you want to, and not because someone is nagging you to do so. The more you meditate, the more you'll want to meditate; but the less you meditate, the less you'll enjoy doing it.

- **Enter immediately** into your spiritual practices from the very moment you assume your meditative posture. Resolutely set aside all attachment to restlessness.

- **Meditate as long as you can do so** with enjoyment, or with keen interest and alert attention. Never sit for long hours merely to test your endurance. And don't sit long, if in doing so you meditate absent-mindedly. Far more important than the duration of a meditation is its intensity. In fact, a good practice is to sit as if your time for sitting were indeed only five minutes.

- **Once a week**, make an effort to meditate a little longer. Longer meditations imitate the ocean tides in their ebb and flow. Let periods of intense concentration alternate with periods of relaxed effort and peaceful receptivity.

- **After a heavy meal**, before beginning to meditate, wait two or three hours. If this delay is impossible, however, or inconvenient, don't worry about it.

### Suggestions for your
## MEDITATION PRACTICE
### from Paramhansa Yogananda [2]

- **To meditate a short time** with depth is better than to meditate for long hours with the mind running wild. Don't feel badly if you find yourself too restless to meditate deeply. Calmness will come in time, if you practice regularly. Just never accept the thought that meditation is not for you. Remember: calmness is your eternal, true nature.

- **Don't force yourself** to sit for a long time. Strive for shorter, but deeper, meditations. Then gradually, as you become accustomed to going deep, lengthen the time you sit in meditation.

- **Be patient.** Do not get excited in your efforts to find God. Be wholehearted, but not anxious about getting results. Move toward your divine goal ever calmly, with tranquility.

- **Be relaxed and natural.** As long as you try to meditate, you won't be able to, just as you can't sleep so long as you will yourself to sleep. Will power should be used gradually. Otherwise, it may become detrimental. That's why it is better, in the beginning, to emphasize relaxation.

- **Meditate more and more deeply,** until calmness and joy become second nature to you. To be ecstatic is not difficult. It is thinking that it is difficult that holds you apart from it. Never think of divine joy as distant from you, and it will be with you always.

- **Stay awake.** A devotee was having difficulty remaining awake during meditation. To him, Yogananda made this suggestion: "Squeeze your eyes shut several times, then open them wide and stare straight ahead. Repeat this practice once or twice more. If you do this, sleepiness will cease to bother you."

- **Behold the light.** Just behind the darkness of closed eyes shines the light of God. When you behold that light in meditation, hold onto it with devotional zeal. Feel yourself inside it: That is where God dwells.

- If, on the other hand, you behold no light in meditation, then concentrate at the point between the eyebrows, and gaze deeply into the darkness that you see with closed eyes. Try, by your devotion, to penetrate that thick veil. In time you will surely behold the inner light, for it is ever there, shining in your forehead. Just as all human beings have eyes, so does everyone have this spiritual eye within his forehead. It awaits only his discovery in deep concentration.

## PART II: *Points to Remember*

- The soul is individualized Spirit. The ego is the soul, identified with the body.

- Ignorance is the mother of all disease. Meditation is the mother of all cures.

- Daily meditation is the best way to stay healthy, build strong immunity to ward off illness, and get in touch with the inner strength to face health challenges and other crises.

- Meditation prepares your mind to perceive your life's circumstances and situations from a broader perspective.

- Meditation improves concentration and strengthens cognitive functioning.

- The rhythm of the breath is connected to the emotions and to the mental processes.

- Dedicate a space in your home exclusively for meditation and other spiritual practices.

- Practiced regularly in the morning, meditation enables you to be more aware of your life's opportunities, and better able to deal with both routine and unexpected situations.

- When practiced in the evening, meditation helps you put your activities to rest and become aware of the gifts and lessons of the day.

- Short "meditation snacks" throughout the day will keep your mind calm and focused, and your body relaxed.

- Try always to practice the self-healing techniques in this book in a state of meditative calmness.

# NOTES | PART TWO

## Title Page

**1** The meditation practices taught by Paramhansa Yogananda are included in the following books by Swami Kriyananda: *The Art and Science of Raja Yoga* and *Awaken to Superconsciousness,* available from https://anandapublications.com/. **Home-study courses** are available from Ananda India Online: https://anandaindia.org/online/online-courses/. **In-person and online live webinars** are available at www.anandaindia.org and the various Ananda centers in India.

**2** Yogananda, "Obtaining Divine Healing," *Inner Culture,* October 1940.

## Chapter One

**1** Yogananda, *Essence of Self-Realization* 20:7.

**2** Yogananda, *The Bhagavad Gita According to Yogananda,* 64, 66.

## Chapter Two

**1** "Meditation and Cardiovascular Risk Reduction," *Journal of the American Heart Association, https://www.ahajournals.org/doi/10.1161/JAHA.117.002218*

**2** Jon Kabat-Zinn, professor of medicine at the University of Massachusetts Medical School, is a foremost researcher on the effects of meditation. https://audiobuddha.org/the-benefits-of-meditation-by-jon-kabat-zinn/. See also https://jdc.jefferson.edu/cgi/viewcontent.cgi?article=1001&context=jmbcimfp

**3** Mekaur, Dora, "Why People Worldwide Are Unhappier, More Stressed Than Ever," July 16, 2022, VOA News, https://www.voanews.com/a/why-people-worldwide-are-unhappier-more-stressed-than-ever-/6658784.html#.

**4** "How stress affects your health," October 31, 2022, American Psychological Association, https://www.apa.org/topics/stress/health

**5** Smith et al., "10 Things We Know About the Science of Meditation," November 12, 2018, Mindful, https://www.mindful.org/10-things-we-know-about-the-science-of-meditation/#.

**6** Yogananda, "Is Life Real?," *Inner Culture,* January 1941.

**7** Yogananda, "Second Coming of Christ," *Inner Culture,* August 1934.

**8** Yogananda, "Meditations and Affirmations," *East-West,* May 1932.

**9** Kriyananda, *Art and Science of Raja Yoga,* 280.

**10** Duke University press release, August 19, 2002. "MRI Studies Provide New Insight Into How Emotions Interfere With Staying Focused," August 19, 2002, Duke Today, https://today.duke.edu/2002/08/pnas0802.html.

**11** Yogananda, *Essence of Self-Realization* 18:1.

**12** Yogananda, "Second Coming of Christ," *Inner Culture,* September 1938.

## Chapter Three

**1** Yogananda, "Second Coming of Christ," *Inner Culture,* September 1938.

**2** Kriyananda, *Rays of the Same Light,* Week 46, Vol. 3:134.

**3** Yogananda, "Meditation and Affirmations," *Inner Culture,* October 1939.

**4** Kriyananda, *Rays of the Same Light,* 134.

**5** Kriyananda, *Art and Science of Raja Yoga,* 77-78.

**6** Kriyananda, 75.

**7** Kriyananda, 76.

**8** Kriyananda, 76-77.

**9** Kriyananda, 77.

**10** Kriyananda, *Art and Science of Raja Yoga,* 280.

**11** Kriyananda, *Awaken to Superconsciousness,* 220.
**12** Kriyananda, 221-222.

## Chapter Four

**1** Kriyananda, *Ananda Yoga for Higher Awareness,* 132.
**2** Yogananda, "Second Coming of Christ," *East-West,* March 1933.
**3** Kriyananda, *Secrets of Meditation,* 2, 3.
**4** Kriyananda, *Meditation for Starters,* 55.
**5** Kriyananda, *Essence of the Bhagavad Gita,* 6:12-13.
**6** Kriyananda, *Ananda Yoga for Higher Awareness,* 132.
**7** Kriyananda, *Ananda Yoga for Higher Awareness.*
**8** Kriyananda, *Art and Science of Raja Yoga,* 81.
**9** Yogananda, "Evaluation of the Science of Curative Methods," *Scientific Healing Affirmations.*
**10** Yogananda, "Second Coming of Christ," *Inner Culture,* September 1938.
**11** Kriyananda, *Art and Science of Raja Yoga,* 61.
**12** Kriyananda, *Awaken to Superconsciousness,* 95.
**13** Kriyananda, *Ananda Yoga for Higher Awareness,* 132.
**14** Kriyananda, *Awaken to Superconsciousness,* 107.
**15** Kriyananda, *Art and Science of Raja Yoga,* 346.
**16** Kriyananda, *Intuition for Starters,* 32.

## Chapter Five

**1** Kriyananda, *Secrets of Meditation,* 13.
**2** Kriyananda, *Intuition for Starters,* 113.
**3** Kriyananda, *Awaken to Superconsciousness,* 123-124.
**4** Kriyananda, *Secrets of Meditation,* 24.
**5** Yogananda, "Second Coming of Christ," *Inner Culture,* January 1939.
**6** Kriyananda, *Intuition for Starters,* 112-113.
**7** Kriyananda, *Secrets of Meditation,* 6.

## Chapter Six

**1** Kriyananda, *Awaken to Superconsciousness,* 217.
**2** Yogananda, *Essence of Self-Realization* 16:12.
**3** Kriyananda, *God Is for Everyone,* 214.
**4** Yogananda, "The Astral World," *Inner Culture,* July 1941.
**5** Kriyananda, *Awaken to Superconsciousness,* 137.
**6** Yogananda, *Essence of Self-Realization* 18:17.
**7** Kriyananda, *Secrets of Meditation,* 17, 28.

## Chapter Seven

**1** Yogananda, "Obtaining Divine Healing," *Inner Culture,* October 1940.
**2** Kriyananda, *Secrets of Meditation,* 29.
**3** Yogananda, "Second Coming of Christ," *East-West,* April 1933.
**4** Kriyananda, *Secrets of Meditation,* 12.
**5** Kriyananda, *Awaken to Superconsciousness,* 235.
**6** Yogananda, "Meditations and Affirmations," *East-West* January, 1933.
**7** Yogananda, "Meditations & Affirmation," *Inner Culture,* January–March 1941.
**8** Yogananda, January–March 1941.
**9** Yogananda, "Meditations & Affirmations," *East-West,* June 1932.

## Chapter Eight

1  Yogananda, *Inner Culture*, October–December 1941.
2  Yogananda, *Autobiography of a Yogi*, 236.
3  Kriyananda, *Conversations with Yogananda* No. 46.
4  Kriyananda, *The New Path*, 421.
5  Information about Kriya Yoga can be found at www.ananda.org.
6  Yogananda, "Second Coming of Christ," *Inner Culture*, June and September 1938.
7  Kriyananda, *The Art and Science of Raja Yoga*, 400.
8  Yogananda, *Autobiography of a Yogi*, 307.

## Chapter Nine

1  Compiled from Swami Kriyananda's books *Awaken to Superconsciousness* (Chapter Seventeen), *The Promise of Immortality* (Chapter Twenty-One), and *Essence of Self-Realization* (16:12).
2  Yogananda, "On Meditation," *Essence of Self-Realization,* 18:1-26.

# PART III

# LIFE FORCE HEALS

Life Force is the only supreme, invariable power by which any or all methods of healing can be made effective. A method of healing is inferior or superior insofar as it is capable of rousing or stimulating the inactive Life Force in any diseased body part, thus electrocuting the disease.

Therefore, all methods of healing are really indirect ways of rousing the life energy, which is the real and direct healer of all diseases…. The method which can directly and quickly rouse the life energy to effect healing I term "Life Therapy," or direct healing by the rays of the inner Life Force.

–YOGANANDA [1]

# The Age of Energy

By deep study, after many years I have
found out in a nutshell how to express health—
by contacting Cosmic Energy.[1] –YOGANANDA

**According to** the astronomical calculations of Swami Sri Yukteswar, the dark age of Kali Yuga, which began in 699 BCE and ended in 1699 CE, was a period that ended roughly with what Western historians call the Dark and Middle Ages.

Throughout Kali Yuga, construction, transportation, and communication were accomplished by material means – primarily by animal and human muscle power. The later centuries of Kali Yuga saw marvels of engineering – all built without the benefit of modern machinery: the Roman cities, monuments, roads, and aqueducts; the Hagia Sophia at Istanbul; the great cathedrals including Chartres, Seville, and the Duomo in Florence; the Palace of Versailles.

Circa 1699, according to Sri Yukteswar's calculations, a new age began to dawn: Dwapara Yuga. Paramhansa Yogananda refers to it as the Atomic Age, and his direct disciple Swami Kriyananda calls it the Age of Energy.[2]

The first signs of the dawning age of energy-awareness appeared as early as 1600, when British scientist William Gilbert published his treatise on electricity and magnetism, *De magnete, Magneticisique Corporibus.* Experiments with electricity followed in Holland, Germany, and France. Near the end of the eighteenth century, Benjamin Franklin discovered the connection between lightning and electricity; inventing the lightning rod and opening the way for other practical inventions that used electric current.

In the early and mid-nineteenth century, significant discoveries in electricity were made by the Italian inventor Alessandro Volta, French physicist Andre-Marie Ampere, British scientist Michael Faraday, and American Joseph Henry, whose works inspired Samuel Morse, inventor of the telegraph.

In 1899, when according to Sri Yukteswar the world entered fully into the Age of Energy, experiments were underway that would lead to the electrification of cities and factories – these included ongoing experiments with direct and alternating currents by Thomas Edison and his rival, Nikola Tesla.

## Healing in the Age of Energy

Startlingly sophisticated healing methods were known in the ancient Orient. In India, in approximately 8000 BCE, Atreya, the progenitor of Ayurveda, wrote the oldest known medical book: the *Atreya Samhita*, which discussed the eight main branches of Ayurveda: internal medicine, surgery, fertility, pediatrics, psychiatry, toxicology, anti-aging, and ears, eyes, and nose.

Chinese medicine, which is based on a sophisticated awareness of the flow of energy through precise channels (meridians) in the human body, was practiced centuries before Christ. Egyptian physicians practiced bone setting, dentistry, simple surgery, and the use of medicinal herbs as long ago as 3300 BCE.

Much of this ancient knowledge, which was lost during the dark period of Kali Yuga, has re-emerged since 1900. Thanks to Albert Einstein's publication of his General Theory of Relativity in 1915, we know that the underlying reality of matter is energy.

Sri Yukeswar's announcement of a dawning age of energy-awareness has proved its validity with a vengeance – all of the significant discoveries since 1900 have been based on a growing understanding of energy and its practical applications. Today, electricity drives indispensable tools in every area of our lives, from medicine to heavy construction, to household devices and smartphones, and from weapons to space flight.

In 1931, Tesla, who was exuberantly ahead of his times, wrote in *The Brooklyn Eagle* newspaper: "I have harnessed the cosmic rays and caused them to operate a motive device. More than 25 years ago I began my efforts to harness the cosmic rays and I have succeeded. Electric power is everywhere present, in unlimited quantities. This new power for the driving of the world's machinery will be derived from the energy which operates in the universe, without the need for coal, gas, oil, or any other fuel."

Since the advent of Dwapara Yuga, the most forward-looking of the healing arts no longer view the human body as a machine whose parts may need repairing or replacing from time to time; rather the body is seen as a material condensation of Cosmic Energy. What Tesla called "the energy which operates in the universe" is the limitless power that Yogananda called 'life energy."

> It is the life energy alone that can effect a cure; all external methods of stimulation can only co-operate with the life energy, and are powerless without it.[3]

## Yogananda's Life Force techniques

Yogananda arrived in America in 1920 with teachings that were intended to help people understand how they could improve their lives in harmony with the new waves of energy-awareness. He emphasized the practical spiritual benefits of the science of Kriya Yoga for the all-round development of human potential. Central to the methods he taught was the use of Life Force for self-healing – he spoke of how we can "harness the cosmic rays and cause them to operate" in our human physical, mental, and causal bodies to keep them in a state of perfect balance.

> Any method of healing is effective according to its Power to arouse or stimulate the Life Force. Medicines and physical manipulations are the grosser methods, while electricity and rays are of a finer nature and effect more directly the electronic constituency of the body, and harmonize the wrong vibratory condition. The Cosmic Electric Force is the direct source of Life.[4]

Yogananda's teachings laid a practical spiritual foundation for all of the alternative healing therapies that would emerge in the new energy-aware era, including therapies that are based on working directly with the Life Force.

> We are made of light. Healing in the future will come more and more by using rays.[5]

The diagram on the following page illustrates how the power of the Life Force that animates the human body flows from Cosmic Consciousness, the divine power that creates and sustains all creation.* Yogananda teaches that Life Force is the bridge between consciousness and matter.

In Part III we will learn to activate the prana that is always present in the body, and how we can increase the amount of life force that flows into the body.

---

* These explanations are from Yogananda's *Advanced Course on Practical Metaphysics*, Lesson 4.

## COSMIC CONSCIOUSNESS

The Spirit vibrating outwards first becomes Cosmic
Consciousness, then as it vibrates into grosser states,
it becomes Conscious Cosmic Energy.

↓

## COSMIC ENERGY

Cosmic Energy is the cause of the creation of planets and
all living organisms.... the source of all living things....
Cosmic Energy is finer than Electrons or any other
vibratory force existing in Nature, and is conscious
(but not self-conscious). It is the missing link
between Consciousness and matter.

↓

## LIFE ENERGY/LIFE FORCE

The Life Energy in the body of all organisms is secretly
supplied by the Cosmic Energy. But the Life Energy loses
this contact the more it becomes individualized, selfish,
body-bound, ignoring its Cosmic Connection....
Invisible mind vibrating as Life Energy is converted into
gross matter. Matter does not exist as it appears to us,
it is nothing but vibrations of Life-Energy which in
turn are vibrations of Consciousness.

↓

## PRANA

The Life Energy [Life Force] in general as present
in the human body is spoken of as Prana in Sanskrit;
it is conscious Energy, it builds the human body
out of a spermatozoon. Its seat in the
human body is the Medulla.*

---

* "Life Force" and "Prana" are often used interchangeably in this book.

# PART III CHAPTER TWO

## The Prana Diet

Man shall not live by bread alone,
but by every word that proceedeth out of
the mouth of God. (MATTHEW 4:4)

### THE YOGINI WHO NEVER EATS*

She was a normal child in all ways but one – she had a voracious appetite. The young girl's mother often chided her for this fault, but to no effect, and for Giri Bala every meal continued to be a banquet that her humble parents could ill afford.

When Giri Bala went to live in her husband's home, her mother-in-law was not as accommodating as her parents had been. She scolded Giri Bala mercilessly and taunted her at each meal. Finally, stung and humiliated to the quick, Giri Bala retorted: "I shall never touch food again as long as I live!"

Little did her mother-in-law know that Giri Bala's outburst signaled an iron determination to discover a way to live without food.

Deeply Giri Bala prayed that God might send her a guru who could teach her how to live by His light alone. So sincere and incessant were her prayers that she entered a state of higher consciousness, which lead her that day to the banks of the Ganges. After immersing herself at the bathing *ghat,* her clothes still dripping, she beheld a saintly figure who materialized before her.

"God has answered your prayer," he told her. "From today you shall live by the astral light, your bodily atoms

*A photograph of Giri Bala is included in *Autobiography of a Yogi,* in the chapter dedicated to her, *"The Woman Yogi Who Never Eats,"* 445.

fed from the infinite current." He taught her a Kriya technique that involved a mantra and advanced pranayama exercises to free her body from its normal dependence on food.

At the time when Yogananda visited Giri Bala in 1936, she had lived without food or water for fifty-six years. He found her to be in glowing good health, with shining eyes and a serene face. In all those years, she had never been ill. Three times investigators had studied her in controlled environments where no food or liquid could pass her lips.

Now a widow, Giri Bala lived with her extended family, performing normal household chores. Her favorite pastime was cooking and feeding the others. Her service done, she filled her evenings with meditation. She could control her breath and heartbeat at will, and would often see her guru and other saints in vision.

"Would you teach this technique to others?" Yogananda asked.

Giri Bala responded, "My guru forbade me to divulge this secret."

"Then for what purpose have you been given such a prodigious ability?

"To prove that man is Spirit," she replied, "and to demonstrate that by divine advancement he can gradually learn to live by the Eternal Light and not by food."

**The fictional Hobbits** of Middle Earth in J.R.R. Tolkien's books gleefully eat seven meals every day: Breakfast, Second Breakfast, Elevenses, Lunch, Afternoon Tea, Dinner, and Supper.

While eating smaller meals more frequently is often recommended, food is not the only, or necessarily even the best, source of sustenance. Yet food is the first thing we think of when we need an extra burst of energy to power the body and mind: a hearty meal, sugar, caffeine, protein, carbohydrates – and chocolate of course!

We often expend more energy in obtaining and preparing our food than we receive by eating it! Think of the cost of getting to market, the money required in obtaining the ingredients, the time spent in shopping, cooking the food, and then eating it. The expenditures do not end here, because once the food is inside the body, it requires significant internal resources to digest. Only after considerable time does the food energy actually become available to the body cells.

Well, then, where else can we turn when we need a pick-me-up?

A nap could do it, like the efficient Spanish *siesta,* but there might not be time or place for it. Sunshine and fresh air can do the trick— unless it is after sunset. A sports activity: a jog around the lake, a bike ride into the hills - unless we are at work and can't take time out.

These common sources of energy are clearly not always available, and often not adequate for our needs.

## Going to the Source

Is it possible to bypass the dinner table and draw energy from a higher, more immediate source? In his autobiography, Yogananda told the story of his visit with Teresa Neumann,* a mystic who, like Giri Bala, had lived for years without food, obtaining nourishment directly from her inner contact with Jesus.

"How can you sustain your body without eating or drinking for so many years?" Yogananda inquired.

"I live by God's light," she replied.

Yogananda responded: "I see you realize that energy flows to your body from the ether, sun, and air."

"I am so happy to know you understand how I live... One of the reasons I am here on earth today is to prove that man can live by God's invisible light, and not by food only."[1]

## Hitting the wall

A common experience of marathon runners is "hitting the wall." This usually happens between eighteen and twenty miles in the 26.2-mile race, when the body has depleted its stores of glycogen. It comes as a sudden feeling of complete depletion, literally from one step to the next. Enthusiasm vanishes, determination becomes a challenge, and the mind insists that it's time to stop.

Speaking from my own experience on several occasions, there is a choice for runners who confront this seemingly impenetrable barrier: you can quit, or you can open a door to a higher source of energy. As a runner, I discovered that one of the most thrilling aspects of sports is the discovery that we can tap into that Source. No food is required; we need only to learn to switch from material food sources to the higher energy source, much like parking a gas-powered car and driving away in an energy-efficient electric vehicle.

However, we don't have to be marathon runners to open a door to the subtle energy source. In Part IV we will learn Yogananda's Life Force techniques that will give us the method.

## Fasting *

Many people have testified to their experiences of accessing an inner flow of prana energy while fasting. Under medical supervision, people have undertaken fasts of up to forty days and longer. After the first few days, most people feel free of hunger and able to continue their normal daily activities, even doing sports. Once the portal to the Life Force is open, the amount of prana we can draw will be limited only by our determination to remain connected to the Source.

World-class athletes like Canadian marathon runner Hussein Hashi and NFL player Hussein Abdullah continue their training through the month of Ramadan, when they abstain from food and drink for approximately eighteen hours from sunrise to sundown. U.S. Triathlete Khadijah Diggs won the Sweetwater Sprint in 2016 while fasting. Weightlifter Kulsoom Abdullah set a personal record in the deadlift while fasting. Hajra Khan, captain of the Pakistan women's soccer team, trains and tours with her team through Ramadan. "Fasting trains you to become a better human being," said Egyptian marathoner and

* You will find Yogananda's instructions for fasting in Chapter Three of Part V.

mountaineer Manal Rostrom, who maintains her training schedule and teaches three fitness classes a day during Ramadan.

## Prana without breath

Most people think of the Sanskrit word *prana* as referring to the breath. But the breath is actually the *result* of the movements of prana in the body. Another definition of prana, which we have encountered elsewhere in these pages, is Life Force. It is the movement of that energy in the body that causes inhalation and exhalation. When the movements of prana become perfectly balanced in the body, outward breathing becomes unnecessary, and the body no longer requires oxygen to survive.

> Once the yogi attains breathlessness..., the body
> is kept alive by the direct flow of energy from the
> medulla oblongata. It is possible in this state to
> remain breathless for days, months, even for years.
> The body appears lifeless, outwardly, but inwardly
> one is filled with the consciousness of infinite life. [2]

We will look more closely at the science of breathlessness in the next chapter. For now, we will consider some stories of people who have been able to live not only without food and water, but even without air.

## Breathlessness is deathlessness

In his book on *Raja Yoga,* Swami Kriyananda reports this interesting discovery.

> In 1961 the director of the Zoological Institute in
> Darjeeling, India, told me of a scientific expedition
> he had once made in the Himalayas. He and his
> companions came upon a yogi seated on the ground,
> well above the snow line, in a state of samadhi.
> The yogi must have been sitting there motionless for
> at least six months, for his fingernails, very long by

this time, had grown into the bark of a tree beside him in such a way that the slightest movement on his part would have snapped them off.[3]

## Hamid Bey

Hamid Bey was a contemporary and associate of Paramhansa Yogananda in the late 1920s. He had received rigorous training in the mysteries of the Coptic Church in Egypt, where he had learned to master his body's voluntary and involuntary functions. He would demonstrate this mastery in spectacular ways, including having himself buried underground in a sealed casket for up to three days. In his book, *My Experiences Preceding 5000 Burials*,[4] he claims to have performed this feat often. When he was released from the airless container, his body would appear dead, with no breath or vital signs. He could willfully suspend his breath while remaining connected to the inner flow of vital energy, and then reanimate his body at will.

## More than a century old

Ananda groups that travel on organized pilgrimages in India have often visited Swami Paramananda, who lives in the foothills of the Himalayas. Paramananda was born in 1889 and met Lahiri Mahaysaya as a child. He also met other Kriya Yoga masters: Babaji, Sri Yukteswar, and Paramhansa Yogananda. At this writing, he is still alive. His eyes sparkle with joy, he looks no older than seventy, and his conversation is engaging. He attributes his health and longevity to his practice of meditation, during which he daily enters the breathless state.

## Storing Cosmic Energy

Just as the body stores calories, the body's cells serve as storage containers for prana.

> There is enough energy in one gram of flesh," Master used to tell us, "to keep the city of Chicago supplied with electricity for a week."

> In a recent experiment [at a Hadron Collidor],
> one human cell was converted into energy.
> The resulting flash of light was reported to have
> been many times brighter than the sun.[5]

Life Force healing techniques accomplish two things: they activate the energy latent in the body cells while opening the doorway at the medulla oblongata to the inflow of cosmic energy.

Prana is also stored in a particular part of the brain: the medulla oblongata. In his early lessons Yogananda writes:

> This life force is stored mainly in the medulla
> and distributed through the sub-dynamos
> in the five plexuses [chakras]. The medulla
> is fed by conscious Cosmic Energy which
> surrounds the body and which is drawn
> into the body by the power of will.[6]

Prana enters the physical body through the doorway of the medulla oblongata, which will be discussed in the next chapter. There are also, however, many doors through which our energy can become dissipated.

## Avoiding Prana leaks

### ❊ THE MILKMAID'S CHAGRIN ❊

Every day, she arose before the others, then stoked the embers and added more wood before going to the barn to milk the cows. Today her milk pail was missing – who could the culprit be? Was it her little brother, playing a prank? Perhaps her mother borrowed the pail to feed the chickens, or a farmhand used it to seed the wheat. She looked around and found a bucket tucked away in the barn, then set about the milking. As she milked, she mused, "I'll churn this into butter before the others get up."

While carrying the milk pail to the kitchen, her thoughts wandered to the village dance, as she wondered who might invite her. While pouring the milk into the churn, she discovered the pail nearly empty – had she been so distracted by her fantasies that she'd spilled it? Retracing her steps to the barn, she found thin trails of milk along the way. Returning to the kitchen, she inspected the pail and much to her chagrin she saw that the bottom was riddled with tiny holes. "My little brother is about to get a good spanking!" she thought angrily as she strode upstairs to wake him.

Every cell in the body is perfectly designed to serve as a storage container for energy – for prana. And while the supply of prana is unlimited, and there are many tools to recharge the cells,* if there are holes in the "bucket," we can easily find our cells drained like the milkmaid's pail. Let us consider some of the many avenues by which our energy can become dissipated.

## Our powers of perception and organs of action

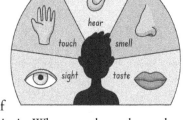

The human body is endowed with five physical senses with which we perceive and enjoy the material world, and five "organs of action" that we might participate in it. When we abuse them, they become the doorways through which our vital energy dissipates.

The five physical senses are: sight, hearing, taste, touch, and smell. They operate through the organs of perception: eyes, ears, tongue, skin, and nose. These organs convey impressions to the mind, which responds through the organs of action: mouth, hands, legs, genitalia, and the organs of excretion. The organs of action are under the **control of the mind.**

The level of our energy precisely reflects how we use our senses and organs. Some actions, such as absorbing the beauty of natural

* In Part IV you will find techniques for recharging the body cells at will.

and man-made objects, inspire us and stimulate a flow of prana – whereas passively watching television programs or videos for endless hours depletes our energy.

Similarly, listening to beautiful music or natural sounds can inspire, stimulate, or soothe us; whereas being bombarded by the disharmonious cacophony of traffic, heavy machinery, and nerve-jarring music is debilitating.[7]

Wholesome food increases our energy reserves, but overeating and junk food can quickly ruin our health.

Harmonious communication is essential for our mental and emotional health, but excessive talking is draining for the speaker and the listeners.

Fragrant flowers and refined perfumes can stimulate uplifting feelings, but in excess they can intoxicate the senses and numb the mind.

Sexual activity can be joyful and loving, but in excess it can drain the vital fluids that the body requires to maintain health.

Work, seen as a service, is fulfilling, but workaholism leads to unhealthy stress and eventual burnout.

Physical exercise is essential to keep the muscles and internal organs functioning optimally, but excessive exercise can lead to injury and depletion.

Keeping our senses and activities under control is vital for healing – though, of course, it is admittedly a skill and habit not easily acquired and maintained. We learn what our limits are through personal experience – usually painful. If we would listen to the sages and follow their wise counsel, we could save ourselves a great deal of suffering.

O Arjuna! Yoga is not for him who eats
too much or who fasts too much, who
sleeps too much or who sleeps too little.

One who is temperate in eating,
recreation, working, sleeping,
and wakefulness attains yoga,
which destroys all suffering.

(BHAGAVAD GITA 6:16-17)

# CHAPTER 2: *Points to Remember*

- Food is not the only, or the best source of energy.

- There is a cosmic source of energy that we can access and tap into directly.

- The cosmic energy flows from the causal to the astral body in the form of Life Force.

- Life Force enters the physical body through the medulla oblongata, where it is stored.

- It is also stored in the cells as prana.

- We can conserve and direct prana for self-healing, or we can dissipate it through the senses.

# Prana, the Spine, and the Chakras

> The connection between the body and the
> mind is the energy (*prana*) in the body. It is energy
> that transmits signals from the senses to the brain.
> It is energy that carries impulses from the brain to
> the body. When the flow of this energy is obstructed
> or set out of balance, there is a corresponding
> inharmony in both body and mind.[1]
>
> −KRIYANANDA

**The physical body** is a masterpiece of engineering. Its intricacies were first explored in the West in the fifteenth century by Dr. Andreas Vesalius in his work, *De Humani Corporis Fabrica* (On the Fabric of the Human Body). In the sixteenth century, Leonardo da Vinci made detailed drawings of the human body and its internal organs that are still studied and appreciated for their accuracy.

Thanks to advancements in technology and medical science, we now know much more about how the body works. However, medical science is still unable to tell us precisely why the body falls ill and how it heals.

Our spiritual search for increasing happiness and freedom does not require that we understand all of the functions of the physical body in the minute detail that medical science requires – but only that we clearly understand the body's relationship to the two subtle bodies that we inhabit, beyond the physical.

In the master scheme of creation, the blueprint for the physical body is first created on the causal plane, which we met in Part I. The master pattern for every created object and being begins with a thought, in the same way that construction of our dream house begins with just that – a dream, a mental concept of our ideal living space. We then communicate our ideas to an architect who, in collaboration with an engineer, creates a blueprint for our new home. If we can find a skilled building contractor, we will, in time, be able to manifest and inhabit our dream home on the physical plane.

Let us look at the blueprint for our "dream house" of radiant health.

## The astral nervous system: the three major naḍis

When developing a healthy lifestyle, we need to also consider our astral and causal bodies. Consciousness is the building block. It directs the creation of the astral body,* including the astral brain and the subtle energetic spine – the *sushumna* – which corresponds to the physical spinal cord. It creates as well the six major dynamos or distribution centers for energy within the sushumna, known as the *chakras*, which correspond to the nerve plexuses in the physical spine. These together correspond to the physical body's sympathetic nervous system.

The astral brain and the chakras communicate through a system of *nadis* – subtle channels through which energy flows. There are three main *nadis*: the sushumna which is the central nerve trunk of the astral body and its deepest energetic channel. On the left side of the sushumna is the *iḍa naḍi*; and on the right side is the *pingala naḍi*. These correspond to the central, sympathetic, and parasympathetic nervous systems.

> There is a subtle connection between the physical
> breath and the movement of energy in the astral
> body. For along the spine, on either side of it, run
> the two ganglionated cords of the sympathetic
> nervous system. These cords have their counterpart
> in the astral body, where they are known in the
> yoga teachings as iḍa (on the left side of the spine)
> and pingala (on the right side). When we inhale,
> there is a corresponding upward movement of
> energy in the iḍa nerve channel. When we exhale,
> there is a downward movement in the pingala.[2]

---

* The astral body includes an astral brain, or the thousand-petaled lotus of light, and six awakened centers in the *sushumna*, or astral cerebro-spinal axis." –Yogananda, *Autobiography of a Yogi*, p. 403.

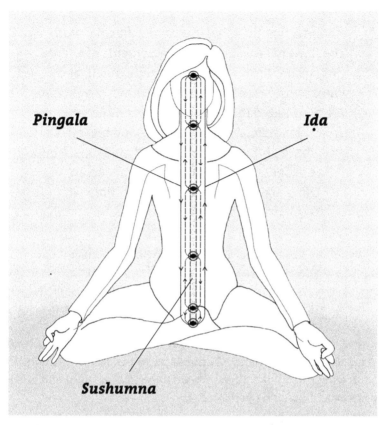

**Pingala**

**Iḍa**

**Sushumna**

The energy current in the astral spine travels upward through the *iḍa naḍi* and is called the *pran* current. This surge of astral energy results in inhalation in the physical body and the oxygenation of the cells. The descending current in the *pingala*, corresponding to exhalation, expels carbon dioxide and other waste products. [3]

Consciously controlled in pranayama and meditation exercises, inhalation can be used to affirm positive mental states, and exhalation can be used to release harmful emotions. In deep meditation, we learn to bring the descending current deeply into the sushumna. When the meditator's consciousness withdraws from the astral left and right, *pran* and *apan*, spinal currents into the central astral channel in the spine—the sushumna—the upward energy current takes us toward soul expansion, while the downward current takes us into deeper *naḍis* that lie inside the sushumna. The physical breath then becomes superfluous, as the body is connected directly to its Source.

> Connecting the inhalation and exhalation with
> the upward and downward movements of energy
> in the superficial spine, which is the origin of the
> sympathetic nervous system, those two movements
> are neutralized in breathlessness. The energy then
> no longer reacts to outer stimuli, and feelings of
> acceptance and rejection cease to trouble the mind.
> One experiences a unidirectional movement of
> rising energy in the deep spine, lifting him
> toward superconsciousness.[4]

In addition to the three main *nadis*, there are thousands of others. It is said that there are 108 main *nadis* and upward of 72,000 minor ones. You may be familiar with the number 108, which is the number of beads on classic necklaces (malas) used in spiritual practices—the 108 beads symbolizing the main *nadi* channels.

For lasting good health, the flow of energy in the *ida and pingala* channels must be balanced. Disturbances in this flow will eventually cause some parts of the physical body to be undercharged and others over-charged, resulting in disease.

### Pranayama: Balancing the flow of Life Force*

As noted earlier, the breath does not cause the currents of prana to flow in the spine. On the contrary, the movement of prana through the ida and pingala nadis causes inhalation and exhalation. Nevertheless, we can use the physical breath to help balance the flow of prana in the spine.

While pranayama is commonly understood to be a system of breathing exercises, in Sanskrit, "Prana" means "energy," and "yama" means "control." Thus pranayama is *control of the flow of energy, or prana.*

> When a deliberate mental effort is made to absorb
> prana from the air that we breathe, then breathing
> can give us psycho-spiritual benefits as well.[5]

* You can find these and other pranayama exercises in Swami Kriyananda's book, *The Art and Science of Raja Yoga.*

Controlled breathing exercises are currently being used in medicine as an effective aid in pain management, stress management, childbirth, and to help prevent and treat panic attacks.

barely managed to jump on the train in time. When I looked in my purse for my annual train pass, it wasn't there. My mind, instantly agitated, told me to run back to the gate and search the platform along the way. Of course – another worry! – I might miss the train.

Suddenly a different thought came: *Stop and breathe!*

I had recently learned a few breathing and meditation exercises – the teacher had told us that we could calm runaway emotions with simple breathing exercises and a mini-meditation.

Instead of rushing about in search of the pass, I stopped for a moment and took a few slow breaths.

In…hold…out. In…hold…out.

As my mind became calmer, a thought floated in with the breath: "Look in your purse again."

And there was my train pass, in a different compartment. Not giving in to panic was an important victory for me, one that I will confidently count on in the future.
–**Silvia**, *Milan*

We will now consider some classic *pranayama* exercises that you can use to equalize the flow of prana. The exercises are demonstrated in a video that is referenced in the Appendices for Part III. Using at least one of them every day will help ensure a healthy flow of vital energy in the body.

All pranayama exercises are best done on an empty stomach. The ideal physical posture for the exercises is seated in a stable position, on the floor or on a chair, with a straight and elongated spine so that no weight is pressing down on the diaphragm and abdomen. The shoulder blades should be brought slightly back, with the chest slightly elevated to expand the chest cavity.

You can enhance the healing effects of the exercises by accompanying them with a visualization. For example, while inhaling feel that along with the air you are inhaling you are absorbing positive qualities of strength, courage, and joy.

While holding the breath, focus at the point between the eyebrows and feel that you are burning up all negative thoughts in a blaze of divine Light.

While exhaling, feel that you are expelling disease, weakness, negativity, and sorrow.

### Regular or triangular breath

The following is a good **warm-up routine** before doing other pranayama exercises. It is also an ideal practice to balance the energy in the spine and body before meditation.

Breathing with the diaphragm, inhale through both nostrils while counting mentally to 6.

- Hold the breath, counting 6.
- Exhale, counting 6.
- Gradually increase the count to 12-12-12, and eventually to 20-20-20 if you can do so comfortably while keeping the count equal for the three phases.
- Repeat this breathing exercise six to twelve times
- If you need to, feel free to start with a shorter count (or count more quickly), and gradually increase the count only if you can do so comfortably.

Deep spiritual awareness occurs as these two currents [the iḍa and pingala] become balanced and neutralized. For the purpose of spiritual awakening, it is important that the period of inhalation and exhalation be equal.[6]

The classic position of the fingers for the following three exercises is called **Vishnu mudra**. Move the index and middle fingers of the right hand (or left hand, if you prefer) toward and then touching the palm. The thumb, ring, and little finger should remain extended, while the thumb is used to control the right nostril, and the other fingers are used to control the left nostril.

## Chandra Bedha Pranayama

*Chandra* means "moon" and is associated with the left nostril, the *iḍa naḍi*. This pranayama cools the body and is used in cases of fever and to relieve tension and stress. It can also be helpful for controlling high blood pressure. While sitting in a meditative posture, with straight spine:

- Close the right nostril with your right thumb and inhale as deeply as possible through the left nostril.
- Close both nostrils and hold your breath as long as is comfortable.
- Open the right nostril and exhale deeply.
- The rhythm of the three parts should be equal (for example, 4 counts in each phase).
- Repeat as many times as is comfortable, always inhaling through the left nostril and exhaling through the right nostril.

## Surya Bedha Pranayama [7]

*Surya* refers to the sun and is associated with the right nostril, the *pingala naḍi*. This pranayama creates warmth in the body and is said to be good for the lungs, heart, and sinuses. It helps to draw energy into the deep spine, the *sushumna*.

- Sit in any meditative posture with a straight spine. Close your eyes.

- Close the left nostril and inhale slowly through the right.

- Close both nostrils, and press the chin firmly against the chest, while holding the breath. Mentally chant AUM at the point between the eyebrows. The breath should be retained only as long as is comfortable.

- Lift the head, then exhale slowly through the left nostril while keeping the right nostril closed.

- Repeat this exercise several times.

## Nadi Shodhana Pranayama

Also known as "alternate nostril breathing," this pranayama harmonizes the flow of prana in the two main peripheral *nadis*, the *pran* and *apan*. It is used especially for purification, and during detoxification programs. Among its benefits: it calms and rejuvenates the nervous system; it is helpful as a preparation for meditation practice; it fosters mental clarity; it enhances the ability to concentrate; it reduces stress and anxiety; it releases toxins.

There are several ways to practice this technique. You may like to try them all and use at least one daily.

- Close the right nostril while inhaling through the left to a count of 8.

- Close both nostrils and hold the breath, counting to 8.

- Open the right nostril and exhale to a count of 8.

- Inhale again immediately through the right nostril, hold the breath, and exhale through the left nostril.

- Start with a shorter count if you require (or count more quickly), and gradually increase only when you feel comfortable doing so.

- Alter the length of the breaths to a 1-2-2 rhythm. For example, inhale to 4 counts, hold for 8 counts, and exhale for 8 counts.

- Increase to a rhythm of 1-4-2. For example, inhale to 4 counts, hold for 16, and exhale for 8 counts. Or try a shorter rhythm of 2-8-4.

Swami Kriyananda cautions us to be prudent.

> One should not practice too many breathing
> exercises at one sitting. When one feels
> nervous or emotionally upset, he should do
> only the most gentle of the breathing exercises.
> Finally, he should always be cognizant of
> the effects of these exercises upon his general
> nervous equilibrium. If they have an upsetting,
> rather than a calming, influence, they should
> be done for a shorter duration, or even
> abandoned altogether."[8]

## Walking pranayama

While walking, inhale and exhale deeply. Inhale for four paces, matching the rhythm to your steps; hold the breath for four paces; exhale for four paces; and hold the breath out for four paces. Repeat this exercise six or twelve times. If this rhythm is too long, start with two or three paces for each phase.

## Sama Vritti Pranayama: box breathing

Research has shown that the above four-part breathing exercise, commonly called "box breathing," has demonstrable benefits for relieving stress, anxiety, panic disorders, insomnia, depression, and that it is useful in lung disease and chronic obstructive pulmonary disease. Instead of performing it while walking, it is done in a simple, relaxed seated position with a straight spine. The four parts are equal in length, and you can begin with 3 or 4 seconds for each part.[9]

## The Standing Full Yogic Breath

- Begin by stooping forward, arms hanging limply. Exhale completely through the mouth.

- Inhale through the nose, starting from the diaphragm, and feel that the downward movement of the diaphragm while pushing the stomach outward is gradually forcing your body into an upright position. Feel as you inhale that you are also filling your lungs from the diaphragm – and not only the lungs, but your whole body.

- Straighten up slowly and bring your arms upward, elbows out to the sides, hands close to the body. Feel that you are stretching your rib cage outward and filling the middle part of your lungs. Then, with a graceful movement, extend the arms upward above your head while filling the upper part of your lungs, and imagine that the air is filling your arms all the way to the fingertips.

- Hold this position momentarily, then exhale slowly through the nose while lowering your arms in the reverse direction until you are stooping forward again in the starting position.

- With each inhalation, feel that you are not only drawing air but strength, vitality, and joy into every body cell from the toes all the way up to the crown of your head.

- With each exhalation, feel that you are expelling from your mind all weakness and negativity.

- With the last exhalation, lower your arms, but remain standing upright.

## Breathlessness

The state of breathlessness mentioned in the last chapter occurs when the flow of prana through the *iḍa* and *pingala* channels is so perfectly balanced that breath is no longer required. At that time, the central *sushumna naḍi* opens and the pran and apan currents continue to flow inside the *sushumna* channel, purifying and vitalizing the body with no need for physical breathing. When we practice meditation techniques, brief moments of breathlessness may occur naturally, giving us intriguing glimpses of the higher states of consciousness that accompany protracted breathlessness.

At Badrinath, a famous pilgrimage spot at over 3000 meters elevation (9842.52 feet) in the Himalayas, the summer residents leave in November, whereupon the bridge over the river is removed, making it difficult to leave. A few advanced yogis remain through the harsh winter months when temperatures fall below freezing and storms drop heavy snow. With only the barest provisions, they keep themselves warm and nourished by practicing prana control. I met a yogi who encloses himself in a steel container, then disconnects his soul from the physical body in a state of breathlessness in which he can continue his spiritual progress untouched by external conditions.

Kriya Yogis (who are not required to winter at high altitude) employ techniques of prana control to achieve states of complete inner stillness and bliss. Yogananda dwells at length on the Kriya technique in *Autobiography of a Yogi*, and we will mention it often in this book.

## Prana and the chakras

During a heat wave in August 2003, a power surge shut down the electricity to most of the northeastern U.S. from New York to Michigan and parts of Canada. For two days, the normal lives of 55 million people were suspended, seriously impacting businesses, hospitals, and other critical services. A month later, a similar power outage shut down most of Italy and parts of Switzerland.

Electric power is generated at high voltage to minimize power losses over long distances. At its destination it needs to be stepped-down with transformers before it can be distributed through electric cable networks and eventually delivered to the electrical circuits of homes and other buildings. Too-high voltage would burn out the relatively delicate household electric wiring, causing damage to appliances and computers.

Similarly, the Cosmic Life Energy that powers the entire universe must be stepped-down as it passes through a network of transformers in the causal and astral worlds before being distributed and delivered through the network of chakras and nadi channels.

A story from India illustrates this concept.

## ✵ THE DESCENT OF THE GANGES* ✵

The goddess Ganga Mata ("Mother of the Ganges") holds a prominent position among the residents of the heavenly realms.

In the causal universe, she represents the Cosmic Ocean. In the astral world, she manifests in Brahmaloka as the river goddess Ganga Devi, the personification of purity and power.

Her waters flowed mightily, and she frolicked unhindered by restraints. Then one day she was summoned to Earth. The astral demons, the *asuras*, at war with the astral gods, the *devas*, had hidden themselves in the waters of Earth. Fortunately, the powerful sage Agastya was sojourning on the planet, and the angelic devas solicited his help in finding their enemies. Agastya complied by drinking all of the water in the oceans and rivers – and thus the demons were revealed and conquered.

Unfortunately, Agastya was unable to restore the waters, as he had digested them already; the Earth was parched and barren. Earth's inhabitants prayed to Brahma for relief, and in his infinite compassion he commanded the river goddess to descend.

Insulted and infuriated at being thus summarily commanded, Ganga resolved that she would indeed descend, but that she would sweep away the entire Earth with her powerful waters.

---

* This is a much-abridged version of the story. I have excluded several portions that are integral to the myth but not to its allegorical significance in this context.

To save the Earth from destruction, Lord Shiva came to the aid of its people. As Ganga Devi descended, Shiva trapped her in his matted hair, where she struggled for a time, until Lord Shiva's calm touch pacified her fury.

Shiva then released her into the many small streams that even now continue to flow from his high Himalayan abode to nourish all India. Having thus been tamed, goddess Ganga Mata is entirely benevolent. Her main stream is the mighty Ganges, India's lifeblood and the object of popular worship, the most holy of rivers on Earth.

Jai Ma! Jai Ganga Ma!

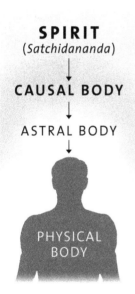

**SPIRIT**
(*Satchidananda*)
↓
**CAUSAL BODY**
↓
**ASTRAL BODY**
↓

PHYSICAL
BODY

The first transformation center for the divine power is the causal body, where pure consciousness – the "Sat" of Satchidananda – is powered-down into archetypical thought patterns and mental attitudes. In keeping with the law of duality, some of these thought patterns are governed by the soul, others by the ego.

These thought forms enter the astral body through the "thousand-petaled lotus" of the astral brain, from which they are distributed through the intricate network of the three main *nadis* and the chakras of the astral energy body.

The astral body has seven "energy centers,"
or chakras as they are called in Sanskrit, that
govern various aspects of our mental and
emotional states. These vortices of energy are
located along our "astral" spine, which is the
counterpart to our physical spine and brain.[10]

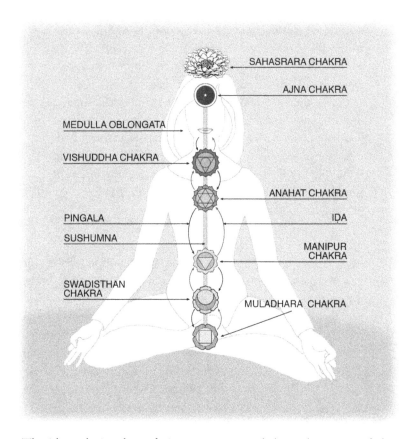

The iḍa and pingala *naḍis* intertwine around the sushumna, and the points where they cross are the chakras.

Each chakra has a positive and negative pole. We can think of the chakras as energy transformer stations with two distribution outlets: an ego portal through which energy leaks outward to become entangled in the dualistic world of Maya, and a soul door that opens inward and upward to allow the river of prana to flow to the higher spinal centers.

## Chakras and Kundalini

When Cosmic Energy enters the astral body through the thousand-petaled lotus, it descends to the point farthest from the brain, slightly below the *muladhara chakra* at the base of the spine, where the Cosmic Energy dwells as *kundalini*. When the kundalini energy becomes activated and flows upward, it harmonizes and balances the chakras.

Kundalini is a primary force for self-healing and Self-realization. Kundalini's dual nature pulls us, on the one hand, into the world of Maya. On the other hand, when properly awakened, kundalini rises upward through the astral spine to the Spiritual Eye, the highest chakra of the sushumna. Passing beyond the sushumna, kundalini reunites with Cosmic Spirit at the Sahasrara chakra, the thousand-petaled lotus at the crown of the head, in a state sometimes referred to as "mystical marriage."

> **When kundalini is raised up the spine, she passes through the chakras, uniting herself with each one of them in turn. In this awakening of inner energy lies the secret of our eventual enlightenment.[11]**

The awakening of kundalini is a universal experience. Saint Teresa of Avila, who lived in Spain in the sixteenth century, said that when the soul enters the ecstatic state it "shoots upward like a bullet out of a gun." We will see how we can naturally and safely activate this healing power, using Life Force techniques.

## The chakras and psychology

As we have seen, each of the chakras has a positive and a negative pole. Before we explore how the chakras nourish the physical body, we will look at the dueling positive and negative mental patterns that are expressed in each of the chakras – of which one of the pair is health-affirming and enables us to conserve its energy, while the other is health-negating and allows energy to be dissipated.

*Muladhara chakra* is the lowest center of subtle energy in the astral spine. It is associated with the Earth element, and its mental patterns reflect earth's solidity. It is described as having four petals, referring to the naḍi channels that emanate from it.

The soul qualities expressed by the vibrations of this chakra, which facilitate an upward movement of life force through the sushumna, are: steadfastness, perseverance, balance, endurance, faith, and commitment.

When this chakra is governed by the ego, attitudes of stubbornness, rigidity, dogmatism, bigotry, attachment, and insecurity block the upward movement of life force and keep us psychologically and emotionally involved in life's inevitable ups and downs.

From the solidity of the first, Earth chakra, we pass upward to the fluidity of **swadhistan chakra**, the Water center, with six petals. Here, the egoic patterns of the muladhara chakra become transformed by soul qualities of mental flexibility, adaptability, open-mindedness, receptivity, and creativity.

The egoic counterparts of the qualities of this chakra include indecisiveness, irresoluteness, vagueness, being easily influenced or manipulated by others, being prone to excessive sense indulgences, rebelliousness, lack of self-discipline, apathy, lack of direction, and lack of commitment. These attitudes create holes in our energy field through which vital healing energy dissipates.

Next is **manipur chakra**, the Fire center at the level of the stomach, with ten petals. The health-affirming mental attitudes of this center include self-control, discipline, determination, enthusiasm, zeal, concentration, tenacity, commitment, and courage. These are antidotes for the health-negating wishy-washy attitudes of the swadhistan chakra.

A way we can easily recognize when the energy in this chakra is governed by the ego is if we are expressing aggressiveness, destructiveness, manipulation of the other people or circumstances in our life, ruthlessness, harshness, intolerance, cruelty, anger, or lack of consideration for others.

The fiery self-purification that the manipura chakra makes possible is a necessary ingredient of a healthy life. When the qualities of the Fire center are active, they may be accompanied by heat on the physical plane, such as a fever that is meant to burn out bacterial or viral infections. On the spiritual plane, the fire element may be celebrated and refined through fire ceremonies such as the *havan* of Hindu and Buddhist traditions which seeks to purify the individual and the environment.

At the level of the heart, **anahat chakra**, with twelve petals, is associated with the Air element. It is the lowest of an upper triad of chakras that express subtler energies and consciousness than the material involvement reflected by the lower three chakras.

Health-supporting attitudes of the anahat chakra include expansive feelings of unconditional love, compassion, kindness, devotion, enthusiasm, and service. When the energy of the heart chakra flows outward, it manifests as conditional human love with its associated attachments, jealousies, and possessiveness. Limited human love can be exclusive, suffocating, and controlling. The positive manifestations of the heart chakra's energies include devotion – the polar opposite of emotion which permits prana to escape into the material world, leading to a roller coaster of hopes and expectations followed by disappointment and disillusionment.

The chakra in the sushumna with the greatest number of petals is **vishuddha chakra** at the physical level of the throat, with sixteen radiating *nadis*. Its element is Ether and it is associated with calm expansion, inner peace, limitless joy, and intuitive perception. When governed by the ego, its energies manifest as restlessness, boredom, seeking constantly varied experiences, changeability, and a mercurial, fickle personality.

Beyond the five elements is **ajna chakra**. It is the highest center in the astral spine, located at the point where the sushumna connects with the brain. This point is actually the negative pole of that chakra, corresponding to the medulla oblongata in the physical body. The positive pole of the sixth chakra is the Spiritual Eye, the point midway between the eyebrows, corresponding to the frontal lobe of the brain. Yogananda refers to this point as the seat of **Kutastha Chaitanya,** or Christ Consciousness. Both of the poles of this chakra play a decisive role in the healing techniques of Life Force Therapy.

Let us look at each of the poles.

Yogananda describes the negative pole – ajna chakra, or medulla oblongata – as the seat of ego in the body. This is where Cosmic Energy injects the soul's three bodies with an awareness of duality – the sense of separation and independence from Spirit. There are only two petals associated with this chakra. In the astral body, they symbolize the ida and pingala *nadis*. The movement of energy in these dual channels is responsible for our mental reactivity, creating our likes and dislikes and subjecting us to the law of karma.

The mental patterns associated with Ajna signal us when the ego is taking control of our inner kingdom. Be on the lookout for the following attitudes: pride, vanity, claiming authorship or ownership, narcissism, a desire for recognition, disdainfulness, craving approval and flattery, seeking to justify our actions and opinions, disrespect, and reactivity.

The positive pole of the sixth chakra, the Kutastha, is known as the Spiritual Eye. It is located at the point between the eyebrows and is the seat of willpower, superconsciousness, radiant joy, intuition, discrimination, and attunement with higher realities. In meditation, even for beginners, it can sometimes be seen inwardly.

> When this light is beheld perfectly, it takes the
> form of a five-pointed star set in a field of deep blue
> or violet light, and circled by a shining ring of gold.
> In a state of ecstasy, the consciousness penetrates
> the spiritual eye and enters the inner realms.[12]

**Sahasrara chakra**, at the crown of the head, is known as the "thousand-petaled lotus," for the myriad *nadis* that bring life energy down from the causal world at that point into the astral body. This is the point beyond duality where the ego and soul reunite in the experience of divine bliss, or *samadhi.*

> The seventh and highest *chakra*, located at
> the top of the brain, is known as the *sahasrara*, or
> thousand-petaled lotus. Albeit the highest center,

it must be approached through the Christ center. By prolonged meditation on the spiritual eye— the circular field of blue light, surrounded by a ring of gold, that appears of itself when the mind is deeply concentrated at the Christ center— a subtle passage opens up from that center to the top of the head. To attempt to approach the *sahasrara* by any other route would be futile; it has even been said to be dangerous.[13]

## Exercise for improving mental health

Review the positive and negative attitudes that correspond to each of the chakras. For each chakra, choose a positive attribute that you would like to develop, and a negative one that you would like to avoid or eliminate. Here are some examples – but you can make your own list.

### Muladhara chakra

*To avoid:* Mental rigidity
*To develop:* Perseverance

✳

### Swadistan chakra

*To avoid:* Indecisiveness
*To develop:* Adaptability

✳

### Manipur chakra

*To avoid:* Aggressiveness
*To develop:* Enthusiasm

✳

### Ananhat chakra

*To avoid:* Possessiveness
*To develop:* Kindness

### Vishuddha chakra

*To avoid:* Restlessness
*To develop:* Calmness

✳

### Ajna/medulla oblongata

*To avoid:* Justifying your actions and opinions
*To develop:* Desire to serve

✳

### Kutashta/spiritual eye

*To avoid:* Intellectuality
*To develop:* Discrimination

Now choose one of the negative attitudes that you feel is disturbing the flow of life force in you. Become aware of when and how the attitude habitually manifests in your thoughts and your interactions with others. Make an effort for a specific period to soften the attitude by substituting the opposite, positive quality that you have identified for that chakra. Evaluate your progress at the end of each day.

You can use meditation to help you unblock this chakra.

When meditating, concentrate on the chakra specifically related to the delusion you want to combat, and from that chakra try to draw the energy upward.[14]

## A technique to awaken the chakras[15]

- Sit upright and straighten the spine to resemble a straight lightning rod. Concentrate the vision between the eyebrows with eyes half open. (Do not frown while doing this; keep the facial expression serene.)

- Now slightly move the spine to the left and right by swaying the body, changing the center of consciousness from the body and senses to the spine. Feel the astral spine and stop swaying the body.

- Then let your consciousness travel up and down several times, from the coccygeal plexus at the end of the spine to the point between the eyebrows. Then concentrate on the coccygeal plexus and mentally chant Om. Again, but slowly travel up the spine, mentally feeling the coccygeal, sacral, lumbar, dorsal, cervical, and medullary plexuses, to the point between the eyebrows, mentally chanting Om in each place.

- When you reach the central point between the eyebrows, return downward, chanting Om at the point between the eyebrows, the medulla, and the five plexuses, and mentally feeling the centers at the same time.

- Continue to chant Om at the seven centers, feeling them while traveling up and down the astral spinal *Sushumna* passage. Practice the above until you distinctly feel that your consciousness is transferred from the body into the spine.

- The practice of the above method will release your soul from the bondage of matter and sense attachment by enabling you to escape through the seven astral doors and become one with the Spirit.

## Sounds of the chakras [16]

Each of the chakras is a dynamo of energy that vibrates at a specific frequency. While you practice the above technique, inwardly try to hear the astral sound that each chakra emits.

- The life current in the *coccyx* is responsible for the solidifying of Life Force and atoms into flesh, and produces the sound of a *buzzing bee* as it operates.

- The *sacral* center sustains the atoms of all the watery substance in the body and makes the musical sound of a *flute* as it works.

- The *lumbar* center keeps up the Astral and electrical heat of the body and oozes out the beautiful sound of a *harp*.

- The *dorsal* center keeps the oxygen and air elements in the body combining with the flesh and sends forth the sound of a *gong* bell.

- The *cervical* plexus maintains the etheric background in the body and times it to all spatial vibrations. This cervical center reverberates with the Cosmic Vibration of *ocean* rumblings.

- The *Christ Center*, in the medulla and at the point between the eyebrows, is the dynamo of consciousness, Life Force, and elemental vibrations, which mainly keep the elements of life, consciousness, flesh, blood, heat, air, and ether of the body continuously recharged.

- By gradual practice you will hear the Symphony of Rolling OM (the vibration of your spiritual or causal body) filling your body and mind.[17]

## Gateway to Life Force: the medulla oblongata*

Overlaying the matrix of the astral body onto the physical body, the *sushumna* correlates to the center of the spinal column; the *chakras* are reflected in the spinal plexuses; and the *naḍis* are reflected in the central and sympathetic nervous systems.[18] But where do these two bodies actually interface?

Yogananda said that the precise point of contact is where the highest spinal center in the astral body, the sixth chakra (Ajna chakra), connects to the medulla oblongata in the physical body. This is the point where the Life Force enters the physical body, infusing it with

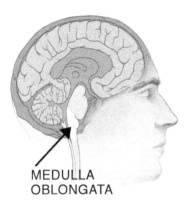

MEDULLA
OBLONGATA

prana. The entire body is nourished by the pranic "lifetrons" as Yogananda calls them,† that make up the Life Force.

Anatomically, the medulla oblongata is the lowest part of the brain stem, as shown in the diagram here. It connects the brain to the spinal cord and is the communication link between the brain and the rest of the body.

---

* The medulla oblongata carries signals from the brain to the rest of the body for essential life functions such as breathing, circulation, swallowing, and digestion. Making up a tail-like structure at the base of the brain, the medulla oblongata connects the brain to the spinal cord, and includes a number of specialized structures and functions. While every part of the brain is important in its own way, life cannot be sustained without the work of the medulla oblongata. –Adapted from Zimlich, Rachael, "The Anatomy of the Medulla Oblongata," Very Well Health, May 30, 2023, https://www.verywellhealth.com/medulla-oblongata-anatomy-4799916.

† See Chapter Four in Part I.

We speak of the medulla as the mouth of
God or the finite opening in the body of man
through which God breathes His Cosmic
Energy or Life into flesh. This medulla [is]
also called the mouth of the astral body.[19]

When the soul passes from one incarnation to the next, it "vacations" for a time in the astral world until the seeds of material desires sprout once again, forcing it to return to the material plane.

When the body of man dies, the astral body
lives on. His desires live on also, for these, forming
as they do vortices of *energy*, belong not to his
physical, but to his astral body. But because desire
directs energy, so long as his desires are for worldly
enjoyment they draw him again and again into
physical incarnation. After death he goes for a time
to the astral plane, but his time there is limited
by the strength of his physical desires.[20]

The time and place of a soul's next birth are governed by a mysterious metaphysical calculation that matches the soul's karma with the best opportunities for its further evolution.

When the sperm and ovum unite, there is
a flash of light in the astral world. Souls there
that are ready to be reborn, if their vibration
matches that of the flash of light, rush to get in.
Sometimes two or more get in at the same time.[21]

Not all matches are perfect. A mother living in an Ananda community told how she was scolding her five-year-old daughter, and how the child retorted: "Just so you know, you weren't my first choice!"

The Soul first enters the nucleus in
the spermatozoa. When the sperm by the
miraculous work of his life force develops into a
body, the nucleus of the sperm remains as
the medulla or the seat of life. This medulla is called
the mouth of God, for through that center He first
breathed the breath of life-force into the human
body. The medulla is the most sensitive of all bodily
organs. Operations can be performed on almost
any part of the body except the medulla.[22]

The intelligent cosmic energy draws a blueprint for a body that will be compatible with the individual's karma. This energy flows through an invisible conduit that connects the astral body to the physical body at the medulla oblongata, similar to the umbilical cord that connects the infant to its mother.

Keep [your] body constantly supplied with
fresh cosmic energy descending into the body
through the door of the Medulla Oblongata.
Strong will pulls energy from the Conscious
Cosmic Rays surrounding the body through the
door of the Medulla Oblongata. Man shall
not live by bread (or food chemicals) alone,
but by every word (vibratory life energy)
which flows (into the body of man) through
the mouth of God (that is, the opening of
the Medulla, through which the Conscious
Cosmic Life Principle enters the body of man).[23]

At birth, the astral doorway remains open for approximately a year. When newborns and infants dream, they may remember their life in the astral world, and even previous lives on this or another physical planet.

As the soul becomes self-aware and the ego takes charge, the astral doorway in the medulla oblongata closes. **Reopening the doorway of the medulla oblongata** is an essential part of learning to use life force as an instrument for self-healing.

## How to stimulate the medulla oblongata

- Slightly lift your chin while relaxing the muscles at the back of the neck.

- Touch the place at the base of the skull, behind the head, in the soft tissue between the head and neck, where you will feel a slight indentation. Considerably inside and well-protected at that point is the medulla oblongata. The medulla generally carries a great deal of tension, both from the weight of head and because it is the seat of the ego.

- Massaging the medulla helps relieve the tension and stimulates the doorway to help re-open to the flow of Cosmic Energy. This self-massage practice is enjoyable at any time and is especially helpful before practicing any of the exercises in this book.

- *Follow these instructions by Yogananda:*

  Concentrate on the medulla, close your eyes, and feeling or visualizing the light there, repeat:

  "Thy cosmic current flows in me, flows in me,
  through my medulla flows in me, flows in me.
  I think and will the current to flow,
  in all my body the current to flow,
  in all my body the current to flow.
  I am charged, I am cured, I am charged, I am cured.
  Lightning flash goes through me.
  I am cured, I am cured." [24]

The most lastingly effective way to stimulate the medulla center is by developing, strengthening, and applying our willpower, the master key that can open the door instantly. In the next chapter, we will discuss that key.

## The Spinal Highway

During an infant's nine-month gestation period in the womb, the astral body feeds its physical body and forms the spinal plexuses. Each plexus nourishes a specific part of the body:

There are subtle centers of energy in the spine that correspond to the neural plexuses through which nerves carry energy to and from the spine and the parts of the body.

- From the lowest plexus, the coccyx, nerves pass to the legs.

- From the next plexus, the sacral, about an inch and a half above the coccyx, nerves pass to higher portions such as the sex organs.

- From the lumbar plexus located opposite the navel they pass to the digestive organs.

- From the dorsal plexus, opposite the heart, they nourish the heart and lungs.

- From the cervical plexus, opposite the throat, they affect the vocal cords, throat, and neck.

- And from the medulla oblongata they reach the brain. At the medulla, indeed, they divide and become the two currents of energy in the spine, taking the energy upward and downward with the breath, and thus connected with the heart and lungs." [25]

When there is a strong and balanced flow of prana through the spine and chakras and their correlated plexuses, the prana is able to keep the body healthy. When the flow is disturbed and insufficient prana reaches the body, the result is disease.

The spine is like a power company that connects the electric appliances in a home (in this case, the body) to the power network (the flow of prana). For optimal health, it is important to keep the spine flexible and relaxed so that the nerves that radiate from the spine will not be pinched. The spinal stretches of the yoga asanas are excellent for this, and doing even a few of them regularly will keep the prana flowing harmoniously. Many asanas can be done while sitting in a chair.[26]

> Yoga exercises also help adjustment of spinal vertebrae, which releases the pressure on the spinal nerves and brings about the normal flow of life-force in the nervous system, which also brings about healing of many diseases.[26]
>
> It is good also to go to an expert once in a while to keep the spine flexible and to be sure that the vertebrae are in their proper places and that they are not shutting off the life force by pinching the nerves.[27]
>
> Spinal adjustments and massages are effective [for]... release[ing] obstructed life-force which can bring about a quicker and surer healing of physical diseases than anything else.[28]

## The five Pranas

Once the Intelligent Life Force manifests the physical body and begins to flow in it, it delegates the creation of the body's inner workings to five "specialists." In the yoga teachings, these are called the "five pranas" or the five *vayus*, meaning winds, or currents. If you are experiencing physical symptoms of disease, and you can correlate them with their associated chakra, it will help you identify which of the spinal centers needs to be stimulated.

The first of the five pranas is **pran vayu**, the "crystalizing current." It is a fundamental energy that is said to create and nourish all the others. Pran vayu is associated with the element of Air, with inhalation, with the *anahata* (heart chakra), and the spiritual eye. It is responsible for the respiratory system, including the heart and lungs, diaphragm, and throat, as well as the brain, eyes, and senses. Its quality is receptivity – to food, to air, to ideas and feelings, and to information and suggestions. When this vayu is not functioning well, respiratory problems result.

The **udan vayu** is the "metabolizing current." It is associated with the subtle element of Ether, and with the *bishuddha* and *ajna* chakras and *kundalini shakti* – the creative, blissful consciousness of enlightenment. Its physical functions include regulating the endocrine and nervous systems. When in balance, this vayu produces a focused, intuitive mind, articulate communications, acute sensory awareness, and the ability to respond to the outside world. When functioning poorly, it can result in metabolic, thyroid, and speech disorders.

The **saman vayu** is the "assimilating current." It is associated with Fire and the *manipura chakra,* and is responsible for transforming food to nourishment for the entire body, as well as for assimilating thoughts and emotions. On an evolutionary level, it relates to kundalini and the expansion of consciousness. When not functioning well, indigestion and stomach disorders may result.

The **vyan vayu** is the "circulatory current." It is associated with the element of Water and the *swadhistan chakra,* and is responsible for supplying blood to all parts of the body. It connects all the functions of the body and regulates the nerves, veins, joints, muscles, and the sense of physical balance and of being grounded. When not functioning well, a lack of physical coordination, mental confusion, anemia, and skin eruptions can result.

The **apan vayu** is the "eliminating current." It is associated with the Earth element, with the muladhara chakra, and with exhalation. It is the energy that governs the removal of waste from the physical body, operating in the genitals, lower intestine, colon, rectum, kidneys, and bladder. When not functioning well, intestinal and stomach problems such as gas, constipation, and even tumors can result. In the mental sphere, an imbalanced apan vayu can result in laziness, dullness, confusion, and indecisiveness.

## Spinal health

A feature that distinguishes human beings from other vertebrates is that our spine is vertical. A properly maintained spine is the highway through which healing energy can nourish all parts of the body. Bad posture compacts the vertebrae, cutting off the flow of energy to the nerves that serve the various body limbs and organs. When sitting, standing, walking, driving, or engaged in any activity, it is important to be aware of and correct our posture so that the vertebrae are not pressing against one another.

Yogananda highlights the importance of correct posture:

> It is slow but sure suicide to walk, sit, rest,
> talk, sit at table, or lie with a caved-in chest.
> The lung cells are starved thereby, and
> maladjustments of the vertebrae occur.
> So it is absolutely necessary always to have
> the chest forward and shoulder blades a
> little backward, even when leaning back
> against a chair for rest.[29]

*Here are some easy checkpoints to monitor your posture:*

- Raise the chest and keep it raised. When walking, lead with the chest.

- Bring the shoulder blades slightly together, to keep the lungs and bronchial tubes open.

- Keep the chin parallel to the ground and pulled slightly inward, to straighten the cervical vertebrae.

- Feel as though a string is attached to the crown of your head, pulling the spine upward.

- Use appropriate exercises to strengthen the abdominal muscles that help keep the lower back in alignment.

- To release muscle tension in the spine, regularly practice hatha yoga, the Life Force Energization Exercises (p. 275), massage, and/or osteopathic/chiropractic adjustments.

- When sitting for long periods, make a habit of standing up at least every hour, and do a few spinal exercises. In the Appendices you will find a video of some easy spinal stretches.

# CHAPTER 3: *Points to Remember*

- Cosmic Energy flows through the causal body to the astral body as Life Force before it reaches and nourishes the physical body as Prana.

- Good health depends on having an abundant supply of prana in the body, and on its harmonious flow.

- The astral body consists of the astral brain, three main energy channels called the nadis (the ida, pingala, and sushumna), and the chakras.

- To maintain good health, it is important to balance the flow of life force in the *nadis* with the aid of pranayama exercises. Practice at least one pranayama exercise for several minutes each day.

- Life Force enters the physical body at the medulla oblongata, the negative pole of the sixth chakra, and is distributed along the cerebrospinal cortex (the brain and the spinal plexuses).

- The doorway to Life Force at the medulla oblongata is generally closed due to ego-centered mental attitudes. Opening this doorway is the key to all effective self-healing methods.

- The mental attitudes that correspond to each chakra either facilitate or block the flow of prana.

PART III    CHAPTER FOUR

# Willpower

A strong will, especially if combined with
awareness of the cosmic energy, can effect miracles.
It can cure diseases, and make a person well.[1]

Strengthen your will and determination
in everything. Your body will then be internally
vibrating with life current...[You can] shake out
disease, failure, and ignorance, but the will
vibration must be stronger than the vibration
of physical or inner disease. The more chronic
the disease is, the stronger, steadier, and more
unflinching should be the determination,
faith, and effort of the will to get well.[2]

—YOGANANDA

**THE GREATER THE WILL,
THE GREATER THE FLOW *of* ENERGY.**
Remember it. Emblazon it in your mind.
Repeat it to yourself several times a day.
This single truth can revolutionize your life.[3]

—KRIYANANDA

## ❊ THE SHINY PAIL ❊

Big Frog and Little Frog were mismatched in size but
were nonetheless good friends. Among all the creatures that lived around the pond, these two were the most
adventurous.

One morning, they set off down the road to the local barnyard, hopping merrily in anticipation of an ad-

venture. No sooner they got there than they spied a glint coming from the direction of the cowshed. When they challenged each other to reach the shining object first, Big Frog with his longer legs and wide-webbed feet was the victor.

When Little Frog arrived, he found Big Frog staring up at a shiny pail – What an interesting sight! – they had never seen such a marvel. In unison, they leapt onto the rim to peer inside, where they saw what appeared to be a deep pond of white water gleaming below. Never having seen white water, they eagerly jumped in.

Although the white pond wasn't big, it was refreshingly cool and had a pleasant smell. Having explored it from side to side and top to bottom, they decided to move on and see what other adventures the barnyard could offer.

Alas! The rim of the pail was too high and their feet found no solid base to jump from. All they could do was keep swimming in the hope that someone would save them.

As time passed and no one came, their swimming became boring, then laborious. Finally, Big Frog exclaimed that he couldn't go on. But Little Frog gathered all his willpower and exclaimed that they must! And so they kept swimming for a while, until Big Frog, legs burning with fatigue, stopped paddling and sank.

Refusing to succumb to what seemed a dire fate, the plucky Little Frog kept paddling. Then, after no more than a few minutes, he felt something soft but solid under his feet, and with his last strength he leapt onto the pail's rim. Looking down, he saw a small yellow mound floating in the white water where he had jumped.

(The farmer's wife was just as surprised when she came to fetch the milk!)

**Before we address** the subject of willpower, it will help to review two points from the last chapter.

- Life Force enters the physical body at the medulla oblongata, where it is distributed as prana along the cerebrospinal cortex (the brain and spinal plexuses).

- The doorway of the medulla oblongata is generally closed owing to ego-centered mental attitudes. Opening the doorway to the flow of life force is the key to self-healing.

One of Yogananda's significant contributions to the science of spiritual healing is an understanding of the connection between willpower and the flow of healing life force.

> **Strong will pulls energy from the Conscious Cosmic Rays surrounding the body through the door of the Medulla Oblongata.[4] Will power is the switch which controls the flow of energy." [5]**

As this diagram shows, the brain's frontal lobes are opposite the medulla oblongata at the base of the skull. Yogananda said that willpower is localized in the frontal lobes of the brain, and that it has a direct connection with the medulla oblongata.

The medulla oblongata in the physical brain is the negative pole of the sixth chakra, the positive pole of which is the spiritual eye, at the point in the fore-

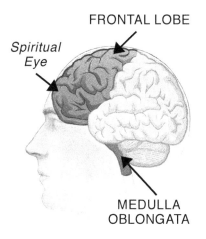

FRONTAL LOBE

*Spiritual Eye*

MEDULLA OBLONGATA

head midway between the eyebrows and directly on the dividing line between the two cerebral hemispheres. We can open the doorway of the medulla by applying our will, and the amount of life force we can draw will depend on the strength of our will. We can then distribute the life force to any areas of the body that need healing. Yogananda said, **"The greater the will, the greater the flow of energy."** It is life force that activates the body's healing powers.

He was an experienced mountaineer. Alone or with climbing friends, he had scaled many of Europe's highest peaks, including a number of first ascents. Yet one climb had eluded him - this time, he would attempt it on his own. He knew the mountain well, having reached the peak on several occasions by other routes, but this would be his first attempt to conquer the impossible north face.

The ascent began with no insurmountable challenges. His equipment was in good order and he was in top condition. Yet, just before the summit, the cliff curved far out over the valley, a thousand meters below. He couldn't go forward, as there were no holds for hands, feet, or pitons (rock anchors). Nor could he return the way he had come. His only option was to climb upside down and out around the jutting rock.

A small ledge supported him as he made his first attempt. At a certain point the force of gravity pulled him back down to the ledge. Again and again he tried, and yet again, always falling painfully from the same point. Bruised and exhausted after more than twenty attempts, he came close to giving up. It seemed he would die there. But what kind of spirit would he die with? Surely that would be up to him. He thought, "If I die, I will do so trying one more time." Summoning all his willpower, he continued.

On one of the "final" attempts, just as he reached the point where he always fell, a force pressed him against the mountain and continued to hold him safely as he progressed around the protruding edge to the top of the jutting boulder. Uncomprehending but grateful, he continued the short distance to the summit.

When he recounted the experience to his climbing companions, they could only conclude that the thin air had caused him to hallucinate. Clearly, there would be no persuading them, yet he knew that the power of the universe had responded to his determination. From then on, he had a deep appreciation of the proverb: "Where there is a will, there is a way."

✵ ✵ ✵

## *What is willpower?*

The true story of the mountaineer is a spectacular and unusual demonstration of the power of will to attract the help of the universe and defy even the laws of gravity.

Willpower is an indispensable element of success in every undertaking. It is the secret weapon of the student who is determined to become a surgeon, the athlete who resolves to win an Olympic medal, the scientist who is eager to discover new worlds, and the innovator who is determined to find ways to make others' lives easier and more fulfilling.

To strengthen our muscles, we need to challenge them. The same is true for the will. Using our willpower for constructive purposes makes it grow stronger. The stronger the will, the more life force we can draw into the body for self-healing and for all our activities.

"If only wishing could make it so." We spend plenty of time wishing that things were better. But wishing has no power to attract a desired result. The same for our good intentions – most of which are quickly forgotten. "I wish I could take a long vacation at the seaside. I'll ask my boss for some extra days."

### The compliant boss

A friend of mine had longed for years to undertake a spiritual pilgrimage to India, but every year she faced the same obstacles. She didn't have the money and her job didn't allow her take time off in February when the pilgrimages happened.

When friends showed her videos of their travels in India, her wish blazed into a powerful desire. She determined that she would go the following year, feeling that her moment had arrived.

The first hurdle was money – she earned a modest salary and had no special skills to earn some extra funds in her spare time. Yet her inner conviction kept her hopes alive.

The universe responded in unexpected ways. An aunt with whom she'd been close as a child passed away, leaving her a substantial amount. Suddenly she had almost reached her goal.

When a letter arrived from the tax service, she worried that it might be bad news but was elated when it was a refund for an overpayment five years earlier. Now she had enough to cover the trip, plus a little extra.

In India, the pilgrimage season is during the hot and humid monsoon months, but for Westerners the ideal weather is at the beginning of the year. Where my friend worked, this was inventory time, with mountains of documents to prepare, and she feared that her boss would never let her go. Yet her desire and conviction were so strong that she steeled herself and knocked on the boss's door.

When she explained that she wanted to go on a spiritual pilgrimage, the boss's eyes grew wistful as she confessed that she, too, longed for such an experience. "Well, go for both of us," she said. "And when you come back, be sure to tell us all about it."

Almost as though living in a dream, she bought her ticket, joined the group and came back with a suitcase full of gifts and a heart filled with inspiration.

❄ ❄ ❄

Willpower is the difference between wistful dreams and actual accomplishments – willpower is the ability to set a course and keep sailing until we've reached it. *Desire* is not the same as wishful thinking, which begins and ends in the mind. When we add energy and emotion to a thought, it becomes a volition.

*Yogananda defines willpower as:*

**Desire plus Energy, directed toward fulfillment.**[6]

❄ PARALYMPIC CHAMPION [7] ❄

E ven as a five-year-old, Beatrice Vio exhibited remarkable skill for fencing; but her career nearly ended at eleven, when she was diagnosed with meningitis. Both forearms had to be amputated, along with both legs at the knee. Although deprived of her limbs, "Bebe" was not bereft of her passion for fencing or her ambition to be a champion.

Bebe was fitted with prosthetic arms and legs, and after only three months of rehabilitation, she returned to arduous training using a specially designed arm to grasp the foil. She had to relearn the sport and develop exceedingly strong abdominal and chest muscles to move quickly and stay balanced in a wheelchair. Now she spends six to ten hours every day training for major competitions, besides attending school.

In 2013, at sixteen, she won the first of eleven consecutive World Cup victories. In the Rio Paralympics in 2016 she won the gold medal, the only competitor with a prosthetic foil arm.

Bebe's motto is: "If it seems impossible, then you can do it." Her inner strength enabled her to turn a tragedy into an opportunity and adversity into victory.

Bebe inspires and encourages others who've suffered severe setbacks: "Don't be pushed by your problems. Be led by your dreams." Together with her parents, she founded a non-profit that helps disabled athletes and raises money to buy them artificial limbs, which are very expensive. She applies her determination and willpower at John Cabot American University, where her goal is to earn a master's in communications and international relations while continuing her fencing career.

*Bebe's story illustrates the willpower formula for success:*
- A strong desire
- A clear vision of the goal
- Relentless, purposeful actions toward the goal
- A willing determination to make our best effort
- The inner strength to remain undiscouraged by adversity

### "Use it or lose it"

Each day presents us with opportunities to use our willpower. Every conscious or unconscious choice will either contribute to building or depleting our health reserves.

When it was time for my run yesterday, I went outside to check the weather. It was cold and windy. The classic struggle followed: to go or not go? With a shiver, I was about to skip the run when I had a thought that hurdled me over to the right side. I asked, "What do I need so that I can do what I know is good for me?"

Remembering that I had a warm hat, running gloves, and a good jacket, I quickly put them on before the ego could join the discussion, and off I went. My initial reluctance and low energy faded with each stride and breath, as I felt prana invigorate my body and brain. My usual forty minutes turned into an effortless hour, and when I returned I was grateful for the physical benefits and the small victory of my will.

A habit of neglecting our willpower weakens the body's protective shield of immunity. A lazy "couch potato" is more likely to fall victim to disease than a person who is dynamically engaged in serving a worthy cause.

Retirement is a transition that we can experience in the manner of our own choosing. Research has shown that retired women tend to remain active in their family and social spheres, and often engage in new endeavors, while retired men tend to have greater difficulty adjusting. Instead of using their free time creatively, they tend toward passivity and experience one illness after another, often culminating in early death.

### Free Will

*Where does our willpower come from?*

We humans are endowed with many abilities that distinguish us from the less-evolved creatures. Physically, we cannot compete with the strength of a lion or the swiftness of a gazelle, much less the sight of a hawk, the hearing of a bat, the olfactory sense of a bear, or the brain size of a sperm whale.

But mentally we excel, thanks to our capacity to reason and think abstractly, conceptually, and sequentially, and to concentrate, discriminate, plan and organize, and express ourselves artistically and symbolically.

We also possess a very real superpower that is the decisive difference between ourselves and the animals: **free will**.

While the lives of animals are ruled by instincts that constrain their behavior, humans alone possess the ability to choose their actions, thoughts, and feelings. We exercise our free will by the use of our willpower.

We have the free will to eat well or unwisely, to give kindness or contempt, to focus our mental attention or succumb to distractions. It is because of the human gift of free will that the Law of Karma applies to us more pointedly than the animals, whose mass karma permits them little or no freedom to determine their individual fate. The freedom to choose comes with the powerful caveat that we are bound to experience the consequences of our choices. In this way, we learn and evolve, slowly or quickly, toward ever greater awareness.

### *How free is our will?*

Our human free will to choose and to determine the course of our lives is unquestionably influenced and conditioned by our family and friends, by the social conventions of our culture, and by our past karma.

We may be intent on doing something bold or unusual, but then someone talks us out of it. Or we decide that "on second thought" we don't want to bother. It takes great inner strength of will and character to swim against the current of "how things have always been done."

In recent years in England and Japan, members of the royal families have married outside of the nobility. The social and economic consequences failed to deter them from their conviction and the inner certainty of the rightness of their course.

The exercise of our free will by using our will pwer plays such a powerful role in maintaining our health and our spiritual progress that it deserves careful consideration. In what ways does our will-power become conditioned and limited? How can we make full use of this superpower that we have so uniquely been granted?*

## What strengthens or weakens our willpower?

Beyond external influences which impact our choices, there are ways that we ourselves undermine or re-inforce our free will. It is no exag-geration to say that day by day and choice by choice we either strengthen or weaken our will, and consequently influence the state of our health. Like

a physical muscle, willpower becomes stronger each time we apply it. As we have already seen: "The greater the will, the stronger the flow of healing life force."

Even the weakest will can be strengthened—by consciously de-veloping attitudes of willingness and positivity, by making efforts to establish healthy habits,† and by having the courage to overcome adversity. Every day life gives us countless opportunities to be will-ing to go the extra mile, to do something difficult or never before attempted, to be positive and courageous in the face of unexpected circumstances.

Attitudes that weaken our willpower include passivity, unwilling-ness, negativity, indulging in bad habits, addictive behaviors, and permitting ourselves to be victims of doubts and fears. The moment we recognize that we are falling prey to these tendencies is the mo-ment to reverse direction.

**Passivity.** While passivity may seem harmless and temporary, it is actually one of Maya's cleverest weapons. Passivity is a devious trick that the ego uses to keep us from realizing our potential.

By definition, passivity means *unwillingness* to engage our energy, mind, and emotions. Its root source can be sheer laziness, apathy,

* In Part VII, Volume Two, we will see the importance of willpower for replacing unhealthy habits with healthy ones.

†See Volume Two, Part VII for detailed instruction on how to establish good habits

or a lack of courage or hope. Often it is simply a symptom of low physical and mental energy that is incapable of rising to the occasion. Unwillingness can become a poisonous habit of doing even the most necessary tasks reluctantly, minimally, or not at all, or of putting off large and small tasks until tomorrow and beyond, whether they involve washing the dishes, filing a tax return, or giving serious attention to a health warning.

In all cases, passivity is a choice that seriously weakens our willpower.

Habitual unwillingness is a common
human condition, suggesting to the mind
endless mountain ranges of problems in the
discharge of the simplest duty. For just
as willingness draws a constantly fresh
supply of energy to the body, so also does
unwillingness block that supply.
"The greater the will, the greater the
flow of energy." The corollary of that
axiom is, "The greater the unwillingness,
the feebler the flow of energy." [8]

The opening story of this book, "Live or Die," provides a glimpse of the results of passivity, and its opposite quality, dynamic willpower.

We each have a personal comfort zone where we feel most physically, emotionally, and mentally secure. When we habitually reject opportunities to go outside the comfort zone and broaden our awareness, we condemn ourselves to a life of comfortable mediocrity.

Yogananda recalled how, as young boys, he and a friend ran away from home and tried to reach the Himalayas. When they were foiled by the arrival of their older brothers, the friend quickly gave up on the quest. Yogananda's resolve remained strong, and, although temporarily thwarted, it would be fulfilled later in his life.

I remember a math exam in my first year of college that nearly all of the students failed. I complained to the professor that the exam was unfairly difficult, and I can still see his penetrating look as he replied: "The material wasn't that difficult – you have a lazy mind." I had to admit that he was right, that I hadn't truly engaged my mental capacities since I had little interest in math. The humiliation of his words roused me from my passivity, and I had no reason to complain about my grades on subsequent exams.

Have you ever been out walking when a pebble got in your shoe? Unwilling to stop and untie the shoe and shake out the pebble, you tried to move it to the arch where it wouldn't bother you. But then it became so irritating that you had to stop and remove it. Why didn't you take it out in the first place?

Passivity, the defining feature of "*shudra* mentality," can become an ingrained and perpetual habit of not putting out the energy to change, improve or grow past our present condition.

**Willingness** is the other side of the coin. Happy, healthy, successful people are willing actors in the drama of their lives. They embrace an attitude of openly and enthusiastically welcoming whatever tasks or challenges arise. The team leader who is eager to see a project through to completion is far more likely to receive a promotion and a raise than the timid individual who jumps ship at the first sign of trouble.

In *Affirmations for Self-Healing,* Swami Kriyananda offers the following insights about willingness.

> Willingness must be cultivated deliberately.
> It is an attitude of mind, and depends
> not on outward conditions.
>
> Most people are willing or unwilling
> depending on their likes and dislikes.
> This habit tends to develop a bias toward
> unwillingness, which gradually becomes
> chronic, and attracts to itself chronic failure.
>
> Don't wait for favorable circumstances to
> awaken willingness in you. Train yourself in
> the attitude of saying yes to life! Often by
> this simple attitude you will find Success
> arriving, unexpected, at your door! [9]

There is another kind of willingness – somewhat ironically, it is the willingness to fail. We waste too much of our power on trying to avoid failure – with the result that we avoid success as well. Our failures are necessary steps on the path to success – and when accepted as such, they can teach us valuable lessons.

### Willing to Fail

Walt was far too young to make his way in the world, yet he resolved that he would no longer passively endure his family's extreme poverty or his father's abuse. Lying about his age, he enlisted in the military and served in World War I.

His destiny was not as a soldier, but as a great visionary.

In his mind, he saw drawings that came to life. With no previous training or financial means, he set himself a goal of creating animated characters on film. His first animation studio went bankrupt. Having failed once, he soon overcame his anxieties and was eager to keep perfecting his animations.

It was at this early stage of his career that he created Mickey Mouse. After three hundred rejections from potential investors to fund a studio, he finally found a backer. And, of course, Mickey Mouse became the most celebrated animated character of all time, and Walt Disney would become known as one of the greatest innovators of his generation.

A soldier will not win every battle, nor will an athlete win every game. An artist will not be able to create a masterpiece with every effort. Walt Disney faced bankruptcy once again thanks to labor shortages during the Second World War. Nonetheless, he embarked on yet another bold venture: Disneyland, which has welcomed more than 700 million visitors since its opening in 1955. Few people today know about Disney's failures, but we do remember his twenty-two Academy Awards, his Congressional Medal of Honor, and his Presidential Award of Freedom.

**Negativity** is a member in good standing of the Passivity-and-Unwillingness Gang. Negativity's unswerving creed is that nothing could possibly be as good as it seems – there must be a hitch, a hidden darkness, which the negative person takes it as his sacred duty to unveil. Given that nothing and no one is perfect in this world of duality, a habit of always looking for the dark side places a lens over our perception which filters out the very real goodness in creation.

In its slightly less deadly form, negativity manifests as **complaining**, a pastime that is not only a complete waste of energy, but drains the complainer's inner resources, sucks the energy out of others, and renders the environment as inharmonious and unhealthful.

Perhaps you have felt the atmosphere in a household where the inhabitants are world-class complainers – how uncomfortable and enervating it is.

> The impulse to carp at everything is a kind of illness of the mind. It prevents people from opening themselves to new ideas, and causes them to see themselves as, in a sense, presiding judges in the courtroom of life. In other words, it is a negative symptom of ego-consciousness.[10]

A darker and even more dangerous aspect of negativity is when we assume that no one is to be trusted, that everyone has ulterior motives or has something to hide, that the deck is always stacked against us, and that people in authority have joined with the members of a secret cabal to control our lives. An obsessive persecution complex is a mental disorder that destroys the mind's ability to discriminate and dupes us into believing even that which we know to be untrue, even disbelieving things we have personally experienced to be true.

**Doubt and fear** are negativity's close friends, and equally capable of closing down the flow of prana.

When I asked a saintly woman in India what she considered the greatest obstacle to spiritual progress, she replied without a moment's hesitation: "Doubt." Once we allow unreasonable doubts to enter the discussion, our willingness to act is put dangerously at risk. One of Maya's favorite weapons, doubt paralyzes us and prevents us from moving forward.

Any decision that we make using only the rational mind will usually be accompanied by a concern that it might be wrong, or that a better decision exists. Perhaps you've signed up for a yoga class, but before the first session you begin to doubt whether Pilates might be better for you, or if perhaps you could find a better yoga instructor. As your doubts pile up and stoke the inner controversy, your will to improve your health will fade and you may soon find yourself utterly paralyzed, unable to decide if you should go forward at all, and which path and which teacher to follow.

After we make a purchase, especially an expensive one, we may suffer from "buyer's remorse." Where we were initially elated with the purchase, doubts being to creep in: will we soon receive news of a better product? Does the product have hidden flaws? Did we research it sufficiently? The internet provides plenty of fuel for doubts.

Yogananda considered **fear** the most powerful saboteur of willpower.

> One of the greatest enemies of will power
> is fear. Avoid it both in thought and in action.
> The life force that is flowing steadily through your
> nerves is squeezed out when the nerves become
> paralyzed by fear, and thus the whole vitality of the
> body is lowered. Fear doesn't help you to get away
> from the object of fear, it only paralyzes your
> will power. You must be cautious but never afraid.
> When fear comes the brain discharges the
> message to all the organs. It paralyzes the heart,
> disturbs the digestive forces, and causes
> many physical disturbances.[11]

**Unhealthy habits** are like black holes that cripple the will and hold it captive, seriously weakening our ability to accomplish.

Habits are a time-saving device. Instead of having to ponder each step of a routine action (e.g., driving), we learn it and relegate it to the subconscious, where it waits like a file in a computer's hard drive.

Habits begin with a desire for a certain fulfillment, followed by a conscious volition to fulfill the desire, and finally repeated actions to satisfy the desire. We need willpower to create a new habit, but once it's established, very little willpower is required to activate it again, as the process has become automatic.

While useful habits make our lives easier – driving, touch typing, riding a bicycle – other habits like smoking; resorting to drugs for a high, a boost, or to quiet our fears; or reacting with anger when we're disappointed – can be devastating to our health. Anger, even when we're aware of how harmful it is to ourselves and others, tends to accelerate along its habitual tracks, leading us even against our better judgment to bitter regrets and possibly devastating consequences.

Two of the best ways to strengthen willpower are by eliminating harmful habits and creating good ones. Part VII is dedicated to the art of mastering habits.

**Routines.** An effective way to reach our goals is by creating routines that can help us get there. A routine isn't the same as a habit, because we can alter a routine anytime in response to changing circumstances. When we're setting out on a trip, we may have to change our yoga and meditation schedule. If we need to finish an important presentation, we may have to meditate a little later in the evening. When the boss schedules an early conference call, we may have to adjust our usual morning routine.

What's the difference between a habit and a routine? Once we've created a habit, it can be difficult to disengage from it. Many of us have committed a great deal of energy and attention to certain habits, not all of which are healthy. We can know that a habit has captured us when it is stronger than our willpower. Of course, it's possible to release our willpower from any habit, but it will always take more time and effort than adjusting our daily routine.

## Overcoming affliction and adversity

When a drunk teenage driver caused a fatal crash, the media reported widely on his lawyer's bizarre defense. He argued – successfully – that his client "had a diminished sense of responsibility due to his wealth and pampered childhood." Quite aside from the hullabaloo that followed the judge's decision, the question arises of whether a young man who is excused from taking responsibility for his actions will ever develop the strength of character to meet life's challenges.

Buddha's father, King Suddhodana, instructed his son's guardians never to let him see anyone who was aged, ill, or dying. When the son, whose name at the time was Siddhartha, convinced his charioteer to take him outside the palace grounds, and he saw human suffering for the first time, he was powerfully driven to understand the ultimate truth of life, and so he dedicated himself to meditation and austerities, and after long and arduous self-discipline he achieved illumination.

I heard a story, which was reported to me as true, about a family that found a bird's nest that had fallen from a tree in their garden. Two eggs were intact, and the children watched over them diligently. One of the eggs soon began to wiggle as the baby bird began pecking its way out of the shell. After long effort, the chick emerged, and lay exhausted for a time. Then it began to move, and after a short time it stood and walked, then flew away.

Wanting to help the other chick, the children delicately helped it break out of its shell. It lay still, but not from exhaustion; it was too weak to move, stand, or fly, and it soon died.

We complain about our adversities, but when we've overcome a challenge we find that it has made us stronger. The following story of an exceptional young athlete illustrates this truth.

### ❖ ENABLED ❖
*The true and evolving story of Kate Foster*

At seven, Kate Foster already showed extraordinary promise in gymnastics. She was strong on the uneven bars, graceful in the floor exercise, poised on the beam, and high-flying off the vault.

When she was twelve, Kate was diagnosed with leukemia. During chemotherapy her leg developed a virulent infection and had to be amputated at mid-thigh. Thanks to a bone marrow transplant and her determined will, she recovered from the cancer.

With the support of a creative coach and her loving father, Kate returned to the gym, and within a year after the surgery she was back in training.

She had to relearn her former skills, but she was undaunted. She had no doubt that she would compete again.

In time, she was competing with her team on the bars and beam – not as in the Paralympics but on equal terms with fully able athletes. The first gymnast to compete with a prosthetic leg, Kate has inspired many others with disabilities to become gymnasts.

Kate graduated from the University of North Carolina in 2021 with double majors in biology and philosophy. While in college she won second place in the women's gymnastics decathlon, helped coach the varsity team, and spent a semester in Greece where she served at a clinic for refugees.

Kate is spending a gap year as a medical scribe in the emergency room at the UNC hospital, and preparing for the grueling pace of medical school. No one is worried that she won't make it. Her strength of will and her determination, her perfect inner balance, and her compassion for others will make her a great doctor.

Through her years of rigorous training, Kate developed the will to return to competitive gymnastics despite a serious, normally disabling disease and the loss of a limb, while earning stellar grades and being accepted into medical school. We look forward to following Kate's career as she helps patients to overcome their afflictions.

## Willpower Recipes

Having gained an appreciation for the link between willpower and well-being, you may enjoy trying some of the following suggestions.

> ~ RECIPE 1 ~
> **Do something different each day**

To help extricate our willpower from the prison of mindless repetitive behaviors, Yogananda recommended that we do something every day that will take us out of our usual routine.

If your morning starts with coffee, try starting the day with one of the energy-boosting exercises in Part IV.

If you drive from your house to the office, ride a bike or take the bus; or weather permitting, leave early and walk.

Be brave – try a different hairdresser, market, or gas station. Instead of watching the entire Downton Abbey series for the third time, go out to a concert or a play.

Try a new restaurant with a different cuisine.

It isn't easy to leave our beloved routines behind. Years ago, while vacationing in Goa, India, my husband and I met a charming couple from Genoa, Italy, and formed a casual friendship. One evening they invited us to their apartment for dinner, where we were surprised by the fragrant aroma of Italian food – food we had never been able to find in India. Where had they found pasta, olive oil, Parmesan cheese, and balsamic vinegar? We needed to know! The wife laughed and guided us to their bedroom. On the bed was a large suitcase full of Italian food. They had brought it all from home!

~ RECIPE 2 ~
**Engage in a creative activity every day
or at least once a week**

Creativity is not the exclusive purview of artists – we all have a creative nature, being creatures of the Creator Himself and made in His image. Even if we are convinced that we can't sing, draw, write, or dance, we might surprise ourselves if we will just try.

Creativity is a secret ingredient that can give anything we do a special shine. Preparing the family's favorite dish? Get creative! Try new main ingredients or toppings. Stay in the creative flow as you dress the dish for serving – you can add special decorative touches to the dish itself or the table: flowers, candles, a hand-written note at each setting.

Yogananda recommends writing down a few sentences in the evening to capture the unexpected gifts of the day. He remarked that when we do creative things, we leave permanent spiritual footprints in the sands of time.

~ RECIPE 3 ~
## Work at overcoming a harmful habit

Bad habits eat away at our will and lower our self-esteem. Overcoming harmful habits brings a wonderful sense of freedom and joy.

As a teen, I was a dedicated smoker. One day, a resident in our student house accused me in a loving but provocative way of being a slave to cigarettes. When I protested indignantly that I wasn't a slave to anything, he challenged me: "Then quit!"

Looking back, I see that it was one of my life's turning points. I accepted the challenge and found it more difficult than I expected. It took over a year to stop smoking, but I still remember the exhilaration I felt the morning I woke up with an absolute inner certainty that I would never smoke again. It felt as if a huge weight had been lifted off me. In that moment, I knew then that I could accomplish anything I determined to.

~ RECIPE 4 ~
## Develop a new habit

While the soul intuitively knows what's good for us, the ego predictably steps in with all the good reasons why we shouldn't bother developing better health habits. Yet when we have succeeded in replacing a harmful habit with a healthier one, we are rewarded with a tremendous boost to our willpower and self-esteem. As mentioned earlier, Part VII will offer helpful suggestions for winning the victory.

Start with a modest goal, something you know you can achieve, and with that victory firmly in hand you'll have the confidence and the memory of the victory that will set you up to achieve even larger goals.

~ RECIPE 5 ~
## Take on a challenge

Replacing an unhealthy habit is a big challenge that demands repeated effort over time. Meanwhile, doing something slightly challenging each day is an excellent strategy for increasing the power of will— take a walk or a longer walk than usual; clean and reorganize a closet or your work area. Any activity will do, as long as it requires more thought and effort than usual.

> ## ~ RECIPE 6 ~
> ## Repeat this will affirmation

Concentrating simultaneously on the medulla oblongata and on the point between the eyebrows, repeat this affirmation, first loudly, then gradually softer and softer, and finally mentally.

*I will my life to charge*  
*With Godly will I will it charge*  
*Through my nerves*  
   *and muscles all*  
*My tissues, limbs and all,*  
*With vibrant tingling fire*  
*With burning joyous power*

*In blood and glands*  
*By sovran command*  
*I bid you flow*  
*By my command*  
*I bid you glow*  
*By my command*  
*I bid you glow.*[12]

> ## ~ RECIPE 7 ~
> ## Exercise every day

Aside from the Energization Exercises that you will learn about in Part IV, daily exercise is an important pillar of a healthy life. Yogananda recommended:

**Walk, run, or take some form of vigorous exercise with deep attention until you perspire, every morning and evening.**[13]

> ## ~ RECIPE 8 ~
> ## Dedicate time and resources
> ## to helping others

Could the elderly person in the apartment upstairs use someone to help her shop or take her to the doctor? Our lives offer us no end of opportunities to serve – by volunteering at a shelter, a refugee training center, an orphanage – or simply by offering a hand. Selfless service builds character, compassion, and willpower. It is a vital element in the divine plan for the evolution of humankind.

## *Suggestions from Yogananda* [14]

To create dynamic will power, determine to do some of the things in life that you thought you could not do. Attempt simple tasks first. Then, as your confidence strengthens and your will becomes more dynamic, you can undertake more difficult accomplishments. Be sure that you have made a good selection, then refuse to submit to failure.

Devote your entire will power to accomplishing one thing at a time, do not scatter your energies or leave something half done to begin a new venture. Use your will power to perfect yourself. You must depend more and more upon the mind because it is the creator of your body and your circumstances. Carrying a thought with dynamic will power means entertaining that thought until it assumes an outward form. When your will power develops that way, and when you can control your destiny by your will power, *then you can do tremendous things.*

I have just given you three important rules to use in making your will power dynamic:

1. Choose a simple task, or accomplishment, you have never mastered and determine to succeed with it.

2. Be sure you have chosen something constructive and feasible, then refuse to consider failure.

3. Concentrate on a single purpose, using all abilities and opportunities to forward it.

# CHAPTER 4: *Points to Remember*

- The greater your willingness to participate dynamically in your life, the more strongly the healing energy will flow through you.

- Life Force enters the body through the doorway of the medulla oblongata.

- Willpower, located at the spiritual eye, is the key that opens that door.

- Willpower is "desire plus energy, directed toward fulfillment."

- Willpower is a spiritual muscle; the more we use it, the stronger it becomes.

- Whenever we rise to meet a challenge, we have won a victory, no matter if outwardly we've succeeded or failed.

- Watch out for and banish the "willpower vampires" from your life: passivity, negativity, laziness, doubt, and fear.

- See Part VII for more suggestions to master your habits.

- Use your willpower every day.

# NOTES │ PART THREE

### Title Page
1 Yogananda, *Praecepta Lessons*, Vol. 3:64.

### Chapter One
1 In his book, *Religion in the New Age*, Swami Kriyananda writes:
> "What makes Sri Yukteswar's analysis so utterly fascinating is that it corresponds amazingly well to objective facts that are now known to science, but that were unknown at the time he wrote his book. At the time he wrote, science had not yet learned that matter is energy. Even more astonishingly, Sri Yukteswar's description of the universe, since verified scientifically in numerous details, was completely unknown to the astronomers of his time."

Kriyananda, Swami, "Ages of Civilization," *Religion in the New Age*, 29.
2 "That year ushered in *Dwapara Yuga*, a 2400-year period of electrical and atomic-energy developments, the age of telegraph, radio, airplanes, and other space-annihilators." Yogananda, *Autobiography of a Yogi*, Chapter Sixteen.
3 Yogananda, "What Cures?," *Scientific Healing Affirmations*.
4 Yogananda, *Praecepta Lessons*, Vol. 3:78/2.
5 Yogananda, "The Astral World," *Inner Culture*, July 1941.

### Chapter Two
1 A photograph of Giri Bala is included in *Autobiography of a Yogi*, Chapter 46, "*The Woman Yogi Who Never Eats*."
2 Kriyananda, *Art and Science of Raja Yoga*, 284.
3 Kriyananda, 284.
4 Bey, Hamid, "My Experience preceding 5000 Burials," https://www.amazon.com/My-Experience-Preceding-5000-Burials/dp/B001OTGYRE. Kindle edition available from https://www.goodreads.com/book/show/803374.My_Experiences_Preceding_5_000_Burials.
5 Kriyananda, *Art and Science of Raja Yoga*, 257-258.
6 Yogananda, *Super Advanced Course No. 1*, Lesson Eleven.
7 Dr. Mattias Basner conducts research at the University of Pennsylvania on how humans process sound. Basner concludes that "(noise) signals, when they hit the amygdalae, start the process through which we secrete stress hormones. Too many stimuli result in excessive stress – as evidenced by the presence of chemicals like cortisol in our blood." Dr. Imke Kirste, a researcher at Duke University Medical School, exposed mice to five different types of sounds, including Mozart's Sonata for Two Pianos in D, as well as the absence of sound. Major cell growth in the brain resulted from listening to silence: "The act of listening to quiet can ... enrich our capacity to think and perceive." Zorn, Justing and Marz, Leigh, "How Listenign to Silence Changes Our Brains," Time, https://time.com/6210320/how-listening-to-silence-changes-our-brains.

### Chapter Three
1 Yogananda, "Resurrection," *East-West*, May–June 1929.
2 Kriyananda, "Basic Principles," *Ananda Yoga for Higher Awareness*.
3 Kriyananda, "Interiorizing the Mind," *Awaken to Superconsciousness*, Chapter Fifteen.
4 The main reason for exhalation is to rid the body of carbon dioxide, which is the waste product of gas exchange in humans. Air is brought into the body through inhalation. During this process air is taken in by the lungs. Diffusion in the

alveoli allows for the exchange of $O_2$ into the pulmonary capillaries and the removal of $CO_2$ and other gases from the pulmonary capillaries to be exhaled. "Exhalation," Wikipedia, https://en.wikipedia.org/wiki/Exhalation#.

**5**  Yogananda, *God Is For Everyone,* Chapter Eleven.

**6**  Kriyananda, *Art and Science of Raja Yoga*, 61.

**7**  Kriyananda, 306.

**8**  Kriyananda, 366.

**9**  Kriyananda, 236.

**10**  Gotter, Ana, "Box Breathing," Healthline, June 17, 2020, https://www.healthline.com/health/box-breathing. "How Box Breathing Can Help You Destress," Cleveland Clinic, August 17, 2021, https://health.clevelandclinic.org/box-breathing-benefits/.

"This breathing technique is widely used by athletes, Navy SEALS, nurses, and people who do yoga and meditate. According to the Mayo Clinic, there is sufficient evidence that intentional deep breathing can calm and regulate the autonomic nervous system (ANS). This system regulates involuntary body functions such as temperature. It can lower blood pressure and provide an almost immediate sense of calm.

The slow holding of the breath allows $CO_2$ to build up in the blood. An increased blood $CO_2$ enhances the cardio-inhibitory response of the vagus nerve when we exhale, and also stimulates the parasympathetic system. This produces a calm, relaxed feeling in the body and mind.

Box breathing can reduce stress and improve your mood. That makes it an exceptional treatment for conditions such as generalized anxiety disorder (GAD), panic disorder, post-traumatic stress disorder (PTSD), and depression. It can also help treat insomnia, by allowing you to calm the nervous system at night before bed. Box breathing can even be efficient at helping with pain management."

**11**  Kriyananda, *Intuition for Starters*, Chapter Two.

**12**  Kriyananda, *The Hindu Way of Awakening*, Chapter Eighteen.

**13**  Kriyananda, *Meditation for Starters*, Chapter Six.

**14**  Kriyananda, *Art and Science of Raja Yoga*, 393.

**15**  Kriyananda, *The Promise of Immortality*, Chapter Twenty-Four.

**16**  Yogananda, *Super Advanced Course No. 1*, Lesson 1.

**17**  Yogananda, "The Six Centers," *Interpretation of the Bhagavad Gita*, East-West, March 1933.

**18**  Yogananda, *Yogoda Course*, Lesson 5.

**19**  "A plexus serves as an area where spinal nerves come together, are sorted, and then travel to their respective areas of the body. (It) is a bundle of intersecting nerves, blood vessels, or lymphatic vessels in the human body. These bundles typically originate from the same anatomical area and serve specific areas of the body. Bundles of nerves that form a plexus communicate information to your brain about pain, temperature, and pressure. These nerve plexuses also send messages from the brain to the muscles, allowing for movement to occur.

**Cervical plexus**: The cervical plexus originates from cervical level one through four and innervates the back of your head and the upper cervical muscles.

**Brachial plexus**: The brachial plexus originates from cervical levels five through eight and thoracic level one. This plexus of nerves innervates your chest, shoulder, and arms. The three major nerves of your arm originate from the brachial plexus, the are the median nerve, the ulnar nerve, and the radial nerve.

**Lumbar plexus**: The lumbar plexus originates from lumbar levels one through four and innervates muscles and skin in your hip and thigh. Two major nerves originate via the lumbar plexus—the femoral nerve and the obturator nerve. These nerves supply motor information to your hip and thigh muscles and communicate sensory information from your thighs and hips to your brain. Branches of the lumbar plexus also innervate areas of your pelvic girdle and genital area.

**Sacral plexus**: The sacral plexus originates from lumbar level four through sacral level four. Your sciatic nerve comes from this plexus and serves the muscles and skin of the back of your thighs, lower legs, and feet. Other nerves that originate from the sacral plexus innervate your gluteal and piriformis muscles of your hips.

**Coccygeal plexus**: This plexus serves a small area near your tailbone."
–Sears, Brett, "What is a Plexus?" Very Well Health, February 28, 2023, https://www.verywellhealth.com/what-is-a-plexus-5079595.

20 "We speak of the medulla as the *mouth of God* or the finite opening in the body of man through which God breathes His Cosmic Energy or Life into flesh. This medulla, also called the *mouth of the astral body*, emanates *a sharp two-edged sword*, or a powerful, two-edged, doubly serving positive-negative current. The one Cosmic Energy must create through the law of duality and relativity, so it sprouts forth the medullary seed current into two positive-negative currents.

The birth of the two astral ganglia chains of the sympathetic system, the Iḍa current on the left and the *Pingala* current on the right side of the spinal cord, is also made possible through the dual (two-edged) creative power of the medulla. The astral and the physical medulla are like two cloven half seeds of the positive-negative physical nervous system. The astral medulla seed sprouts forth into the vital tree of life, extending its pairs of branches into the two brain hemispheres, eyes, ears, hands, feet, as well as the two pairs of numerous inner organs. The two astral sympathetic nervous currents (*Iḍa* and *Pingala*) act in conjunction with the astral main central or spinal *Sushumna* current. These two branches of life current emanate from the medulla seed and intertwine themselves with the *Sushumna* vital current at the spinal centers."
–Yogananda, *Super-Advanced Course No. 1,* Lesson 1.

21 Kriyananda, *The Art and Science of Raja Yoga,* 434.
22 Kriyananda, *Conversations with Yogananda* No. 177.
23 Yogananda, "Practical Application of the First Stanza," *Interpretation of the Bhagavad Gita, East-West,* August 1932.
24 Yogananda, "Vibratory Healing," *Inner Culture,* September 1936.
25 Yogananda, *Yogoda Course,* Lesson 8, 1.
26 Kriyananda, *The Promise of Immortality,* Chapter Twenty-One.
27 For programs in Ananda Yoga see https://www.expandinglight.org/yoga/.
28 Yogananda, "Second Coming of Christ," *Inner Culture,* September 1938.
29 Yogananda, "Super-Method of Overcoming Nervousness," *East-West,* November 1932.
30 Yogananda, "Second Coming of Christ," *Inner Culture,* September 1938.
31 Yogananda, "Yogoda" brochure, 1925.

## Chapter Four

1 Yogananda, *Essence of Self-Realization* 8:1.
2 Yogananda, "Vibratory Healing," *Inner Culture*, September 1936.
3 Kriyananda, *Art and Science of Raja Yoga*, 258.
4 Yogananda, Vibratory Healing," *Inner Culture,* September 1936.
5 Yogananda, *Praecepta Lessons*, Vol. 1:8.
6 Yogananda, *Essence of Self-Realization* 8:1.
7 Orenstein, Hanah W., "The Invincible Beatrice Vio," Assembly, August 6, 2020, https://assembly.malala.org/stories/the-invincible-beatrice-vio.
8 Kriyananda, "Attunement to God's Will," *Rays of the Same Light*, Week 40, 71.
9 Kriyananda, "Willingness," *Affirmations for Self-Healing,* 50.
10 Kriyananda, "The Sovereign Lord of All," *Essence of the Bhagavad Gita,* Chapter Twenty-Two, Verse 9:1.
11 Yogananda, "Life Energy and Will Power," *The Attributes of Success.*
12 Yogananda, "Will Affirmation," *Scientific Healing Affirmations.*
13 Yogananda, "The Art of Living," *East-West*, May 1933.
14 Yogananda, "The Dynamic Power of Will," *Scientific Healing Affirmations.*

# PART IV

ENERGIZE

The energization exercises are a wonderful system that was originated by Paramhansa Yogananda, and that represents his unique contributions to the science of yoga. The energization exercises are based on an ancient teaching that the entire physical universe is a condensation of energy. Scientists have known for some time now that matter is energy – thus we can explode the atom, essentially converting matter into energy.

We live surrounded by cosmic energy, which we draw indirectly into our bodies through the food we eat, and through oxygen and sunlight. Yet these sources of energy, as Paramhansa Yogananda explained, are akin to the water that you put in a car battery. When the battery runs down, no amount of water will bring it back to life. You must recharge the battery from another source.

Similarly, our bodies are sustained indirectly by food, but directly by the cosmic energy, which enters the body through the medulla oblongata, at the base of the brain, in the little dip there at the bottom of the skull. This is the energy we live by. This is the mouth of man [pointing to the mouth], because this is where we eat physical food. It is the mouth of the physical body. But the medulla, on the other side of the head, inside at the base of the brain, is where we draw to ourselves divine energy.

We draw more or less energy according to our mental attitudes. You've probably found that when you feel reluctant to do something, you don't have the energy to do it, even if you've eaten a full meal. Whereas if you really want to do something, even if you've been fasting, you have all the energy you need to accomplish it.

Yogananda's axiom is: "The greater the will, the greater the flow of energy." Now, willpower can be understood rightly or wrongly. When it is true willpower, it is not the kind of tense effort that says,

---

* Excerpted from a lesson with Kriyananda about the Energization Exercises recorded in 1979. https://www.anandaedizioni.it/shop/materiale-didattico/swami-kriyananda-gli-esercizi-di-ricarica-di-yogananda/.

"I'm going to do it if it kills me!" Rather, it is the kind of effort that we call willingness, enthusiasm, and joy.

When you have willingness, when you are happy, when you want to do things that make you cheerful, you find that you have energy – you can even have the energy to heal yourself. People who are happy are far less prone to be ill.

The energization exercises are a means of using willpower and willingness to draw energy into the body at will. The movements are physical, but their purpose is to feel the consciousness behind them – to feel the flow of energy, to be conscious of that flow, and then by the use of our willpower to direct energy and make it act upon the body. "The greater the will, the greater the flow of energy." As you become aware of that energy, you will be able to increase its flow.

# PART IV CHAPTER ONE

## Take Charge of Your Health

### ✵ Was it Mozart or Beethoven? ✵

I don't remember if the piece was by Mozart or Beethoven – this was many years ago. My only memory is that it was sublime. Our choir had rehearsed for months, and I was thrilled to sing in the soprano section.

On Friday morning I was late as usual, and as I dashed across a rough field I twisted an ankle and fell hard. Friends nearby came to my rescue. Soon my foot was plunged in ice water, then warm water, despite my cries of pain which were compassionately acknowledged but firmly ignored.

The doctor told me to stay off my feet for several days and rest in bed with the leg elevated. This was not what I wanted to hear – my desire and determination outweighed the condition of my body. My will was strong and I *would* sing with the choir!

Meanwhile, the ankle swelled and throbbed. How would I stand for over an hour? This had to stop! I knew what I had to do – I would use Yogananda's energization methods.

Mentally I stimulated the medulla oblongata at the back of my head while I tensed all the muscles of my body, and then relaxed. Next, I concentrated on the ankle and gently tensed the area. With each inhalation I mentally sent rays of healing energy and light to the ankle, and with each exhalation I allowed the healing light to expand and saturate the cells.

I kept at my practice from morning to night, visualizing my swollen ankle reduced to its normal size, tendons healed and muscles strengthened.

When I awoke on the morning of the Saturday concert and tentatively moved my foot around, there was no pain or restriction. I swung my legs to the ground and gingerly rose to my feet – no pain! A few cautious steps – no pain! I walked outdoors and around the house – no pain!

Very happily I did the full set of Energization exercises, then meditated and did some vocal exercises, then drove to town to shop for a concert blouse. In the afternoon I was able to stand for the hour-long dress rehearsal without pain, and again during the two-hour evening and morning concerts.

I believe the piece was by Mozart. When the choir rejoiced at the conclusion of our performances, I rejoiced twice over, grateful for the rapturous music and to Paramhansa Yogananda for the healing power of the Energization Exercises. –*Shivani* (*the author*)

## Taking charge

**Before we begin** to learn to control the life force in our bodies and use it to heal ourselves and others, it will be a good idea to review some of the key concepts we've covered so far:

- We are surrounded by an unlimited and immediately available supply of cosmic energy.

- We can draw upon the cosmic energy and use it to heal ourselves and to succeed in all our worthy endeavors.

- The key to opening the medualla oblongata and drawing a flow of prana into the body is willpower.

- "The greater the will, the greater the flow of energy."

Paramhansa Yogananda's guru, Swami Sri Yukteswar, prepared him to bring India's ancient wisdom to the West. After studying with his guru for ten years and earning a bachelor's degree, the young Swami Yogananda first created a school for boys in India.

As a reluctant student who had been uninspired by the traditional methods of education, he made the curriculum as engaging as possible for his students. He conducted most classes outdoors in natural settings and encouraged vigorous physical activity to help the boys develop their willpower and concentration.

In their youthful exuberance, the boys sometimes let their energy run wild, and the young schoolmaster conceived the idea of exercises that would teach them to control their energy.

Years later, he would introduce these exercises to his adult students in America. The "Yogoda System of Physical, Mental, And Spiritual Perfection" became a cornerstone of his teachings. In time, they became known as the Energization Exercises.

A century has passed since Yogananda devised the exercises. Today they are practiced by people of all ages and in all walks of life: by school children and the elderly; working parents and single mothers; artists and craftsmen; musicians, actors, and filmmakers; athletes and martial artists; business managers; yoga instructors and their students; those recovering from illness; and people who follow diverse spiritual traditions. They are an important foundational element of what Yogananda called "Life Therapy."

> It is the life energy, the cosmic
> electrical force in all cases which cures....
> The method which can directly and quickly
> rouse the life energy to effect healing
> I term "Life Therapy," or direct healing by
> the rays of the inner Life Force.[1]

Hundreds of thousands of people the world over practice these exercises, and use them for self-healing. We include here a selection of their stories.

### ✴ MORAL STRENGTH ✴

My father was still in the hospital after a sudden, massive heart attack – it was so unexpected and emotionally taxing for me that I wasn't sure I could deal with the roiling feelings I was experiencing.

Before I left for the hospital in the morning, I would do the full set of Energization Exercises so that I could feel connected with a greater power and have the physical, psychological, and moral strength I needed in that dark moment. After three days, my father passed. I am grateful for

the Energization Exercises, as they helped me to let him go with greater serenity and to support the rest of the family.
–**Priya Alessandra,** *Siena, Italy*

## Overall physical vitality and mental awareness

In Part III, we learned about the distribution system for subtle energy – the chakras and *naḍis* – in the astral energy body just behind our physical form, and the corresponding nervous system in the physical body that delivers prana to all parts of the organism. Regular practice of the Energization Exercises greatly increases the amount of prana available to the brain and body and enables us to overcome physical and mental fatigue.

### ✦ EXECUTIVE RECHARGE ✦

I was tasked with recruiting 800 highly skilled people in a short span of time – and I admit, it was a stretch for me. In addition to responsibility for coordinating the entire large project, I had to travel frequently between India and Germany to attend important meetings.

Instead of resting during the flights, I would prepare my notes, then immediately grab a taxi from the airport to the meeting, where I urgently needed a bright, alert mind the moment I walked in the door. The return trips were pretty much the same, as I returned to my daily hour-long commute and a full week's backlog of work that awaited me.

Determined to conquer jet lag, I began doing the Energization Exercises in the airport lounge immediately before boarding and again upon arriving, during the long wait for my luggage. Having set this routine, I found that I could walk into any meeting with fresh energy and mental focus and get the work done.

Jet lag is no longer a problem. During my ten- to twelve-hour work days I do an extra set before lunch, amazing my younger colleagues with my high energy and productivity.
– **Latha,** *Pune, India*

## Overcoming Fatigue

The days when we feel filled with energy and enthusiasm from awaking to bedtime are precious, and sadly too rare. The amount and quality of our energy will vary from day to day, depending on how well we have slept, our diet, our enthusiasm for what we're doing, and our level of stress.

Our energy reserves will generally fluctuate during the day, from high after breakfast, and waning as lunch nears. We will often experience a sleepy spell after lunch, followed by an uptick in energy from mid- to late afternoon, and then a final downhill slide through the remainder of the day.

> Chronic fatigue is one of the most widespread ills of our age. It is not due to overwork...but rather to a scattering of our forces.... Countless influences pull us in conflicting directions. We find ourselves trying to do a hundred things hastily, rather than one thing at a time carefully and well.[2]

Coffee and energy drinks can help us stay perky, but not for very long. Yogananda offers a better way:

> The internal way of dispelling fatigue is to vibrate your body by your willpower.[3]

With regular practice of the Energization Exercises, supplemented by life-force snacks, it is possible to maintain our energy, enthusiasm, and concentration throughout the day.

> Life energy can be continually supplied in the body, by stimulating it by the power of conscious will. The will serves to bridge the gulf existing between the life energy in the body and the cosmic energy surrounding it.[4]

As the cells are but condensed will and energy,
they can be instantaneously renewed by the power of
strong, unflinching will. Therefore, one should never say
or think he is tired, for by doing that one becomes twice
as tired and paralyzes the will which must be active
in order to draw Cosmic Energy into the body.[5]

### ❆ No more naps ❆

In May 2015 I was diagnosed with an auto-immune disease that made me so tired, I was sleeping sixteen hours a day or more, and I couldn't make it through a whole day without a nap.

Taking care of my husband and small daughter stretched me to the limit of my resources. Whenever I overdid it, I would lie in bed for two or three days with inflammatory pain and fatigue. My knees were so compromised, I couldn't bend or put any weight on them.

Seven months after the diagnosis I enrolled in the Life Therapy School of Self-Healing where I learned the Energization Exercises. I began practicing them daily, and on the days when I couldn't get out of bed I would practice the series while lying down, sometimes doing them mentally.

For the next four years I combined the medications I had been prescribed with daily Energization and other Life Therapy techniques, until the day came when my body no longer wanted the medicine. For the last full year I have been medication-free and nap-free. The crippling fatigue is a thing of the past, and I have enough vital energy again to garden and volunteer with needy children.

The doctors had told me that the disease might stabilize, but I would never be free of fatigue. I can only conclude that they may know a lot about disease, but they don't know nearly enough about the life force. –*Jenny, Switzerland*

## Pain management

Pain is a messenger. The body regularly reports to the brain through the "wires" of the nervous system. When the body is injured or seriously ill we perceive the signals as pain, which generally increases in proportion to the urgency of the message. The body also sends upbeat messages of health and harmony, indicating that all systems are working well.

Pain messages are meant to alert us that we've done something harmful to the body, for example, touching a hot stove. Or the nerves may send a message in the form of an upset or alarmed emotion that alerts us to a physical or psychological danger.

Some pain medications prevent the message delivery system from sending pain messages to the brain. Other medications prevent the brain from receiving the pain messages. These medications may bring quick relief, but they may mute the body's pain messages that are urging us to identify and treat the underlying cause of the pain.

In some situations, the Energization Exercises can help relieve pain without harmful side-effects. The exercises enable us to take conscious control of the energy in the body, rebalancing the nervous system and sending soothing energy to body parts in need of healing by enhancing the circulation of endorphins.

❋ MIGRAINES BE GONE! ❋

My younger sister and my son and I seem to have inherited my mother's migraines. For forty years, my life was a constant struggle to survive the crippling headaches that drove me to the hospital at least once a month. I spent lots of money on doctors and took so many drugs that my body became poisoned by them.

Five years ago I discovered the Energization Exercises and meditation. When I began to practice the Exercises twice a day, I was amazed to find that after just two weeks the headaches were almost gone. Since then, I haven't needed medication or doctors because the migraines have disappeared. Doing the Exercises every day strengthened my willpower and raised my overall energy – and in some marvelous way, it healed me. This miraculous healing has changed my life and the lives of those around me. *–Silvia, Arezzo, Italy*

he first shot of anesthesia failed to numb my mouth. The dentist thought that a second shot would do the trick, but when he began to drill, I cried out for a third.

Mumbling and dribbling, I left the dentist's office in a daze. A few steps outside, the anesthesia started to wear off, and I experienced such a powerful pain in my mouth, jaw, and head that my world shrank to a bubble of agony.

Across the road from the dentist's office there was a small park with a statue of the Madonna. Somehow, I managed to cross the street and find a bench to sit on at the foot of the statue.

At first I tried to meditate the pain away, but it wasn't working. Desperate for relief, I tried sending healing energy as I had been taught when I learned the Energization Exercises. I clenched my teeth, and with deep concentration and willpower, I began drawing healing energy into my body and directing it to my painful mouth. I strongly visualized healing light and energy entering through the medulla and arriving at my mouth as I clenched my teeth. When I relaxed, I visualized the energy spreading and being absorbed by the traumatized tooth, gums, jaw, and cells.

After starting slowly, I continued to tense and relax, and after no more than a minute the pain was almost gone! I got up and began walking while I continued tensing to draw healing energy, then relaxed to let it saturate the painful areas. After ten minutes, not only was the pain completely gone, it was replaced by a state of deep joy such as I had never experienced.

This was one of my first and strongest early experiences with applying Energization for healing, and it showed me what a powerful tool it is. –*Arudra, Ananda Assisi*

✖    ✖    ✖

## Strengthens the immune system

When we practice the Energization Exercises regularly, they boost the immune system.

> By energizing the muscles, the white and
> red blood corpuscles are specially charged
> with vital force. This electrification of blood cells
> helps to make them immune to disease and
> helps to surround them with a charged
> barbed wire of life force which electrocutes
> all invading inimical bacteria.[6]

At the first sign of a cold or flu, use Energization to send it on its way.

### ❊ BANISH COLDS ❊

As part of my teacher training program, I was asked to record a video, but all I wanted to do was go back to bed. I was shivering, sneezing, and coughing, and I asked if I could postpone the recording for a few days. But it wasn't possible, and I realized I needed a quick fix for my aching body.

That evening I did two sets of Energization with total concentration and commitment. The following morning, I woke up feeling healthy, vibrant, and alive, without the slightest signs of a cold. The videoed teaching exam went much better than I could ever have expected. **–Victoria,** *USA*

❊

Regardless of the season, whether it was winter or summer, for seven years I regularly experienced such severe throat soreness that any effort to swallow was accompanied by excruciating pain.

When I learned to energize the body, I began to apply the tension and relaxation technique to send energy to the muscles of my neck and throat. As time passed, I found that I was suffering from fewer and fewer sore throats, and for the last several years I have had no colds or throat difficulties at all. **–Tatiana,** *Russia*

his is the story of how I fell in love with the Energization Exercises. I was preparing to leave on a long trip, followed by a full week of teaching. For several weeks I had been fighting an acute outbreak of chronic bronchitis and an annoying cough. No treatments seemed to work. Clearly, if I was coughing all the time I couldn't be very effective as a teacher or while interacting with others. I realized that I had better get serious and find a way to get better quickly.

I thought, "Let me try Energization. Maybe it will help." I decided to do the full set five times the first day – before breakfast, before getting in the car, and at several rest areas along the highway – where I did them while smiling at the passers-by who stared at me. By the time we reached our destination, the cough had already begun to diminish, and day by day it steadily improved. By the third day, it was almost gone.

I was grateful for the physical healing, but what truly surprised me was how happy I felt each time I energized. I couldn't wait for the next time I could stop and do the exercises.

Now, years later, my love affair with Energization continues, and I always look forward to our daily trysts.

–**Gitanjali,** *Ananda Assisi, Italy*

※　　※　　※

## Hastens recovery time from illness and injury

The body's self-healing abilities are marvelous. We can enhance its healing powers and greatly shorten the recovery from illness with the Energization Exercises.

※ **FAST-ACTING** ※

was on the tractor, plowing a field in the evening, when a wheel hit an obstacle and the tractor lurched, throwing me off. As I fell, I slammed a knee against the tractor, and by the next day I couldn't walk.

The following day, I attended a seminar where we practiced the Energization Exercises in the morning and again in the afternoon. That evening, I was able to take the dog for a walk, and I realized that I was practically running to keep up with him, without pain. I have never had such a quick healing! –**Francesca,** *Gerace, Italy*

※ COVID CURED ※

I certainly hadn't planned on getting Covid, and definitely not this severely. I had been vaccinated three days before, but the full protection hadn't set in, and before I was even sure that the symptoms weren't simply a vaccination reaction, I was in intensive care and the doctors refused to say with certainty that I would survive.

By the third day, I was gaining some mental clarity, and the thought came that the spiritual laws hadn't been suspended even in these challenging conditions. I did several of the Energization Exercises, first in bed with pillow support, then on my feet after unplugging the oxygen machine. Each day I added a few exercises until I began to feel that I was re-connecting with the cosmic source of healing, which I experienced as an instantaneous sensation of light and energy filling and repairing my lungs.

By the time I was discharged, the whole hospital was talking about my "minor miracle" – not only of surviving such an extreme case of the virus, but doing it all so joyfully and quickly. –**Giulia,** *Milan*

※ AFTER THE FALL ※

It was a beautiful sunny day in the Swiss Alps as we sat enjoying a picnic outside the village church. When we left, I fell head-first down a flight of stone stairs. In slow motion, I was aware my knees, then my hands, my shoulder, and finally my head slamming onto the hard stones. Finally, when I reached the bottom of the stairs, I lay motionless and winded. Intuitively, I started to breathe in at each point of impact, checking to see if anything was broken. Surprisingly, I experienced no pain, but only a warm wave of healing energy saturating each part.

After taking some time to focus my breath and direct prana to each area, I assured my family and the gathered crowd that I was fine and that no ambulance was needed. I got up, and we proceeded home.

For the next few days, whenever I did the complete Energization routine I used the slight bruising at the points of impact to help direct my mind, breath, and energy to the center of those body parts, while feeling that the *prana* with its inherent intelligence was completing the healing process until my body was as good as new.
—**Jenny,** *Switzerland*

⁂　　⁂　　⁂

## Surgery

When we're scheduled for surgery, we put our faith in God and our trust in the surgeon, but as the following story suggests, we can influence the outcome with the Energization Exercises.

### ⁂ PREPARING FOR AN OPERATION ⁂

We all have images stored in memory that will remain forever prominently displayed in the album of our lives. One of my special memories is seeing my mother, age 79, and my father, age 87, on the computer screen in the midst of the Covid pandemic, telling me that the doctors had diagnosed Mom with uterine cancer.

During subsequent computer calls, I began teaching her the Energization Exercises, and soon it was a daily appointment. My father joined us, and he learned the prayer to the Infinite Spirit that we say before we begin – it was another special image, as I had never seen my father praying with folded hands.

We continued our regular practice daily leading up to the operation. When the day arrived, I was able to join my mother on the drive to the hospital. The mother who arrived at the hospital with my father by her side, with her small suitcase in his hand, was no longer sick or sad. She looked like someone who was simply on the way to do something that needed to be done, with a peaceful smile and in the certainty of divine protection.

The surgery was successful. No further therapy was needed, and my mother does her Exercises every day.
–*Giulia, Assisi*

##  MIRACULOUS RECOVERY

Where am I? How did I get here? Why am I here? I must go and find someone to ask them, but I can't move.

The intensive care nurse told me that I had been in a near-fatal highway accident and that my husband and I were lucky to be alive. In my case, the "luck" was that I had not perished but had "only" seventeen broken ribs, two fractured knees, an injured spine, and broken teeth.

The doctor said that I must lie perfectly still and unmoving. Nevertheless I began to do the Energization Exercises mentally, and it wasn't long until I could feel the healing energy reaching my broken bones and aching muscles.

The next morning, with the nurse's help, I was able to stand as we walked slowly to the bathroom.

For the next two weeks I continued my practice, and soon I could do the Exercises physically as well. After fifteen days I was dismissed from the hospital, and after three months I am pretty much back to my normal life. The doctors had said that my recovery would take at least twelve months, but they didn't know about the secret healing power of Energization. –*Vinu, New Delhi*

### The effect of Energization Exercises
### on the nervous system

The central and peripheral nervous systems play a primary role in maintaining health. The brain, spinal cord, and nerves extend to every part of the body, carrying nerve impulses that control our physical movements and our sense perceptions and heart function, breathing, digestion, body temperature regulation, endocrine functions, and the body's response to external stimuli.

Messages from the senses arrive through the peripheral nerves to receptors in the brain, which communicates with the rest of the body, telling it what to do in response to the information.

More than a billion nerve cells (neurons) make up the nervous system. These neurons carry messages through neurotransmitters in the brain, then up and down the spinal cord and across the synapses at a speed of up to 431 kilometers (268 miles) per hour.

The nerves are negatively affected by stress, trauma, and disharmonious emotional reactions such as anger or fear, as well as by the use of drugs and alcohol. Bad habits are debilitating to the integrity of the nerves. Restlessness, irritability, and anxiety can signal more serious impairment of the nervous system.

Yogananda observes:

> Nervousness is the deadliest disease.
> It looks very simple, but has far-reaching
> consequences.... Nervousness burns the nerves,
> cutting off the supply of current or energy....
>
> The disease of the nervous system is the cause of
> all diseases...You can revive tissues if you have
> burned them out...by sending energy into nerves
> that have been destroyed. Each cell and tissue in
> the nervous system is a living thing. Each nerve
> tissue and cell is intelligent. Nerves take messages
> from the brain to the outer world. You must
> know how to treat nerve cells so that they will not
> be destroyed. Keep them cheerful always.[7]

When we do the Energization Exercises, we are sending messages from the brain to each muscle group, consciously telling it to tense and relax. With regular practice, the cumulative effect is that the Energization Exercises strengthen the nerve fibers, stimulate synaptic growth, and enhance neuroplasticity (the brain's ability to change its structure in response to specific stimuli). One of the most outstanding benefits of the exercises is that they help maintain the nervous system's health and harmonious functioning.

## Calms emotional reactions

When we allow ourselves to indulge in an emotional tantrum, we are doing great harm to our health. The nervous system becomes overloaded, and messages between the body and brain are dangerously distorted. Our feelings are exaggerated, our mind is confused, our breathing and heart rate are erratic. We burn up our energy reserves and become exhausted, much as a child will fall asleep after a temper tantrum. Emotional fits can cause us to lose our appetite, our sleep, and our friends. Continued emotional reactivity invites psychological and physical disease by disturbing the flow of live-giving prana.

If you habitually experience emotional meltdowns, don't despair. Even though your will may be at a low ebb when you are feeling deeply upset, the Energization Exercises can come to the rescue! Consciously tensing and relaxing the various body parts will help ground your awareness in physical reality. The left-right sequences of the exercises rebalance the nerve currents responsible for the healthy functioning of the brain and heart – all of which helps us come back to our senses.

❄ IN TEARS ❄

A heated argument with a close friend was deeply upsetting to me. We had disagreed in the past, but now the rift seemed irreparable, and I was devastated. I was scheduled to attend an important meeting later in the day, and I couldn't arrive in tears so I started doing the Energization Exercises, and by the end of the practice I was completely calm. The meeting was a great success and it led to new and welcome opportunities. *–Tatiana, Russia*

❄    ❄    ❄

## Stress relief

Deep-seated, prolonged anxieties about money, work, relationships, and health create harmful mental and physical toxins. Work-related stress is pandemic everywhere today – job burnout is now recognized as a mental health condition, with 77% of the workers surveyed in a recent U.S. study saying that they experienced stress in their jobs. As many as 120,000 deaths annually are related to stress and its consequences. The statistics in other countries are similarly alarming.

When we feel overwhelmed and unable to deal with personal or social situations, stress hormones such as cortisol are released, and the flow of nerve impulses that normally regulate the connections between brain and body becomes unbalanced and diminished. With prolonged stress, the body's ability to recover and heal is compromised, making it more vulnerable to auto-immune disorders, anxiety, depression, and heart and digestive problems.

A common remedy for stress is regular exercise. The Energization Exercises are even better, since they specifically balance the neural communication between the left and right hemispheres of the brain, improving communication and coordination, and stimulating a stronger right-left flow of energy.

The contraction and relaxation of muscle groups during the Energization Exercises helps us consciously relieve the tensions that accompany and exacerbate stress.

Regular practice of the Energization Exercises alters the brain's chemistry by encouraging production of peptide neurotransmitters that calm the body's response to stress. The stress response becomes attenuated or eliminated as the harmonious flow of prana adjusts and re-educates the brain.

### ❊ MIDNIGHT ANXIETY ❊

During a period when I was experiencing great stress, there was a night when the tension and worries became so extreme that I awoke in the darkness with a severe anxiety crisis. I experienced so much fear and tension that it was truly frightening, and didn't know what to do. But I made the effort to get up and do the Energization Exercises, and they helped me calm down and drive the focus of my mind away from the fearful thoughts. When I went back to bed I fell asleep immediately, and in the morning I woke up feeling well. –*Julia, Spain*

## Alleviates depression

While depression has many causes, it is always accompanied by low energy and a diminished flow of life force. When our energy reserves fall below a certain level, we are prey to negative moods and depression, which usually result in a loss of willingness and enthusiasm.

> If we are unwell, depressed, or life negating, it is primarily because our energy is low.[8]
>
> Moods come to us because our energy has descended to the lower part of our bodies. When we raise our level of energy, the moods vanish for lack of native air to breathe.[9]

At the first sign of depression, and at the very first thought of disappointment, frustration, or failure, the quickest and most effective way to pull out of the slump before it can become a downward spiral is to get up and move. Doing the Energization Exercises, or even the shorter Life Force Full Body Recharge, can help us forestall entire days of sadness.

### ❄ MONSTER MOODS ❄

I was a normal kid in most ways, with a happy family and a good environment, and I was pretty smart at school – except when the monster came: a depression that placed a black veil over my eyes, turning everything dark. Negativity reigned, life was hopeless, and I couldn't do anything about it.

The moods haunted me for days, weeks, even months. There was nothing I could do but let them run their course.

Meditation kept me on an even keel, but when I fell into the dark state it didn't help me. Then I discovered the Energization Exercises, and they completely transformed my life.

First, they've made me more aware of my level of energy throughout the day. When I feel the energy curve taking a downward turn, I know that I am able to choose: I can let the depression take over me, or I can take charge of the flow of energy and send it upward.

Each time I respond this way, my determination to take charge becomes stronger, because I know from experience the sad consequences that the other choice brings. Nine times out of ten, I am able to conquer the mood in the short time it takes to do the exercises and quickly return to my normal world view.

Energization is now my favorite spiritual tool. I energize three times a day, and I am no longer a slave to the moods that try to sabotage my happiness. *–Aryavan,* Mumbai

*Affirmation*

I am not my moods, and I am not subject to the moods of others. I am ruler in my kingdom of thoughts and feelings! [10]

## Energization and the brain

Until the 1990s, neuroscientists believed that the brain could no longer create new cells after we emerge from adolescence. Since then, researchers have confirmed that the brain is capable of regenerating itself throughout life. The process of neurogenesis – the formation of new brain cells – occurs every day, as the brain creates thousands of new neurons.

Neurogenesis is stimulated by physical exercise and supported by a healthy diet.[11] Even more important, brain renewal is advanced by mental activity. Regular use of the brain's ability to concentrate on new and complex activities – such as learning a new language, playing an instrument, playing chess, enjoying artistic endeavors, solving math problems, performing information analysis, and similar brain-stimulating challenges – combined with the use of willpower, helps create new synapses.

This is what happens when we practice the Energization Exercises. We begin each exercise by focusing deep attention on a specific muscle group. We then apply our willpower to draw life force into the body through the medulla oblongata and distribute it through the nerves to the muscles and organs of the body part. The exercises and their accompanying breathing practices bring an increased supply of oxygenated blood to the brain, aiding in neurogenesis and facilitating mental clarity and creativity.

## *Energization and creativity*

Creative inspiration is received at the superconscious level of our awareness – and one of the most reliable ways to access our creative powers is through regular meditation. When we are engaged in creative pursuits, it is also important to prepare the body to serve as a channel for superconscious inspiration by keeping the physical brain oxygenated and energized. One of the best ways to accomplish this is by doing the full set of Life Force Energization Exercises before we start our creative work, and pausing at intervals for a quick energy pick-me-up with the Full Body Recharge.

❋ THE MIDNIGHT POET ❋

I began to write poetry many years ago, and by 2003 two collections had been published. Then one day a powerful, almost mystical revelation came to me: I should write books sometime in the future. The titles of these books appeared along with the themes for each of them.

Many years after the revelation, on the eve of the New Year of 2016, I was visited by decisive inspiration for the next step in this important matter for me. The inspiration was so strong I set out to write the first book immediately, and then daily contributed to it.

My daytime is devoted mainly to work and family responsibilities, so the only time I could really devote to writing was after midnight. Needing a flow of creative inspiration and the energy to write so late at night, I started every session with a full set of the Energization Exercises. They powered my body and raised my mind into a constant flow of creative inspiration. In only thirty days the book was completed. It is an invitation to have a heart-to-heart talk about life, called "Shall We Talk?" With Energization as my midnight companion, I am confident that the other books will soon see the light of day. *–Gennadiy, Minsk, Republic of Belarus*

### Cellular rejuvenation

Cell damage can occur during many illnesses. The Energization Exercises enable us to deliver life force to the intelligent cells so that they can repair themselves.

> Exercising with will and concentration produces
> excellent results because it creates energy
> *directly*, by will development. This energy is
> quickly absorbed by the muscles, blood, bones,
> and sinews, for cellular rejuvenation.[11]

> [Energization] teaches how to surround
> each body cell with a ring of super-charged
> electrical vital energy and thus keep them free from
> decay or bacterial invasion. It keeps not only the
> muscles, but all the tissues of the body, bones,
> marrow, brain, and cells in perfect health....

> [Energization] insures the strengthening
> and multiplication of all cells. It spiritualizes
> the body cells, converting them into
> undying soul and electrical life-force.[12]

## Longevity

A phrase from the prayer that Yogananda recommended at the start of the Exercises is: "Eternal youth of body and mind, abide in me forever, forever, forever!"[13] When we daily nourish and cleanse the cells and organs, their vitality remains high. Dead cells are efficiently replaced with new ones, the body retains its youthful vigor, and the mind remains sharp and creative even in advanced age.

> Longevity depends not only upon proper eating,
> but also upon breathing less, not overworking the heart,
> proper elimination, control of sex-force, and proper
> recharging of the body from the Divine Source.[14]

## Energization and regeneration

In a correspondence lesson that Yogananda created in 1930, he asserted that we humans possess an inner power not only to regenerate our bodies and brain cells, but also our organs.

> Humanity can regain the power to recreate lost limbs,
> organs, etc., only by learning to convert the somatic
> cells back to their original obedient germ-cell state.
> By freeing life force and mind from bodily slavery,
> by increasing vitality and mental power, the somatic
> cells can be made to change into germ cells.[15]

Many decades later, biomedical researcher Dr. Shinya Yamanaka was awarded the 2007 Nobel Prize for his research on reprogramming human adult skin cells to behave like embryonic or pluripotent stem cells that are capable of developing into any type of cell in the body. His "induced pluripotent stem cells" soon became known as "Yamanaka factors."

Serious scientific research has also been conducted in the field of organ and limb regeneration in animals. Orthopedic surgeon Dr. Robert Becker[16] was an early pioneer in this field.

He might have won the Nobel prize, if he hadn't crossed the line.

Dr. Robert Becker, whose work on cell regeneration is described above, was the go-to orthopedic surgeon with the Veterans Administration Hospital in Syracuse, New York, where he served as chief of orthopedic surgery, chief of research, and head of a research laboratory devoted to studying the role of bioelectrical phenomena in growth, healing, and tissue regeneration. When other doctors encountered cases of severely crushed bones, they sent their patients to Dr. Becker.

Through extensive trials, Becker had developed a protocol by which he implanted small electrodes around the vicinity of the broken bones and sent microamperes of electricity through them at intervals. Subjects of his research were: where to implant the electrodes, how much electricity, and how often. His success rate was high.

He became known as the Father of Electromedicine and was nominated as a Nobel candidate. He applied his findings from observations of the natural regenerative abilities of the salamander to an animal not equipped with this ability: a frog. Using his electrode protocols, he was able to induce the frog to produce some regenerative tissue. The results convinced him that during healing, some cells in the vicinity of the injury became transformed into stem cells, a process known as dedifferentiation, as a consequence of electrical signals that originate in the nervous system.

When he observed similar electrical pulsations running along the skin of mammals, he hypothesized that they were coming through the nervous system. And when he measured these pulsations in human beings in different states of awareness – in sleep, under anesthesia, and when hypnotized – he surmised that there was a controlling mechanism in the mind.

Becker hypothesized that the underlying scientific explanation for the ancient Chinese method of clinical treatment known as acupuncture involved the flow of information via electromagnetic energy along channels in the body that were invisible to Western imaging techniques, yet were regarded in China as ontologically real.

His book, *The Body Electric, Electromagnetism and The Foundation of Life*,[17] recounts the results of his research in the field of cellular regeneration and its relationship to electrical currents in living things, challenging the established mechanistic understanding of the body.

Far ahead of his time, Dr. Becker did not receive the Nobel prize, although his research on how growth and healing are controlled is being carried forward by a handful of his successors, bringing modern science closer to empirically verifying the methods used for centuries by Oriental physicians and sages.

❊   ❊   ❊

These experiments lend scientific weight to Yogananda's claim, quoted above, that cells can be made to change their functions, that they can be reverted to a "dedifferentiated, pluripotent non-specialized state" and made to multiply and then redifferentiate into new cells of any type – as seems to have occurred in the experiments with regenerating a frog's upper leg.

Nearly a century ago, Yogananda predicted that the healing of the future would employ electricity, and that as human consciousness evolved, self-healing through the direct use of the life force would become known. The power that life force techniques direct through the nervous system has the same healing potential as the minute electrical impulses that Dr. Becker applied. Becker holds the very unorthodox belief that "there is a second nervous system, previously unrecognized by science, which parallels the one we're all familiar with. This second nervous system controls growth, healing, and the regeneration of broken bones."

## *Energization and the spine*

The spine is the primary conduit for communication between the brain and body: thus, keeping it flexible and properly aligned is important to our overall health. During the time we spend sitting in chairs, the vertebrae become compacted, pinching the nerves and diminishing the flow of prana in the body. Several of the Energization Exercises are dedicated to stretching the spine and realigning the vertebrae. The spine is engaged in one way or another in all of the exercises. A flexible spine is a healthy spine.

## *Tones and strengthens the muscles*

Muscle tone and strength diminish rapidly when we are physically inactive. More than we realize, strong muscles are involved in maintaining general health and well-being. Healthy muscles help the body perform important activities, beyond simply movements – these include supporting a healthy metabolism. They guard against breaks and fractures and decrease the risk of falling. Muscular activity is a contributing factor in the prevention of high cholesterol, diabetes, cardiovascular disease, and cancer.

While a distinguishing aspect of Energization relative to other forms of physical exercise is that it intentionally strengthens the mental muscle of the will, its benefits for the physical muscles should not be disregarded. The conscious contraction and relaxation of the muscles helps to keep them strong and maintain muscle tone. All of the muscles in the body are affected by Energization, from the twenty small muscles in the foot, to the hundreds in the head and face.

A study led by Masatoshi Nakamura at the Niigata University of Health and Welfare in Niigata, Japan found that men and women who contracted their arm muscles as hard as possible for a total of three seconds per day increased their bicep strength by as much as twelve percent after a month. The study concluded:

> "Every muscle contraction counts, and contributes to building strength, assuming you lift a weight near the maximum you can handle and it lasts at least three seconds." [18]

People who enjoy sports use Energization to prepare their muscles for training and competition. Yoga and martial arts enthusiasts find Energization an ideal warmup.

Ananda Yoga is a unique approach to the practice of the traditional yoga asanas. It includes a conscious intent to become aware of the flow of vital energy, not only through the physical movements of the postures, but also mentally, through the use of affirmations that accompany each posture to help the practitioner become aware of its subtle energetic and spiritual effects.

In the Ananda Yoga teacher training courses, the students begin each session with a warmup that includes some, or at times, all of the Energization Exercises.

As an Ananda Yoga teacher for many years, I have found that the exercises give the students access to a deeper experience of yoga. They learn to *feel* the energy movements characteristic to each asana, and to *withdraw* the energy, especially during the moments of stillness after the asana. They learn to *draw* cosmic energy, especially during the warrior poses, and how to *uplift* the energy to the spiritual eye, especially during the inverted poses.

It has been rewarding for me to observe how combining Energization with yoga enlivens the atmosphere of the session and inspires the future yoga teachers to perceive the art and science of yoga in a deeper light that they can pass on to their students. –*Jayadev,* co-*founder of the* Yogananda Academy of Europe *and director of the* School of Ananda Yoga

## ❋ Black belt ❋

I learned the Energization Exercises when I was already a second-degree black belt and part-time karate instructor. However, the only time I could find to practice them was between my afternoon postgraduate classes and my evening karate sessions. Yet after only a few weeks, I noticed some remarkable results:

- I did not need a nap between the classes and the karate practice.

- It took me less time to warm up for the karate sessions.
- I had more physical strength and greater stamina.
- My entire body felt lighter and more agile.
- I had more control of my muscles: I was able to quickly contract and relax the necessary muscles while performing karate movements. This gave more power to each movement, with less effort.
- When I did the Exercises after a training session, I was able to recover more quickly.

After a year of doing Energization Exercises, I started learning a new karate style – it is an Okinawan style called *Uechi Ryu*. It is one of the most efficient and powerful karate styles – its practitioners are known for their strength, speed, power, and what is known in martial arts as "the body armor" – a body that is tolerant to punches and kicks. The foundation of this style is a sequence of movements that require certain muscles to be quickly tensed and relaxed before each action. I was able to learn and excel in this style quickly, thanks to my Energization practice.
–**Nebojsa**, *Belgrade; Serbia*

## *Energization and the heart*

Heart disease is the leading cause of death worldwide – in 2019 approximately 15 million people died of heart attack and stroke. The heart is a muscle: Although we rarely think of it in physical terms, it is, in fact, our most essential and hard-working one. Every day it pumps approximately 7,200 liters (1900 gallons) of blood. Unlike other muscles, it doesn't rest at night. Like other muscles, it is weakened by a sedentary lifestyle and strengthened by daily physical exertion.

The most universally prescribed prevention for heart disease is exercise. Cardiologists recommend thirty minutes daily of even mild physical exercise such as brisk walking or gardening: 150 minutes a week of mild exercise or 75 minutes of vigorous exercise will keep the heart in good condition. Another way to strengthen the heart is with weight-bearing exercises, which tone all of the muscles, including the heart.

The complete set of Energization Exercises, which can be completed in about fifteen minutes, brings both kinds of benefit to the heart and arteries: each exercise involves the heart muscle, along with others, moderately increasing the heart rate. The weight-lifting exercises (using imaginary weights with mental and physical resistance) tone the entire body. Sluggish circulation receives a healthy boost, and oxygenated blood is sent to all of the cells and organs.

## Nourishes the organs and glands

You may recall (from Part III) that prana maintains the body through five primary systems: circulation, metabolism/endocrine, respiration, digestion, and over-all immunity. Due to stress, age, environmental pollution, and unhealthy lifestyle choices, these systems will slow or become impaired over time, leaving the organism vulnerable to disease and premature aging.

The Life Force Energization Exercises specifically reinforce all of these systems. Many of the exercises include deep breathing which improves respiration and lung flexibility, while others bring prana and fresh blood to the stomach, pancreas, and intestines, improving digestion, metabolism, and glucose assimilation. Yet others stimulate the brain, helping to maintain cognition and protect the neurons. All of the exercises improve heart and lung efficiency and circulation.

Sluggish circulation often culminates in poison deposits in the system. By energizing the muscles, the white and red blood corpuscles are specially charged with vital force. This electrification of blood cells helps to make them immune to disease and helps to surround them with a charged barbed wire of life force which electrocutes all invading inimical bacteria. The Yogoda tensing exercises are especially helpful in stimulating sluggish circulation.[19]

I didn't recall eating beets for dinner, yet the water in the toilet bowl was decidedly tinged with red. I wish it had been beets, but it was blood. In addition to this unwelcome symptom, I had strong stomach cramps and intestinal pain. An inflamed digestive track was causing fever, headaches, and general weakness – it was colitis, which if unattended could get seriously worse.

I recalled that Yogananda had recommended some stomach energization exercises to cure abdominal problems.* I decided to try them before seeing the doctor. I started with ten to twelve cycles in the morning and evening on an empty stomach, slowly increasing to the recommended maximum. After three days, I felt better, and after four weeks of daily practice, the inflammation, pain, and weakness were gone. I could digest well, my energy had returned, and the toilet bowl was no longer red. *–Arudra, Ananda Assisi*

## Energization and the bones

Osteoporosis affects more than 200 million people globally. Loss of bone density weakens the skeletal structure and can make bones vulnerable to breaks and fractures, which in turn can severely limit movement and overall health. Weight-bearing and muscle-strengthening exercises are recommended to help prevent or delay loss of bone density. Appropriate exercise routines are freely available online – they often include exercises similar to some of the Energization Exercises, such as biceps curls and running in place.

In the Energization Exercises, weights and resistance straps are replaced by tensing muscles with willpower to create resistance. A majority of the Exercises employ this approach to strengthen the legs, arms, back, shoulders, and neck.

*"These are special exercises for those who particularly want to improve digestion and eliminate constipation and other abdominal troubles by increasing the peristaltic movements of the intestines and more uniform secretions of the glands – liver, pancreas, etc. – in a proper way... (They) are to be done at least 15 times; 20 or more if needed...up to 40 times, increasing a few each day until you reach the maximum number." –Yogananda, "Yogoda, Tissue-Will System of Physical Perfection," 1925 edition.

Aside from strengthening the body's skeletal structure to help prevent fractures, Energization can be helpful to hasten healing after injury.

※ NINETEEN DAYS ※

It happened with amusing consistency – whenever I was scheduled to teach a course in self-healing, I would have a health crisis, usually a cold or flu. While these episodes were more annoying than debilitating, this time it was serious: a fractured ankle.

I was descending a set of stairs in wet weather, and on the last slippery step my foot twisted under me. "Just a sprain," I thought. But the next day as I taught the first class, my foot throbbed and the swelling had increased.

At the emergency room, an x-ray revealed a fracture, and when the swelling had subsided after a day, the foot, ankle, and shin bone were encased in an old-style heavy plaster cast. When I asked how long I'd have to wear it, the tech said, "At least a month, perhaps longer." "I'll be back in nineteen days," I declared. He replied, "You can come back if you like, but you'll just have to return when the ankle is healed after four weeks."

Why nineteen days? Because Easter was approaching, and I didn't want to be hobbling during the celebrations.

The class I was teaching was about Life Therapy, and it provided excellent motivation for my healing. I had my first experience of doing the Energization Exercises in a chair. I found that they worked just as well in that position, but the leg cast was a challenge – which I tackled with the following routine:

I **visualized** healing prana entering through the medulla oblongata and flooding the ankle.

I **energized** – while the cast prevented tensing and vibrating the calf and ankle, I did those exercises mentally, with more repetitions.

I **willed** that the life force I was sending to the ankle was knitting the bones together.

**I affirmed,** "My ankle is well!"

**I imagined** the amazed look on the face of the x-ray technician when he discovered that the bones had, in fact, healed in just nineteen days.

And so it was, precisely nineteen days later. The surprised discussion amongst the doctors and technicians, the removal of the burdensome cast, a remarkably short period of physical therapy, and another story to tell about the value of Life Force healing techniques. –**Shivani** (*the author*)

※ TWENTY YEARS LATER ※

Sport has always been my passion. As a young boy I loved to ski, and later I would take up tennis, though my performance and pleasure were hindered by an old injury to my ankle.

When I was twelve, I fell on the ski slopes with the ski attached to my leg, resulting in a break of the tibia (shinbone). The doctors applied a cast, and I had to keep the leg immobilized for more than a hundred days. When they finally removed the cast, my leg had become so thin, it looked as if only bone remained.

The doctors said that there was no need for physiotherapy, that the leg would return to normal on its own. But it didn't – over the next several years I sprained the ankle many times, rupturing ligaments and further compromising my athletic performance.

For more than twenty years I sought a solution, but every therapy I tried proved either ineffective or unable to help me live with an ankle that was still partially compromised.

For spiritual reasons, I signed up with the Ananda Raja Yoga School, where I learned the Energization Exercises. When the instructor said that the exercises could be used to help heal a weak or injured body part, I thought I would try them on the ankle. Throughout course, I practiced them three times a day.

To my surprise, one day as I was doing my usual yoga routine, I discovered that I could bend both ankles to a near-equal degree, and that after more than twenty years my body could enter the asanas without limitations, and without resorting to strange postural devices.

Since that day, my ankle has become fully functional and has no longer bothered me during sports, nor have I had any additional complaints. –**Marco,** *Siena, Italy*

## Joints and tendons

S everal months ago, I underwent rehabilitation for severe tendonitis and calcification in my shoulder. When I showed my therapist the Energization Exercises I was doing daily, he was surprised and said, "If you want to cure this tendonitis, you will have to do them at least four times a day." After just three months of energizing four times every day, and only four sessions of osteopathic manipulations, the tendonitis was healed completely. –**Valerio,** *Sicily*

## Anytime, anywhere

For many people, the first option they think of when they feel a need to increase their energy is to sign up at a gym and dedicate at least an hour a day on the treadmill and strength machines. Or they acquire expensive home equipment, buy special shoes and clothing, take energy drinks, protein smoothies, and vitamins. And, let's face it, any exercise at all will yield a satisfying improvement in our energy, health, and happiness.

But do we really need to spend all that time and money? We can practice the complete set of Energization Exercises almost anywhere, anytime, in any comfortable clothes, in about fifteen minutes.

Yogananda specified that the exercises should be done slowly and in the prescribed order. He said that it's best to do them outdoors, or indoors with windows open. As my story above shows, although they should be performed while standing, we can, if need be, do them while sitting.

They can be done almost anywhere – while sitting at the computer, while listening to a conference speaker, while commuting in the bus, flying in an airplane, or at the airport. If we are unable to stand or sit, we can even practice them lying down, with actual physical movements, or only mentally. In all cases, what's most needed is a powerful desire to feel better, and to do them with fully focused attention, and a firm knowledge of the correct method and sequence.

### ❊ PITCHING OUR PROJECT ❊

We were preparing an oral presentation for a prospective client, and I had been appointed the program director. It would be an important meeting for our company, and for me. On the morning of the meeting, I prepared by doing a full set of Energization, along with my usual Kriya practice, and offered a prayer that the meeting might go well and be fruitful for both sides.

Both teams were seated around a large table in the client's conference room. As my colleagues introduced themselves, I was silently doing the Full Body Recharge mentally without drawing the participants' attention. When it was my turn to speak, I gave a short presentation about our approach to the project, and responded to their questions.

The atmosphere turned a bit tense when someone on the client's team made a few negative observations and asked some aggressive questions. A member of our team became flustered while attempting to respond, and gave less than satisfactory answers. At that point, I calmly and courteously intervened and clarified the issues. The meeting ended on an inconclusive note, with our team feeling a bit demoralized, imagining that we had lost the contract.

A month later, the client informed us that we had been awarded the job. The project began, and at lunch one day, one of the client's representatives mentioned that she had been quite displeased with her colleague's aggressive behavior, and that she had noticed how calm and centered I was while responding with clarity and respect. I told her my secret: Energization and meditation, a winning combination in all circumstances. –**Ahmet,** *Milan, Italy*

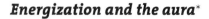

## *Energization and the aura**

In the last chapter, we considered a principle that Yogananda affirmed many times: "The greater the will, the greater the flow of energy." We also pondered its corollary: "The greater the flow of energy, the stronger the magnetic field."

Regular practice of the Energization Exercises generates a powerful magnetic field that we can employ to protect ourselves from unwelcome influences.

We are constantly surrounded by an astral energy shield which is commonly known as the *aura.* A powerful magnetic aura can repel negativity, disease, and even, to a degree, bad karma – but its protective power will depend on the quantity, quality, and constancy of the flow of life force. The strength of the flow of energy will vary from day to day, and even from hour to hour. When it is low, the magnetic field becomes weaker and more porous, so that disease can enter more easily.

With regular practice of the complete, and also the abbreviated Energization series, we can keep the flow of life force strong in us, and the protective shield of the aura can become impenetrable.

### ✳ SHIELDED ✳

I was undergoing a particularly difficult situation in my life, and feeling energetically attacked by negativity that was coming from all directions. It was stressing me to the point where I was having actual dizzy spells. And then I remembered that we can use the Energization Exercises to strengthen our aura. As soon as I practiced them, I began to feel much better, psychologically and physically. This experience encouraged me to practice them daily to keep my aura always strong. –*Clarita, Rome*

* We will consider more ways to protect ourselves from negative influences in Part XII, Volume Three.

## Energization and Self-realization

As we saw in Part II, the main obstacle to Self-realization is the ego which compels us to identify ourselves with a limited material reality. No amount of well-reasoned persuasion will ever succeed in convincing the ego otherwise. Actual experiences of blissful, non-material realities, however, provide a convincing contrast, encouraging the ego to expand its narrow horizons.

With the regular practice of Energization Exercises, we begin to have a direct and immediate experience of the flow of energy. As we increasingly gain mastery over that flow, we soon begin to identify ourselves as a conduit for a higher energy. With repeated, regular ongoing practice, we eventually enter into the flow of the Cosmic Energy that is always streaming from its Source into our being, and which will lift us into Cosmic Consciousness.

When the ego finally reunites with the soul, the resulting union is experienced in eight ways: "I am peace. I am joy. I am calmness. I am love. I am wisdom. I am light. I am Aum. I am Energy." The experience of cosmic energy is often our first taste of Self-realization. Getting to know ourselves as being that energy is an important step toward realizing who and what we are.

### ✵ MAGIC WAND ✵

I am an energetic, go-getter kind of individual, yet I am rather prone to stress. The many self-help books I have avidly read on dealing with stress have all said that meditation can help clear and calm the mind.

And so I sat and began doing what I thought was meditating. Being from Thailand, I thought that meditation was part of my DNA, and that I could figure it all out on my own. When my thoughts threatened to overwhelm me, I tried to calm them with forceful breathing practices – which only resulted in raw nostrils and an even more restless mind!

Then I came across the Energization Exercises, and it was like being touched by a magic wand. The tensing and relaxing of individual muscles, the gentle breathing, the harmonious physical movements – it all worked together to prepare my body to relax and my mind to be calm. I was surprised at how painless and joyful meditation could be.

For me, it is an unbeatable combination: Energization plus meditation equals a more stable, constructive, and joyful life. –**Bhiti Pokae,** Thailand

## *Energization and meditation*

Any technique of meditation can be greatly enhanced by warming up with the Energization Exercises. They serve to vitalize the body, release physical tensions, focus the mind and calm emotional reactivity. Students on the path of Kriya [20] first learn these Exercises and practice them daily before meditation, both to improve the quality of the meditation session itself, and also to prepare themselves for the more advanced practice of the Kriya techniques by harmonizing the flow of energy in the astral body.

PART IV    CHAPTER TWO

# Life Force Energization Exercises

It is the Life Energy that will cure, and
that method which exerts the most power
over the Life Energy is the superior method.[1]
—YOGANANDA

## ☀ LIGHTNING FLASH FLOWS THROUGH ME ☀

I had always been strong and healthy, until the day
when I started to feel uncharacteristically tired. When
I began having trouble walking, I went to the doctor, and
after lots of tests and misdiagnoses, it was discovered that
I had fourth-stage non-Hodgkin's lymphoma cancer.

There was a tumor close to my spine, and initially
they tried treating it with electric shocks. The treatment
was extremely painful and left me lying on the floor like
a baby, unable to stand or walk. That was when I brought
to bear the Energization Exercises that I had practiced for
several years.

Because I had no feeling in my legs, I was unable to
make the muscles tense and relax. As I lay in the hospital
bed, I did the exercise mentally, sending energy through
the medulla oblongata to the legs, while visualizing the
muscles, in turn, contracting and relaxing, and receiving
healing light. I could feel the energy flowing and moving
through many blockages. The longer I could focus on the
exercise, the more I could feel the energy healing my legs.

After three days, I started to walk. The doctor and
nurses said that it was impossible to be able to walk so
soon – they had planned to keep me in the hospital for
a long time, but when they saw how quickly I was progressing, they dismissed me.

This kind of cancer is curable, and I had the good fortune to receive a new therapy that targeted only the specific cancer cells. During the long treatments, while the medicine flowed into my veins and did its job, I was doing mine, connecting by another kind of IV to the Cosmic Energy, and mentally willing it to flow through me and wash away the cancer cells.

The immunotherapy cycles are now successfully finished, and I need to go for a checkup only twice a year. One or more times every day, I tense with will, relax and feel – always thankful for the cosmic energy therapy that is keeping me healthy, happy, and productive.

—*Rinus, Netherlands*

## The Energization Exercises

In a metaphorical sense, disease can be described as "constipation"– blockage to the flow of vital energy. Yogananda's Energization Exercises remove energy blocks by increasing the flow of life force to a degree where it is sufficiently strong to open the energy channels.

In this chapter, we will see how, by activating our willpower and using concentration, we can draw limitless energy through the portal of the medulla oblongata and distribute it to the trillion cells of the body and brain.

The thirty-nine Energization Exercises belong to what Yogananda called "the Yogoda System of Physical, Mental, and Spiritual Perfection." Today, they are more commonly known as the Energization Exercises. In this book I call them the Life Force Energization Exercises, or at times simply Energization. You can learn them at home while watching the videos referenced in the Appendices, which will give you guided instructions.

If you already know them, you can enhance your practice by following the Advanced Practice Guidelines listed in the Appendices, which include commentary from Yogananda's lessons, Swami Kriyananda's writings, notes I took in 1971 when Kriyananda instructed us in their proper practice, and from my own experiences practicing them for fifty years.

All of the Energization Exercises are based on the now familiar principle, "The greater the will, the greater the flow of energy." They strengthen our willpower, which in turn increases the flow of healing life force.

It is worth emphasizing this point: *self-healing comes down to the strength of our will.* Thus, practices that reinforce our willpower are a tremendous investment in our good health.* The difference between sports and Energization is that while willpower is an obvious requirement in sports, its use is more or less automatic, and it lacks a specific intention to vitalize the entire body with a superior form of energy.†

Mechanical exercises generally teach one to concentrate on the muscles and to consider oneself a Muscular being only. They help stimulate the animal consciousness in man and not his subtle nature. "Yogoda"....teaches...the maximum use of conscious Will and Life Energy, in exercising and vitalizing not only muscles but all tissues and cells of the body....It teaches...that strength comes from within and not from the muscles, and that life does not solely depend on food and exercise but is sustained from within.[2]

The focus of this chapter is the core Energization exercise that Yogananda taught in his first set of lessons, which he authored in 1923. In this book we call it the **"Full Body Life Force Recharge,"** sometimes abbreviated as "Full Body Recharge." This single exercise is the key to understanding all the others. Its practice brings many of the healing benefits of the entire set. If you practice it several times a day, rest assured that the quality of your life and health will improve.

* The importance of willpower is a frequent theme in Yogananda's teachings. It is mentioned often throughout this book, especially in Chapter Four of Part III. We will meet it again in Part VI, as one of the superpowers of the conscious mind, and again in Part VII as an essential factor for eliminating unhealthy habits.

† In addition to Energization, daily physical exercise is an important requisite for health and vitality. See Part V.

### Tense with will — relax and feel!

The seat of willpower in the body is located in the frontal lobes of the brain, at the point between the eyebrows, which is the positive pole of the sixth chakra. Its corresponding negative pole is the medulla oblongata, located at the base of the brain.* It is the doorway through which life force enters the body. The more strongly we can exert our willpower, the greater the flow of life force that we will be able to draw into the body at that point.

Each energization exercise is designed to strengthen the power of will by what appears to be the simple act of consciously tensing certain areas of the body, and then consciously relaxing them. Yogananda instructs: "Tense with will – relax and feel."

A deliberate act of will is required to tense specific muscle groups and relax them in a controlled manner. Similar to a physical muscle, the "muscle" of will power becomes stronger, the more we exercise it by regular Energization. And, of course, the stronger it gets, the more energy we are able to draw into the body.

In addition to strengthening our will, tensing and relaxing each body naturally increases the flow of blood and oxygen to the cells.

One of the key functions of blood is transport. Blood vessels are like networks of roads where deliveries and waste removal take place. Oxygen, nutrients and hormones are delivered around the body in the blood and carbon dioxide and other waste products are removed. Blood flow within muscles fluctuates as they contract and relax. During contraction, the vasculature within the muscle is compressed, resulting in a lower arterial inflow with inflow increased upon relaxation. The opposite effect would be seen if measuring venous outflow.

This rapid increase and decrease in flow is observed over multiple contractions. If the muscle is used for an extended period, mean arterial inflow will increase as the arterioles vasodilate to provide the oxygen and nutrients required for contraction. Following the end of contractions, this increased mean flow remains to resupply the muscle tissue with required nutrients and clear inhibitory waste products, due to the loss of the inhibitory contractile phase.[3]

* See the diagram on p. 209.

Both greater oxygenation – caused by
deep breathing; and fuller circulation –
due to the tension of particular parts –
are reinforced by the distribution of motor
Life Energy to the different parts through
willpower. This complete coordination,
gives health, power, freshness and
long life. By this process you store up
more cellular energy than you use up
during daily activities.[4]

The body eliminates waste and toxins during the tension phase of Energization, when the venous blood is pushed back to the heart, and the lymph fluids are pushed back into the bloodstream where waste products are eliminated through the kidneys and liver. During the relaxation phase, an increased flow of blood carries oxygen and nutrients to the muscles.

There is also more squeezing of
the waste materials out of the tissues,
this waste being finally expelled
through the nostrils, pores, etc.[5]

With daily practice, toxins are expelled, damaged cells are repaired or eliminated, and the cells of body, brain, and nervous system are invigorated with prana – the intelligent energy-architect that creates healthy cells. In a real sense, we are cleansed and born anew each day.

By intensity of effort you can heal
yourself very soon, since Yogoda gives you
the power to bring the only curative source,
the Cosmic Life Energy, into contact
with diseased tissues.[6]

When I undertook my annual internal body cleanse this time, I felt that it would be helpful to do a particularly deep cleanse, and so I made my customary natural herbal preparations rather strong.

At first, I seemed to be doing quite well, but then I noticed some discomfort in my body due to what appeared to be an accumulation of the toxins that my body was releasing into my system to be eliminated – but my body didn't seem to be eliminating them properly.

At a certain point I received an intuition that I could use the Energization Exercises, specifically the Full Body Recharge, to help expel the toxins.

I did the exercises many times with full determination, while visualizing the healing energy burning out the toxins. I felt an immediate relief, and during the night I perspired a great deal. In the morning, my body was ready to evacuate with great intensity. After twenty-four hours I felt much lighter, freer, and grateful that I had remembered the cleansing power of Energization. –**Cristina**, *Spain*

## *Relax and feel*

"Tense with will – relax and feel." The second phase requires that we very consciously and completely relax the muscles. Why is this important? Because the relaxation phase is when prana flows into and vitalizes the area. It is therefore important to relax as completely as possible.

Tension blocks the natural flow of energy in the body. It paralyzes one's normal sense of physical and mental harmony. Human ills all derive more or less directly from impairments in the body's energy-flow. The main reason for eliminating waste from the body is to permit the free flow of energy. Tension, the chief obstruction to this flow, is the first obstacle to be overcome if the body is to return to its divinely natural state.[7]

When we are stressed, muscle tension spreads throughout the body and prevents vital energy from reaching organs and cells, initiating a process of deterioration and opening the way for disease. Thus Yogananda taught that it is important to learn to release these tensions every day.

> The first step in rejuvenation is relaxation, both physical and mental. If you are tensed even slightly in any part, you are burning up energy in that part. The burning of energy results in a breaking down of bodily tissues and decay.[8]

Try to become more aware throughout the day of those muscles that become tight, and take immediate action to diffuse the tension.

> Whenever you want to relax any body part, gently tense it, hold the tension in it, counting from 1 to 3 then relax quickly and feel the energy retire.[9]

Always remember that the kind of effort required for these exercises is more mental than physical, since it is our willpower, and not our physical strength, that draws energy. With regular practice our ability to tense strongly and relax completely will improve, and the exercises will increasingly help us develop our healing power.

> Whenever you direct your Will into any part of the body as you tense it, you are sending down a quantity of nerve energy – Pranic current or vital energy – from the brain to that part. The greater the flow of this Pranic current, the stronger and better is its action on that particular part, and the greater is the chance of the tissues of that part being revitalized by more rapid circulation and healthier Pranic adjustment.[10]

## Life Force Full Body Recharge

In this exercise you will mentally locate and try to isolate each of the twenty body parts, with full concentration. Before you start, it will help to touch each body part; you can do this while sitting or standing. Touching the part will help you become aware of the neural pathways between the body and mind.

**1,2** Touch your left foot and curl your toes, then relax. Do the same with the right foot.

**3,4** Touch and squeeze your left calf, then the right.

**5,6** Touch and squeeze the front, side, and back of your left thigh, then the right.

**7,8** Touch and squeeze the left buttock, then the right.

**9** Place your hands over your lower abdomen and squeeze the lower abdominal muscles.

**10** Move the hands over the stomach and squeeze the upper abdominal muscles.

**11** Grab the left forearm, then **12** the right.

**13** Grab the left bicep, then **14** the right.

**15** Place your right hand over the left side of your chest (the pectoral muscles).

**16** Place your left hand over the right pectorals.

**17** Place your left hand on the left side of your neck.

**18** Place the right hand on the right side of your neck.

**19** Place either hand over your throat.

**20** With either hand, squeeze the muscles at the back of the neck.

## Concentrate at the center of each part

Each exercise begins with **concentrating in the center** of the body part.

The moment we form an intention to act, our willpower becomes activated at the level of thought. When we visualize ourselves performing the action, our willpower becomes even more deeply engaged and activated. This, in turn, activates the portions of the brain related to the action.

Through the power of Will, the brain
receives an increased supply of
Life Energy from Cosmic Energy residing
in and surrounding the body.[11]

When we concentrate deeply on something we want to do, neurotransmitters initiate a cascade of communication through the nervous system, creating a bridge between the brain and the body. When we do the Full Body Recharge or the Energization Exercises, the mind needs to be deeply focused at the center of the muscle group that's involved in each exercise in order to initiate a full flow of energy to that body part.

Concentrate on the *inside* of the
muscles—in the center, as it were,
of any part you are tensing.
Become keenly aware, first,
of the sensation of tension.
Then try to feel, behind that tension,
the causative flow of energy.[12]

### Use your will power to control the amount of tension and relaxation

With the mind concentrated on a body part, the next step is to *tense* that part *slowly*, increasing the tension gradually from low to medium to high, and finally making the part vibrate. Yogananda said that the exercises should be done calmly and harmoniously, thus the flow from low to high and the vibration at the end should be executed in a smooth flow, and the vibration should be done with deep, calm concentration for up to three seconds.

The relaxation should also be done gradually and harmoniously, from high to medium to low, ending with complete relaxation. During complete relaxation, try to "feel" the concentration of prana in the body part. At first you might have difficulty in achieving this level of control, but with practice it becomes easier.

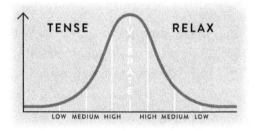

In doing the exercise in this controlled fashion, heart activity increases—fresh blood and oxygen flow both from the brain to the muscles and back again to the brain through a continuous loop, greatly benefitting the heart muscle and arteries, as well as the body cells. Even without the addition of Cosmic Energy, the miraculous operating system of the body is able to refresh and regenerate itself. Consciously opening the doorway at the medulla oblongata to a higher octave of healing power, exponentially increases the efficacy of the body's own reserves.

Exercising with will and concentration produces excellent results because it creates energy directly, by will development. This energy is quickly absorbed by the muscles, blood, bones, and sinews, for cellular rejuvenation. Therefore, the highest degree of energy accompanied by the least tissue destruction is derived from the Yogoda will exercises.[13]

## Practice slowly and deliberately

Yogananda emphasized the importance of doing each cycle slowly.

> The *more slowly* the exercises are done,
> with *deliberate application of the Will Power* to
> the particular parts, the greater is the flow of
> Life Energy from the brain to those parts,
> and the more harmonious its coordination
> with the cellular energy of the tissues.[14]

> The...exercises are all to be done slowly at first,
> gently and rhythmically. Never give jerks.
> Every movement must be harmonious.... Slow and
> attentive exercise performed once produces more
> beneficial results than hasty and inattentive
> exercise performed many times.... No results are
> obtained if the exercises are done quickly.[15]

## How to breathe during the exercises

Breathing exercises are a central part of virtually every system of yoga meditation. The Energization Exercises employ a practice called **"double breathing"** that more fully fills and empties the lungs, bringing in more oxygen and expelling more carbon dioxide. The Full Body Recharge begins and ends with double breathing, and some of the Energization Exercises are done with double breathing as well.

During double breathing, we take two inhalations through the nostrils in rapid succession: a short, quick inhalation followed by a longer and stronger inhalation. Double breathing allows us to draw more oxygen and prana into the body. Try it now, while sitting or standing with a straight spine.

Without pausing after the second part of the inhalation, exhale through the mouth and nose, forcefully emptying the lungs with a short, rapid exhalation followed by a longer and slower exhalation.

While doing double breathing, consciously use the muscles of the diaphragm to move the air in and out of the lungs. Vigorous double breathing helps strengthen the heart and lungs.

Slowly practice three of these cycles in succession to accustom yourself to this kind of breathing.*

Dr. Andrew Huberman, a neurologist at the Stanford University School of Medicine, is testing what he calls "physiological sighs" as a way to short-circuit the body's sympathetic stress response by balancing it with a parasympathetic relaxing response.

Two inhalations through the nose are followed immediately by a single forceful long exhalation through the mouth. Huberman suspects that the alveolar sacs of the lungs, over time, deflate and are unable to take in sufficient oxygen and expel carbon dioxide adequately, and that this deficiency plays a significant role in triggering the stress response. With double inhalation, the alveolar sacs quickly inflate and take in more oxygen, and with forced exhalation more carbon dioxide is offloaded. He recommends doing at least three cycles of "sighs" at the first sign of stress, noting that the simple exercise can be done anytime, anywhere, even while driving, and that they effectively interrupt the stress syndrome.[16]

## Test your willpower and concentration

This exercise will help you understand how to use maximum concentration and willpower while contracting and relaxing a muscle group.

- Extend one arm to the side at shoulder height. Bend the arm at the elbow and bring the forearm straight up, creating a 90-degree angle.

- Touch the biceps of the bent arm for a moment with the other hand, then put the hand back down at your side.

- Close your eyes and keep your concentration in the bicep throughout the exercise.

- While concentrating in the bicep, contract the upper arm as if resisting a one-kilo weight (2.2 pounds) for about five seconds.

* This practice is demonstrated in the instruction videos found in the Appendices.

- Increase the contraction to resist two kilos (4.4 pounds) and hold for about five seconds.

- Slowly and smoothly increase the contraction to resist five kilos (11 pounds).

- If you are able, increase the weight a bit more, contracting as hard as you can, causing the muscles to vibrate. Hold the vibration for about ten seconds.

- Now, very, very slowly begin to relax the tension in the upper arm, reversing the process until you have brought the arm back down to your side, completely relaxed.

- Hold your attention in the arm for a few seconds and notice the sensations there.

People commonly report feeling a sensation of warmth and tingling in the entire arm, and a sense that the arm is bigger, stronger, lighter, and more alive.

Now evaluate how your other arm feels at this moment. Compared to the arm that has been "energized," it will likely feel heavier, stiffer, and less alive, perhaps even cold or dead.

The sensations you felt in the energized arm are the result of the process described above: the motor portions of the brain were activated; messages were sent through the nervous system; the heart started to work harder; blood, oxygen, and prana arrived at the point of your concentration and were diffused throughout the bicep.

The work of holding your arm steady as the weight got heavier was accomplished by your willpower, which increased in intensity as the weight got heavier.

As you gradually reached the level where the muscle was vibrating and you were exerting your willpower to the maximum, the doorway of the medulla oblongata opened wider and a flood of Cosmic Energy entered the body.

During the Full Body Recharge, when you recharge each of the body parts, make an effort to bring the tension to the highest level possible for your present condition.

For maximum results you need to give your full attention to each phase: tensing with maximum willpower, and releasing the tension completely. Each person's "maximum" will be different, and it will naturally take practice to be able to give the exercises your own maximum effort. Make sure not to harm the body by over-exertion, or over-tensing weak or injured parts.

It also takes time to perfect the phase of complete relaxation. Proceed gradually, and as you practice, give equal attention to both phases – by doing the exercises correctly the healing effects will occur more quickly.

> *The purpose of tension and relaxation is dissociation of life force and mind from the consciousness of the body.* When that is accomplished, the will and life force actually own the whole body and can, through their healing rays, remove chronic defects from any body part.[17]

## *Cautions*

If your muscles are tight due to accumulated tension, you might experience some pain during the tension phase of the exercise. With regular practice, this should subside, you should gradually be able to exert more tension without pain. It is not necessary or desirable to do the exercises to the point of pain.

If you have high blood pressure, adjust the "high" tension phase so that you are never straining. If you have low blood pressure, do not exaggerate the number of repetitions of the exercises that use double breathing. Conscious practice of the Exercises should help normalize any blood pressure issues.

### ✷ PRECIPITOUS ✷

I t was very hot, and I was feeling unwell. My blood pressure is usually normal, but when the heat is extreme it can fall to an alarmingly low level. Now it was 72-58 and I needed to do something quickly to survive.

I knew that my habitual resource in an emergency, the Energization Exercises, would save me. I did them there and then with deep concentration, trying to be aware of the prana flowing into my body with each movement and helping to normalize the blood pressure.

When I finished my practice, my pressure had risen to 82-67, enough to get me through the day without fainting. I use the exercises every day to stay well, and in emergencies like this one, they have never failed me. –*Alessandra, Siena, Italy*

## *Twenty Body-Part Recharge*

We will now apply the lessons we learned during the bicep exercise – exerting gradual, controlled tension, vibration, and relaxation – to energize twenty muscle groups. We start with the feet, and work our way up the body to the head, always beginning on the left side. Follow the proper order by referring to the diagram on page 282.

Before you begin, concentrate on the medulla, close your eyes, and feeling or visualizing the light there, repeat this affirmation:

> Thy cosmic current flows in me, flows in me,
> through my medulla flows in me, flows in me.
> I think and will the current to flow, in all my body
> the current to flow, in all my body the current
> to flow. I am charged, I am cured, I am charged,
> I am cured. Lightning flash goes through me.
> I am cured, I am cured.[18]

Starting with your left foot, curl your toes and concentrate on the arch of the foot. Tense slowly in a wave from low to high tension, then vibrate the foot, holding the tension for several seconds. Now, gradually reduce the tension until the foot is completely relaxed. Pause for a moment to experience the results. The entire cycle should take about ten or twelve seconds – likely longer while you are learning.

Proceed to the right foot, repeating the same procedure, and onward up the body – always starting on the left side, then the right. Begin each cycle of tension and relaxation by first concentrating in the center of the part before you start to tense.

As you learn the exercise, you will be creating new neural pathways between your brain and body. It is important to establish these pathways carefully and deeply. Once created, you can turn your focus from the physical performance to the flow of Cosmic Energy that is being drawn through the medulla oblongata to nourish each part.

I suggest a rhythm of 3-3-3-1: take about three seconds to tense gradually; three seconds to focus deeply on the part and make it vibrate strongly; three seconds for gradual, controlled relaxation; and about a second (or more if you wish) to hold your concentration on the part and experience the results.

For those already practicing this exercise as part of the full set of Energization Exercises, this rhythm may be somewhat different from your normal practice. Doing the exercise more consciously and slowly brings greater healing results.

---

### FIVE PHASES *of the* FULL BODY RECHARGE*

As mentioned, you will be creating neural pathways between the brain and body as you practice the exercises regularly. These pathways will take time to form, so in the beginning, practice only Phases One, Two, and Five as described here:

*Phase One.*
Start the full-body prana recharge with one or more cycles of **double breathing**.

*Phase Two.*
Move on immediately to the next phase: tense and relax each of the twenty muscle groups (again, refer to the diagram) consciously and slowly (but at an energetic pace), starting at the feet and progressing up the body to the neck muscles, repeating each muscle or each pair of muscles two or three times. There is no required breathing pattern during this phase.

*Phase Five.*
At this point, repeat Phase One to conclude your practice.

---

* This exercise is demonstrated in a video that you will find in the Appendices.

Repeat this progression, moving from the feet to neck, in **a standing position**. Then try it while **sitting down**, and then in a **prone position**. You can practice this exercise in any of those positions whenever you need to fill your energy "tank" with prana.

Yogananda recommends that whenever we practice the Full Body Recharge, we should do each exercise two or three times. You can do each pair – left foot/right foot – two or three times, always slowly and with deep concentration.

Once you are more or less able to locate these areas and you feel comfortable with the exercise, you can add the third and fourth phases.

### Phase Three.

Tense each part with medium tension and *hold the tension in each muscle group* as you pass on to the next group, ending with the neck muscles. Now slightly increase the tension simultaneously in all of the muscles from medium to high, then vibrate, holding the tension and vibration for a few seconds.

### Phase Four.

This is the most challenging phase. Release the tension in each muscle group separately in reverse order, starting with the neck muscles and proceeding downward. Release first the right side, then the left. At the start of relaxation, first release the four parts of the neck simultaneously while lowering the chin to the chest. Then proceed to relax the right side of the chest, then the left, and so forth.

### Phase Five.

Once you've relaxed the tension in the feet, immediately repeat Phase One: double breathing while tensing the whole body and increasing tension gradually to high with vibration, then exhaling while gradually releasing the tension in all body parts simultaneously.

A final note about Phases Three and Four. Once you are able to coordinate the various movements comfortably, you should do Phase Three with one slow inhalation (not double breathing), and you should do Phase Four with a single slow exhalation.

Be patient as you get comfortable with Phases One, Two, and Five before attempting Phases Three and Four. When the neural pathways are established and retained in your muscle memory, you will be able to do the phases in a harmonious flow, and you can turn your focus to the breathing pattern.

### Wake-up call

The manner in which we wake up in the morning can set the tone for the rest of the day. "Toast" people pop up as soon as they open their eyes, while "potato" people roll over and pull the covers up over their head to "cook" a little longer. Whether you are a toast or potato person, you may find Yogananda's recommendation helpful:

> When you wake up in the morning,
> don't jump out of bed suddenly. Go through
> the routine of energizing your body while in bed.
> Close your eyes. First relax all parts and then
> give them a breakfast of energy by tensing your
> whole body slowly, then relaxing. Tense and relax
> gradually; do not jerk. Then get up and repeat the
> routine three times while on your feet.[19]

### Mental practice without physical tension

There are situations when it will not be possible or advisable to do the Exercises with physical tension: when a muscle is weak or injured (for example, when an arm or leg is sprained or fractured), when you are experiencing tendonitis (inflammation of the muscle tendons), during a debilitating illness, or when recovering from surgery. Because willpower activates a flow of healing energy, and concentration directs the energy to the desired body part, you can do the Energization and Full Body Recharge exercises mentally, as your situation allows.

was just settling into my chair when the opening prayer began. As I moved my arms to fold my hands together in Pranam Mudra, I experienced excruciating pain in my shoulder that prevented me from completing the movement. The beauty of the ceremony was lost to me as my mind was overwhelmed by agony.

Somehow I managed to sit until the end. When I arrived home, my first instinct was to look for pain medication, but my higher Self told me that I should try the Energization Exercises, practicing them mentally as I had learned to do in the meditation teacher training program. Summoning my willpower, I mentally did the shoulder rotations several times, then went to sleep.

My first thoughts in the morning went to the shoulder. Even though I had only done a few rotations mentally, I realized that the pain had improved by about forty percent. I did the complete set of Energization Exercises and finished with some extra shoulder rotations. By that evening I was totally free of discomfort and felt absolutely normal. What an amazing gift I had received through this powerful healing instrument. My pranams to Yoganandaji.
–**Sumitra,** *New Delhi*

When doing the exercises mentally, Yogananda suggests:

> Keep your mind on the medulla and
> imagine the energy flowing into your body
> through the medulla and from thence to every
> part of the body. By keeping your mind thus
> fixed upon the medulla, you will soon learn to
> draw in energy from the ether and send it to all
> parts of your body at will, without the physical
> process of tensing and relaxing.[20]

Mentally visualizing the physical movement can bring the same results as when we do them physically, as numerous studies using magnetic resonance mapping have shown:

"We stimulate the same brain regions when we visualize an action and when we actually perform that same action. For example, when you visualize lifting your right hand, it stimulates the same part of the brain that is activated when you actually lift your right hand.

A striking example of how visualization increases brain activation is seen in stroke.

When a person has a stroke due to a blood clot in a brain artery, blood cannot reach the tissue that the artery once fed with oxygen and nutrients, and that tissue dies. This tissue death then spreads to the surrounding area that does not receive the blood any more. However, if a person with this stroke imagines moving the affected arm or leg, brain blood flow to the affected area increases and the surrounding brain tissue is saved. Imagining moving a limb, even after it has been paralyzed after a stroke, increases brain blood flow enough to diminish the amount of tissue death. This is a very clear indicator of the power of visualization."[21]

### Awaken me

"O Eternal Energy! Awaken within me
Conscious Will, Conscious Vitality,
Conscious Health, Conscious Realization.
Good-will to all, Vitality to all,
Good Health to all, Realization to all.
Eternal youth of body and mind
abide in me forever, forever, forever."[22]

was enjoying a casual dinner with friends in New York City, when the conversation turned to me and what I do. I told my friends about meditation and the healing effects of Yogananda's Energization Exercises. I briefly outlined the basic principles – that energy is universal, that we can draw it into the body through the medulla oblongata by tensing and relaxing muscle groups and directing the healing energy to them. I mentioned that even when muscular movement is not possible, the exercises can be done mentally with the same effect.

It was a pleasant dinner conversation; not a class, nothing terribly detailed.

Years later, I received a letter from one of the people who had been at the dinner. He told me that he had experienced numbness in his limbs and had fallen on the stairs, unable to move. No doctor and no amount of testing could explain it. He was essentially immobilized, not knowing what was afflicting him, how it might progress, or how to cure it.

He then remembered our conversation at dinner, and while lying in bed, he began to draw in cosmic energy mentally in the way I had explained, and directed it to his limbs. He wasn't sure if it was having any physical effect, but it helped him overcome his rising panic and helplessness. While doing the exercise mentally, he was able to stay calm, centered, and focused.

Slowly, the symptoms began to reverse as he continued to bring energy into his body through the medulla oblongata. In the letter he said that whatever had caused the paralysis, it had completely disappeared, and that he is back to enjoying his life, with a sense of deep gratitude.

– *Nayaswami Uma,* *Ananda Europa*

## Life Force snacks

While our cell phones can take an hour or longer to recharge, it is possible to replenish the body's prana reserves in three minutes or less. With the Full Body Recharge, the entire body and brain are instantly supplied with life force. No time is required for digestion, there are no harmful side effects, and the healing energy is instantly metabolized and absorbed directly by the body cells.

While there is a limit to how much coffee, chocolate, or sugar the body can absorb in one day, there is no limit to the number of times we can enjoy a life force snack. Since we can easily and effectively practice the Full Body Recharge while standing, sitting, or lying down, we can do it often during the day, even every hour, to keep ourselves in top form.

**The power snack.** An even faster super recharge is the "double breath" – using the diaphragm to inhale forcibly while using our will-power to strongly vibrate all of the body parts simultaneously – and then using the diaphragm and abdominal muscles to expel the breath and empty the lungs.

Three cycles of double breathing in rapid succession take about twenty seconds and will give the brain and body an immediate energy boost. We can practice the cycle anytime, anywhere – even while walking or driving. It is also very effective for calming an agitated mind and an over-charged nervous system.

When we allow our energy reserves to become depleted, the protective shield of our aura is weakened, and negativity and illness can get in more easily. Keeping our will active and our energy tank full is our best health insurance.

I have made it a habit to snack on life force once an hour. If I miss one or more snacks, my energy begins to flag and my mind starts to get foggy. When my smart watch insistently reminds me every hour to stand up, I massage the medulla oblongata, do several cycles of double breathing, and finish with the Full Body Recharge. I have found that keeping my energy tank full is the best way to stay healthy and productive!

### Learn the complete *Life Force Energization Exercises*

In the Appendices you will find a video tutorial I created that includes five short energization sessions with accompanying written materials.

It takes some time to commit the Energization Exercises to memory, and you may find the video and audio guided practice session helpful for learning and remembering the sequence. After you have experienced the benefits for your health and all your life's activities, you will be motivated to make them a part of your daily regime. A common comment about Energization is: "I don't know how I could live without it."

## POINTS TO REMEMBER
### *while practicing the Full Body Recharge*

- An unlimited supply of cosmic energy is available at the touch of your willpower.
- The greater the will, the greater the flow of healing energy.
- Consciously tensing and relaxing stimulates and opens the medulla oblongata.
- By deep concentration we can direct healing life force to targeted areas in the body.
- Use your willpower consciously to modulate the degree of tension and relaxation.
- Tense with will – then relax and feel.
- Remember, while inducing high tension in a muscle or group of muscles, to use maximum Will.[23]
- Exercise very slowly, willingly, and pleasantly, with eyes closed. With eyes closed our concentration is keener and the energy currents are unable to escape through the eyes.

## More Life Force Exercises

Practice of this technique enables man to
recover control of his inner life force and thus realize
his oneness with the universe. –YOGANANDA [1]

**The exercises** in this chapter are derived primarily from Yogananda's
original writings regarding health and self-healing.* The elements of
the Full Body Recharge that you learned in the last chapter come to
bear in these additional exercises:

- Use of the will to draw life force into the body
- Concentration in the area being vitalized
- Contraction and vibration of certain parts of the body, fol-
  lowed by relaxation
- A specific pattern of inhalation and exhalation

It is worth noting that many of these exercises are intended to be
done while the breath is suspended, after we exhale. Yogananda said,

"Breath is the cord that ties the soul to the body." [2]

When the breath is suspended and the soul is no longer circumscribed by the body, higher powers can operate.

Of special note are Yogananda's heliotropic exercises which combine the power of the sun with our willpower, concentration, and
breath for a greater healing effect.

---

* These exercises are from Yogananda's original correspondence lessons, written between 1925 and 1935, as well as from early editions of *Scientific Healing* Affirmations,
and from Yogananda's commentaries on the Bhagavad Gita and "Second Coming of
Christ," as they appeared in his magazines *East-West* and *Inner* Culture. They are also
derived from a series called "Health Recipes" and other articles from the magazines.

## For general vitality

☀ **EXERCISE 1** [3] ☀

- Stand erect with arms stretched straight above your head.
- Relax while holding this position.
- Throw the breath out and keep it out while counting from 1 to 12.
- Inhale and feel that you are drawing energy in through the fingertips and into the medulla and body parts.

☀ **EXERCISE 2** ☀
### For the vital healing of any body part

- Inhale and hold the breath, and in quick, rapid succession:
- Feel the breath in the lungs being converted into energy, which is being reinforced by energy flowing through the medulla oblongata.
- Then concentrate on the point between the eyebrows and centralize the energy there, feeling it as a warm force.
- Then, with a slow exhalation, divert the energy from there to the diseased part, feeling that power burning up all disease.[4]

☀ **EXERCISE 3** ☀

- Stand erect, shoulders back, chest out, chin up, hands down at the sides.
- Now exhale slowly while dropping the chin on the chest, and bend forward at the waist with the arms coming down as far as you can comfortably manage.
- Then inhale slowly, bringing the arms straight in front you and upward over the head.
- Still holding the breath, bend the body and arms backward as far back as you can stretch.
- Then exhale slowly, coming back to the starting position.
- Repeat the exercise three times.[5]

## ☼ EXERCISE 4 ☼

In order to receive electronic energy from the ether, expel the breath, remain calm while sitting in the erect posture, and feel the electronic energy surrounding your body and entering through your body cells; or lift your hands above your head and feel the energy arrive through your fingers.[6]

## ☼ EXERCISE 5 ☼

Sit upright on a chair. Close your eyes. Expel the breath quickly, but start inhaling very slowly through the nostrils, thinking that the air is filling your brain, lungs, heart, spine, stomach, abdomen, thighs, legs, arms, and so forth.

You can also inhale quickly and fill the whole body with the atomic power in the oxygen.[7]

## ☼ EXERCISE 6 ☼

Rubbing the whole stripped body vigorously and rapidly with the palms before taking a bath generates life force and is also very beneficial.[8]

## To improve eyesight and inner vision

## ☼ EXERCISE 1 ☼

- Exhale and keep the breath out.
- With the eyes closed, contract the eyelids and brows very lightly.
- Hold the contraction, with deep concentration, to the count of 20.
- Release the contraction and inhale.
- Repeat 7 times morning and night.[9]

- Concentrate with closed eyes first on the medulla, then feel the power of vision in the eyes flowing through the optical nerves into the retina.
- Concentrate on the retina. Dilate eyes and then relax.
- Turn eyeballs upward, then downward, then left, then right.
- Then rotate them from left to right, and right to left.
- Fix the attention of the eyes on the spot in the middle of the forehead, thinking that the Life Energy flows into and transforms both eyes into two searchlights.

*Learn and repeat this affirmation while doing the above exercise*

I bid you
O rays of blue
To glide through my
    optic nerves
And show me true,
    and show me true
His Light is there
His Light is there.
Through my eyes
Thou dost peep
Thou dost peep.
They are whole, they are
    perfect.
One above and two below
Eyes three, eyes three
Through you unseen,
    what light doth flee
Through you unseen,
    what light doth flee.
Lotus eyes, weep no more
Weep no more

The storms thy petals hurt
    no more.
Come quick and glide
    like swans
In the blithesome water
    of Bliss
In the peaceful lake of peace
In the hour of wisdom's
    dawn.
The light of Thine
O shines through mine
Through past, present and
    future time
I command you
My eyes two
Be one and single
Be one and single
To see all and know all
To make my body shine
To make my mind shine
To make my soul shine.[10]

nother benefit of Energization was how it restored my vision. In the last year of school I studied a great deal as I prepared to enter the university, and as a result my vision deteriorated – when I looked at the night sky, I could no longer see the stars. This lasted for six or seven years, until I learned about Energization. A year later, after more or less regular practice, I looked up at the night sky and was able to say hello again to all the stars!"
—*Tatiana, Russia*

## For toning the nerves

- Inhale and hold the breath.
- Gently contract the entire body, tensing all the muscles at once.
- Hold to a count of 20, with deep attention on the entire body.
- Exhale and release the contraction.
- Repeat three times whenever you feel weak or nervous.[11]

## For the heart and brain

In order to aid in the healing of cardiac or cerebral disorders, we may send energy mentally to the affected area by concentrating on it without tensing. By this method one can send a feeble current of energy to any body part. Actually tensing with will, of course, produces more energy than concentration alone, but very gentle conscious tension and relaxation of the whole body also sends healing energy, vitality, etc., to the heart and brain. It must be remembered, however, that in tensing and relaxing the whole body with a view to curing heart or brain disorders, our concentration must be centered on the affected organ.[12]

## Targeted practice

*A weak muscle or injured part of the body can be strengthened by sending healing energy to the body part with the tension and relaxation method.*

If any part of the body is especially weak,
send the energy very slowly and gently.
It will be gradually strengthened....
You can feel the actual current of energy
being switched on in your body,
wherever you want it.[13]

Anytime you feel a need to energize,
or to heal, an individual body part, tense
that part with will power, sending energy
to it from the medulla; then relax it...
While tensing, be aware of the body *inwardly*,
not outwardly. Concentrate in the center of
any part you are tensing. Once you become
inwardly aware of that tension, you will
gradually become aware of the energy creating it.
The more aware you are of the energy, the
greater will be your control over it.[14]

## To strengthen or heal limbs or muscles

*To remove pain in an arm or leg, or to strengthen a limb:*

- Contract the muscle gently while exhaling, to a count of 20.
- Release the contraction and inhale.
- Repeat 6 times.[15]

## For headaches

*Headaches are often caused by alimentary disturbances such as constipation, and by impurities in the blood. Use this exercise at the first sign of a headache.*

- Press the palm of one hand against the back of the head and press the other palm lightly on the forehead.
- Inhale, hold the breath, and with deepest attention gently contract the muscles at the top of the head. Exhale and release contraction.
- Repeat 4-6 times.[16]

*You will find more suggestions for curing headaches in the Appendices.*

## For brain power

- Exhale and keep the breath out.
- With full concentration, contract the muscles of the head gently to a count of 15.
- Inhale and release the contraction.[17]

## For the teeth

### ✸ EXERCISE 1 ✸

- With eyes closed, clinch the upper and lower left teeth together, then relax.
- Clinch the upper and lower right teeth together, and relax.
- Clinch the front upper and lower teeth together, and relax.
- Then clinch the entire set of upper and lower teeth.
- Hold each state for one or two minutes, concentrating on the "clinching teeth sensation" – thinking that the healing energy is vitalizing all the roots of the teeth and is removing all inharmonious conditions.[18]

## EXERCISE 2

Why disobey God's little laws that govern the body beautiful? You take your lunch, give your lips a hasty napkin rub, and rush out feeling that everything is all right. But what about your teeth – why deny them a cleansing shower bath after they have worked so hard for you? Diseased teeth produce many ills. The Hindu pundits say to rinse your mouth with water ten times after each meal if you have no toothbrush handy.[19]

## For the chest

### EXERCISE 1

- Close eyes. Very gently contract both breasts. Put whole attention there while contracting them.
- Hold the contraction, counting 1 to 30.
- Then release contraction.
- Repeat six times, morning, noon, and night.[20]

  [Author's note: *No breathing pattern is given with this exercise. However, given that other, similar exercises are done with an exhalation and the suspension of breath during the contraction, that pattern can be tried with this exercise as well.*]

### EXERCISE 2

Exposing the chest to direct sunlight has been found to be very beneficial.[21]

### EXERCISE 3

- Stand erect.
- Press your left hand on the right chest, and the right hand on the left chest.
- Slowly tense both sides HIGH simultaneously.
- Relax completely.[22]

# For the stomach and digestion

*These are special exercises for those who particularly want to improve their digestion and eliminate constipation and other abdominal troubles. They increase the peristaltic movements of the intestines and the secretions of the glands, the liver, pancreas, etc., in a proper way. Those without any abdominal troubles may equally well do them without any harm. They are indispensably necessary for all. To be practiced daily in the morning after leaving bed; either early in the morning or four hours after a heavy meal.* [23]

## ☀ EXERCISE 1 ☀

- Stand erect, with closed eyes.
- Pressingly place both hands on abdomen, one above the other.
- Contract with high tension the lower portion, and hold, while contracting and tensing the upper portion.
- While concentrating deeply in the abdomen, hold the tension as long as comfortable.
- Simultaneously relax both parts.
- Repeat eight times. [24]

## ☀ EXERCISE 2 ☀

- Stoop forward, grasping the arms of a chair, holding the arms straight.
- Exhale completely.
- With the breath suspended, slowly cave in the abdomen as far as possible, then push it out as far as possible.
- With the breath still suspended, repeat four or more times.
- Inhale as you stand up, and relax.
- Repeat at least five times, increasing the number of repetitions up to a maximum of forty times. [25]

- Exhale and hold the breath out.
- Contract the abdomen and stomach while concentrating deeply on the navel.
- Hold, with the breath suspended, to a count of 20.
- Release and inhale.
- Repeat 6-12 times in the morning and evening on a light stomach.[26]

◈ **EXERCISE 4** ◈

*to strengthen the stomach muscles*

- Lie down on your back on the floor.
- Balance on the hips with head and feet up from floor [to the extent you are able].
- Then rock up and down and sideways first on one shoulder, then on the other, like a rocking chair or boat.

  This is very strengthening for the stomach muscles, [and] also gives great spinal strength.[27]

## For the spine

◈ **EXERCISE 1** ◈

*This exercise is wonderful for the spine, as it adjusts the vertebrae.*

- Lie down on floor and, balancing on the hips, bring the head and feet up about twelve inches [30 cm] from the floor.
- Place your hands pressingly on the stomach.
- Inhale and while holding the breath, mentally count to six.
- Exhale, relax, and drop hands and feet to the floor.
- Repeat thrice.[28]

- Stand erect, with feet apart, both arms stretched in front.
- With a little force, swing your arms, body, and face all the way to left, and then all the way to the right.
- Alternate three or more times. [29]

## The healing power of sunrays

*Affirmation*

Today I shall find God's vitality in the Sun.
I shall bathe my body directly in
sunlight every day and appreciate the
life-giving, disease-destroying gift of
the ultra-violet rays from God. [30]

The following techniques are part of what Yogananda calls the "magnetic diet."

> "The magnetic diet consists of
> such food substitutes as rays and oxygen
> which can be easily assimilated and
> converted into energy by the latent life
> forces in the body. Magnetic foods
> give energy more quickly than solids
> and liquids which are less easily
> converted into life force." [31]

## GENERAL RECOMMENDATIONS*

- Bathe your body in the bacteria-killing sunshine every day.

- Take a sun bath and concentrate deeply upon the sun-bathed surface of the body, and drink the sunshine in through every pore of the body. Concentration on the sun rays gives one hundred times greater results than taking a sun bath absentmindedly.

- The ultraviolet rays one absorbs in one whole day on a bathing beach exert a beneficial vitalizing effect on the body that lasts about three months.

- Take sunbaths as often as you can, from ten minutes to one-half hour, according to the strength of the sun.

- Bathing in sunlight-heated or ultraviolet ray-saturated water is very beneficial.

- Energy may be drawn from the sun by covering the whole body with a piece of thick blue silk or a blanket and keeping the medulla exposed with the sun shining there, on the back of the head. Concentrate on the back of the head and feel it getting warmer and warmer. Feel the energy being stored in the brain and distributed through the body.

- When using a sun lamp on the affected body part, concentrate your entire thought on the feeling of warmth and know that you are absorbing energy into the atomic composition of the body, and thus electrifying your cell batteries.

- If you have no time for a real sun bath, then open your window, and with eyes closed and head bared, absorb the ultraviolet rays of the sunshine.

---

* These recommendations are from Yogananda's *Super Advanced Course No. 1*, Lessons 1 and 5; and articles in *East-West* magazines in July–August and November–December, 1926.

### OBSTRUCTERS OF SUNLIGHT[32]

- Glass windows. Sunlight coming through a closed window is of no value as the vitalizing rays are shut out. It is necessary to use the direct rays of the sun.
- Clothing.
- Clogged pores. Exercise often and bathe frequently, rubbing the skin vigorously.

The body's energy requirements can be supplied partly by sunshine and oxygen, which are absorbed by the pores. For this reason, the surface of the skin must be kept scrupulously clean at all times."[33]

## Helio-Therapy: Life Force plus sunrays *

*The following methods use life force and sunlight to heal specific parts of the body. Practice them whenever you are in the sun – not only to cure disease or heal a part of the body, but regularly to vitalize the body and strengthen your immunity to disease.*

The method of simultaneously using Life Force and sunlight is the great new Heliotropic or Heliotherapic method of healing. [Each] of the following methods is based upon quickening the Life Force and sun's rays to combine into a greater force for the healing of different body parts.

### For wounds, sores, and skin troubles

- Expose the diseased or injured part to the sunlight.
- Gently contract and relax that part for ten minutes.
- During the exercise, think that the Cosmic Life Force is healing the sore.
- *Optimum Practice Time: ten minutes.*

* Most of the exercises in this section, unless otherwise indicated, are from the *Praecepta Lessons*, Vol. 2:39.

## For getting rid of colds, and for stimulating the vocal cords

- Daily, at any time, lie flat on your back on a woolen blanket in the sun, exposing your chest, thighs, and feet.
- Open your mouth wide and turn your head so that sunlight can penetrate the nostrils and mouth.
- Gently quiver the head by tensing. Concentrate on the mucous membranes of the nose and throat.
- Visualize the energy you are sending by vibrating is absorbing and transmuting the sunlight into a hot, healing force passing through these passages and banishing disease germs.
- *Optimum Practice Time: 15 minutes daily.*

* * *

- With mouth closed, roll your tongue backward and forward.
- Put your chin on your chest. Tense the [front of the neck].
- Then force the chin upward [with high tension], relax, and drop chin back onto the chest.
- Practice four times, repeating often during the day.[34]

## For chest colds

- Sit or lie in the sun, letting the sunlight fall on your chest.
- Rapidly but gently rub the chest, consciously injecting energy into the chest through your fingers and hands.
- Mentally visualize, and gradually become aware of, by feeling, that the energy in your hands is acting on the sunlight falling on your chest to create a new, healing force.
- As you experience the sensation of the sunlight and the rubbing, consciously absorb this energy into the chest and use it to destroy the disease germs in the respiratory organs.
- *Optimum Practice Time: half hour, twice daily when the stomach is empty.*

## For headaches

- Sit so that sunlight falls freely on your head and face. Keep your eyes closed.
- With your fingers, rapidly rub your entire scalp, forehead, back part of head, and sides of head.
- As you rub, think that you are mixing the Cosmic Life Force flowing through your fingers with the sunlight shining on your head, and feel that you are pouring this mixed solution of healing light into your head, saturating your pores and brain cells.
- Practice for 10 minutes, then sit quietly while you experience the great healing power you just channeled.
- *Optimum Practice Time: 10 minutes.*

## For rheumatism

- Expose the affected body part to the sunlight.
- Gently contract the part and hold.
- Then while the part is contracted, rub it rapidly with the fingers, visualizing the Cosmic Life Force in your fingers, in the contracted body part, and in the sunlight, mixing together and creating a healing force that will eliminate the trouble.
- Do this for two minutes, then relax, quietly experiencing the healing force at work in the body part.
- *Optimum Practice Time: two minutes, five times daily.*

## For anemia and nervousness

- Sit facing the sunlight with chest, arms, and thighs exposed. Gently tense the entire body, energizing it; then relax.
- With your palms, rapidly rub your forehead, throat, chest, abdomen, and thighs for two minutes.

- Now turn so that the sunlight is falling on your back. Tense the entire body, energizing it, and then relax. Briskly rub back of neck, shoulders, back, and buttocks.

- Feel the Cosmic Life Energy in your hands, your body, and the sunlight combining to make a powerful healing light that will soothe and rejuvenate the entire body.

- Repeat this exercise ten times.

- It is also beneficial to contract the feet and rub the soles with the fingers while exposing them to the sunlight.

- *Optimum Practice Time: two minutes each, ten times.*

## For the eyes

*The energy in the eyes should be developed to its full potential. One exercise for developing this potential is amazingly effective also in curing weak vision. It strengthens the flow of energy through the nerves to the eyes. Indeed, this exercise is primarily a cure for faulty vision. Here is how it is to be practiced:*

- When the sun is close to the horizon – within half an hour of sunrise or sunset – gaze into it deeply. (At this time its harmful rays are filtered out, and the tremendous healing power may be drawn into the eyes without injury.)

- Gaze unblinking for one minute to start with, gradually increasing the time over several weeks to a maximum of nine minutes.

- By the force of your will, draw the sun's healing rays into your eyes.

- Then turn your back to the sun, and blink your eyes fairly rapidly for about one minute.

- Close the eyes, and cover them first with the right hand, then with the left (so that the left hand covers the right), and gaze into the after-image that you see.

- The sun's rays should strike on the area of the medulla oblongata.

- The light that you see in the after-image will be partly due to the energy flowing into the eyes from the medulla oblongata. The more deeply you concentrate, the more this flow of energy will be strengthened.

- Gaze into the after-image as long as it lasts.

- Then turn your eyes far to the left, up, right, and down. Repeat this rotation three times.

- Then squeeze the eyes tightly, sending energy to them.

- Open the eyes, and stare at an object.

- Repeat this squeezing and staring process three times.

You will be amazed to see how, in a comparatively brief time, your vision improves, and also how *alive* your eyes feel. [35]

## BATHING DAILY IN GOD'S OCEAN OF X-RAY
*By Swami Yogananda*

When the sun shines, everything seems to smile with its halo of golden rays. Gloomy, dark places seem to forsake their mystery-dreaded atmosphere. The sun seems to cheer the mind. It is the life of all Nature's living children, the trees, flowers, and human beings….

Sunlight and ultra violet ray baths are also necessary to fill the tissues and pores with life-giving energy from without. They redden the hemoglobin of the blood, recharging it and making it richer and healthier. As an ordinary bath washes away and clears the bacteria and dirt from the human body, so also the ultra violet rays in the sunlight not only cleanse the body of bacteria but also destroy them. The ultra violet rays are the death rays which penetrate the homes of enemy bacteria hiding in the fingernails and body pores, and scorch them out.

By all means, if you have not time for a walk, open your glass windows and let your life-giving, soliciting friend, Sunlight, fall on you and bathe you all over. Keep on jumping up and down, if you are afraid of catching cold, but each morning do bathe in the ocean of X-Ray which God has created for you. Without a daily bath in God's sea of X-Ray, you cannot be healthy. And remember, only healthy persons are happy. [36]

# NOTES | PART FOUR

## Chapter One

1 Yogananda, *Praecepta Lessons*, Vol. 3:64.
2 Kriyananda, *The Art and Science of Raja Yoga*, 119.
3 Yogananda, "Recipes," *East-West*, May–June, 1927.
4 Yogananda, *Yogoda Course*, Lesson 1.
5 Yogananda, *Super Advanced Course No. 1*, Lesson Eleven.
6 Yogananda, "The Chemical Battle of Life," *Bhagavad Gita Interpretations* 1:1.
7 Yogananda, "Overcoming Nervousness," *East-West*, July–August 1927.
8 Kriyananda, Foreword, *The Art and Science of Raja Yoga*, 15.
9 Kriyananda, *Do It NOW!*, September 30.
10 Kriyananda, *Secrets of Emotional Healing*, 5.
11 Yogananda, *Yogoda Course* No. 1, Lesson 5.
12 Yogananda, *Yogoda Tissue-Will System of Body and Mind Perfection*, 1923 edition.
13 Yogananda, *Yogoda Course*, Lesson 1.
14 Yogananda, "What Is Perfect Diet?" *Inner Culture*, October 1940. See also this interesting article in the Harvard Medical School News and Research Journal, "Decrease Oxygen to Boost Longevity?" https://hms.harvard.edu/news/decrease-oxygen-boost-longevity#.
15 Yogananda, *Super Advanced Course No. 1*, Lesson 11.
16 https://en.wikipedia.org/wiki/Robert_O._Becker.
17 Becker, *The Body Electric, Electromagnetism and The Foundation of Life*, available at https://www.amazon.com/Body-Electric-Electromagnetism-Foundation-Life/dp/0688069711.
18 *New York Times*, "Stronger Muscles in 3 Seconds a Day," https://www.nytimes.com/2022/03/02/well/move/stronger-muscles-health.html.
19 Yogananda, "The Chemical Battle of Life," *Bhagavad Gita Interpretations* 1:1/20.
20 https://anandaeurope.org/books/kriya-yoga/;https://www.ananda.org/kriya-yoga/; https://anandaindia.org/kriya-yoga/.

## Chapter Two

1 Yogananda, "Evaluation of the Science of Curative Method," *Scientific Healing Affirmations*, 29.
2 Yogananda, *Yogoda Course*, Lesson 1.
3 "Blood Flow in Skeletal Muscle," *LibreTexts Medicine*, https://med.libretexts.org/Courses/James_Madison_University/AandP_for_STEM_Educators/24%3A_Cardiovascular_System-_Blood_Vessels/24.08%3A_Blood_Flow_Through_the_Body/24.8C%3A_Blood_Flow_in_Skeletal_Muscle.
4 Yogananda, "Introduction," *Yogoda Tissue-Will System of Physical Perfection*, 1925 edition.
5 Yogananda, "Introduction," *Yogoda Tissue-Will System of Physical Perfection*, 1925 edition.
6 Yogananda, *Yogoda Course*, Lesson 3.
7 Kriyananda, *The Art and Science of Raja Yoga*, 53.
8 Yogananda, *Praecepta Lessons*, Vol. 3:78/3.
9 Yogananda, Vol. 2:34.
10 Yogananda, *Yogoda Tissue-Will System of Physical Perfection*, 1925 edition.
11 Yogananda, 1925 edition.
12 Kriyananda, *Art and Science of Raja Yoga*, 263.

**13** Yogananda, *Super Advanced Course No. 1*, Lesson 5.
**14** Yogananda, *Yogoda Tissue-Will System of Physical Perfection*, 1925.
**15** Yogananda, *Yogoda Course*, Lessons 2 and 3.
**16** Doctor Andrew Huberman is a neuroscientist and associate professor in the Department of Neurobiology at the Stanford University School of Medicine. In 2020, the Huberman Lab initiated a collaboration with the laboratory of David Spiegel in the Stanford Department of Psychiatry and Behavioral Sciences, to systematically study how particular patterns of respiration influence the autonomic nervous system, stress, and other brain states, including sleep. https://scopeblog.stanford.edu/2020/10/07/how-stress-affects-your-brain-and-how-to-reverse-it/,https://www.youtube.com/watch?v=bQ7B3bxGVjs&list=WL&index=65&ab_channel=StanfordUniversitySchoolofEngineering.
**17** Yogananda, *Super Advanced Course No. 1*, Lesson 11.
**18** Yogananda, *Yogoda Course*, Lesson 8.
**19** Yogananda, *Praecepta Lessons*, Vol. 1:9.
**20** Yogananda, Vol. 1:9.
**21** Pillay, Srinivasan, "The Science of Visualization," *Huffpost*, https://www.huffpost.com/entry/the-science-of-visualizat_b_171340. See also https://www.sciencedirect.com/science/article/abs/pii/S0168010217304418; and Mental Training Effects on Voluntary Muscle Strength, https://grantome.com/grant/NIH/R01-NS035130-03.
**22** Yogananda, *Yogoda Course*, Lesson 8.
**23** Yogananda, "Introduction," *Yogoda Tissue-Will System of Physical Perfection*, 1925 edition.

### Chapter Three

**1** Yogananda, *Praecepta Lessons*, Vol. 5:114.
**2** Yogananda, *New Super Cosmic Science Course*, Lesson 1.
**3** Yogananda, Lesson 2.
**4** Learned from Swami Kriyananda, who learned it from Yogananda.
**5** Yogananda, *Advanced Super Cosmic Science Course*, Lesson 1.
**6** Yogananda, Lesson 1.
**7** Yogananda, *Super Advanced Course No. 1*, Lesson 5.
**8** Yogananda, *Praecepta Lessons*, Vol. 2:34.
**9** Yogananda, *Scientific Healing Affirmations*, 95-97.
**10** Yogananda, *Praecepta Lessons*, Vol. 2:34.
**11** Yogananda, *Super Advanced Course No.1*, Lesson 11.
**12** Yogananda, *Yogoda Course*, Lesson 3.
**13** Kriyananda, *Awaken to Superconsciousness*, 150.
**14** Yogananda, *Praecepta Lessons*, Vol. 2:34.
**15** Yogananda, Vol. 2:34.
**16** Yogananda, Vol. 2:34.
**17** Yogananda, *Scientific Healing Affirmations*, 99.
**18** Yogananda, "Recipes," *East-West* magazine, January–February, 1926.
**19** Yogananda, *Praecepta Lessons*, Vol. 3:70.
**20** Yogananda, Vol. 3:70.
**21** Yogananda, *Yogoda Tissue-Will System of Physical Perfection*, 1925 edition.
**22** Yogananda, 1925 edition.
**23** Yogananda, *Yogoda Course*, Lesson 1.
**24** Yogananda, *Yogoda Tissue-Will System of Physical Perfection*, 1925 edition.
**25** Yogananda, *Praecepta Lessons*, Vol. 2:34.

**26** Yogananda, *Yogoda Course*, Lesson 3.

**27** Yogananda, Lesson 3.

**28** Yogananda, *Yogoda Tissue-Will System of Physical Perfection*, 1925 edition.

**29** Yogananda, "Meditations and Affirmations," *East-West*, January, 1933.

**30** Yogananda, *Super-Advanced Course No. 1*, Lesson 5.

**31** Yogananda, *Praecepta Lessons*, Vol. 2:9.

**32** Yogananda, *Super-Advanced Course No. 1,* Lesson 5.

**33** Yogananda, *Yogoda Course*, Lesson 2.

**34** Kriyananda, *Art and Science of Raja Yoga*, 369-370.

**35** Yogananda, "Recipes," *East-West*, March–April, 1930.

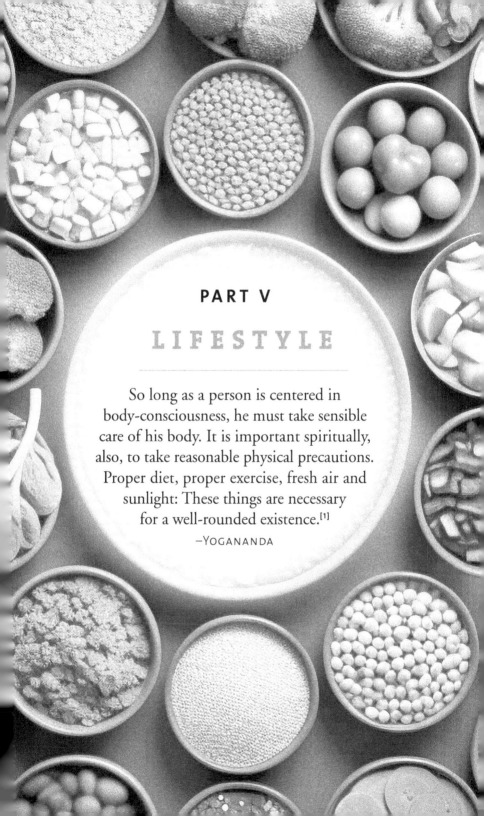

# PART V

# LIFESTYLE

So long as a person is centered in
body-consciousness, he must take sensible
care of his body. It is important spiritually,
also, to take reasonable physical precautions.
Proper diet, proper exercise, fresh air and
sunlight: These things are necessary
for a well-rounded existence.[1]

—YOGANANDA

PART V    CHAPTER ONE

# Your Pranic Diet

> Obey the material laws of the body by
> sensible choice of food. Since you have to eat,
> eat the right kind of food. Choose a balanced
> diet, stick to it, and then forget the body;
> devote your time to the more important
> studies and problems of life.[1]
>
> The life energy in the body battery is derived
> from Cosmic Energy through the medulla,
> and from food. The life energy in the body breaks
> up the foods and converts them into energy also.
> It is the intricate task of the life force to distill
> more life force from the nourishment taken into
> the body. Therefore, one's diet should be confined
> to foods which are easily converted into energy,
> or which are productive of fresh energy.[2]
>
> Diseases are not due to "fate" but to wrong eating
> and over-eating and transgression of God's laws.
> Over-eating, lack of exercise, immoderation in
> sex life, and eating wrong things – these are the
> physical causes of disease. Diseases are nothing
> but poisons trying to get out of the system.[3]
>
> – YOGANANDA

**Hippocrates,** who is widely regarded as the father of Western medicine, said that health can only be assured by proper diet: "Let food be thy medicine and medicine be thy food." The word 'diet' derives from Greek *daita*, which means "healthful living according to the proper selection of food." [4]

Centuries before Hippocrates lived, the ancient healing science of Ayurveda was established in India on four pillars, the first being diet: "Health begins in the kitchen." [5]

In modern terminology, "You are what you eat" is widely accepted by lay people as well as doctors as the basis for the science of nutrition, a major factor for health and longevity.[6]

Dietary recommendations have a prominent place In Yogananda's teachings on the science of Self-realization. His earliest writings include detailed dietary instructions, which form the basis for this chapter.*

Yogananda had a practical and transcendental relationship with food. He enjoyed cooking and often prepared meals for his guests.

> Yogananda was a great cook and he told us that when he prepared food he tasted it at the spiritual eye. One time he came into the room very blissfully and said, "I've been trying for years to get just that taste in this dish. I could taste it at the spiritual eye, and it was just right." He felt great bliss because it was divinely inspired, and, sure enough, it was very good.[7]

Yogananda started a restaurant in the India Center building at the Self-Realization Fellowship church in Hollywood.

> India Center was formally opened to the public on April 8th, 1951....
> A large hall downstairs was dedicated as

---

* Yogananda published his health advice in his correspondence courses (1925 to 1935); in the "Recipes" articles that appeared in *East-West* and *Inner Culture* magazines; and in his commentaries on the Bhagavad Gita and the teachings of Jesus Christ, "Second Coming of Christ." Nearly all of the citations in this chapter, unless otherwise indicated, are from these sources. You will find some of his original articles in the Appendices for Part V.

a "meeting place for men of goodwill of
all nations." Upstairs, a public restaurant
served delicious vegetarian meals,
the recipes for which were Master's own
creations. Over the years both meeting hall
and restaurant were to become famous.[8]

## *Proper-eatarianism*

To my first generation of students, I didn't say much about
a vegetarian diet; it was too unusual, then, for the people in
this country. Diet was secondary in importance, anyway, to
the teachings of yoga.

For the next generation, I recommended that they eat
less meat. Most of them, on an average, became healthier.

For this third generation, I've recommended a completely vegetarian diet, and find that, of the three groups, the
present one is the most healthy.

I don't care much, however, for that word, "vegetarian."
Too many people are fanatics on the subject. I've coined what
I consider a better word: 'propereatarian.'" [9]

Becoming a "proper-eaterian" is a process of reducing the consumption of meat and consuming plant-based foods in a judicious
and nutritionally balanced way.

Meat is concentrated food and is strengthening, but it is highly constipating and acts as a retainer of body poisons and a
harbinger of disease....Vegetables and fruits, having a natural
laxative action, are conducive to health and to the elimination
of diseases.[10]

For some people this transition happens easily and naturally, while
for others it may take time for the body to adjust to the new diet.

For best results one should abstain from all beef and pork products. Do not make a habit of eating even chicken, lamb, or fish every day...Lamb is best and then chicken and fish.... Once a week, or better, once a month is enough, if your system demands flesh foods at all....Nuts, cottage cheese, eggs, milk, cream, and bananas are very good meat and fish substitutes. If you eat chicken, lamb, or fish, have a salad with them....Lettuce prevents the protein from excessive acid reaction, and thus avoids overtaxing and injuring the kidneys.[11]

## Meat substitutes

*The best meat substitute is ground nuts*: Almonds give vital strength; pistachio nuts give fat; pine and cashew nuts give harmonious development of all parts of the body; peanuts are for elimination and general strength; pistachio nuts for brain development and memory.... Nut loaves, nut products in general.... Nuts should always be ground or chewed very thoroughly before swallowing.[12]

*Combine ground nuts with fresh orange juice in these ways:*

- 1 tb. unsalted, unfried, ground, or whole pine or pignolia nuts with one glassful of orange juice
- 1 tb. ground cashew nuts with one glassful of orange juice
- 1 tb. ground pecans with one glassful of orange juice
- 1 tb. ground pistachio nuts with one glassful of orange juice
- 1 tb. ground almonds with one glassful of orange juice
- 1 tb. Brazil nuts or peanut butter with one glassful of orange juice

A bowl of orange juice and pulp served with a banana sliced to paper-like thinness is not only delicious but nourishing and can take the place of meat. Bananas contain more nutrition than fish, lobsters, or crabs. They are grown by nature and free from all poisons.[13]

Yogananda used avocado as a meat substitute in some of his health recipes, and also eggs and cheese. Although the strict vegetarian diet in India prohibits the consumption of eggs, Yogananda recommended them as a suitable source of protein, especially the yolks.

- Nuts, cottage cheese, eggs, milk, cream, and bananas are very good meat and fish substitutes.[14]
- Those who can dispense with meat can use fish and eggs.[15]
- It is better to eat eggs and nuts in place of meat.[16]
- Boiled eggs with half a head of lettuce.[17]
- Fresh cottage cheese with half a head of lettuce.[18]
- Eat mostly raw vegetables and one-half of a boiled yolk of an egg a day.[19]
- A glass of orange juice with a beaten yolk of one egg makes an ideal breakfast.[20]

---

### MOCK LAMB LOAF

- Soak ¼ cupful of barley in ¾ cupful of water over night.
- Then add 3 cups of water, ¼ cupful of ground walnuts, one bay leaf, one teaspoonful of salt, ½ teaspoonful of pepper, ½ clove of garlic, ¼ teaspoonful of thyme, and one tablespoonful of butter.
- Let simmer for about two hours. Then strain, leaving the liquid for gravy.
- To the thick mixture add one cup of ground onions and one egg.
- Place in a well buttered pan and bake for one hour.
- Serves for about four.[21]

## NUT LOAF

- 1 cup ground walnuts
- 1 cup finely chopped walnuts
- 3 cups fresh whole wheat bread crumbs
- 2 tablespoons tamari
- ½ cup tomato juice
- 2 eggs, well beaten
- 3 tablespoons butter
- 3 medium onions, chopped fine
- 1 clove garlic, minced

Mix together the nuts, fresh bread crumbs, tamari, tomato juice, and eggs. Sauté the onions and garlic in butter until golden, stirring frequently. Add the onions to the nut mixture; you may need to add a little water to create the right consistency for a loaf. Press into oiled 9" x 5" loaf pan. Bake at 350° for about 45 minutes. Makes 4–6 servings.[22]

## *Importance of raw foods*

Nearly a century ago, well before vegetarianism and veganism entered the mainstream of public awareness, Yogananda recommended a diet that included an abundant amount of raw food.

Let half of your diet be raw food. Eat more ground nuts.[23]

Try to include in your daily diet as much raw food as possible. Cooked vegetables should be eaten with the juice in which they were boiled.[24]

Raw food is nature-and-sun-cooked food with even temperature. Use it abundantly. But if you eat cooked food, let it be steamed or baked food without loss of the natural juices which boiling evaporates.[25]

Do not eat vitamin-killed boiled dinners. Vegetables have been ripened and cooked in Nature's kitchen with the cosmic fire—ultra-violet rays. Why do you want to cook them again? Scientific experiments show beyond question that cooking destroys the vitamins. Without vitamins, the swallowed food goes into the stomach without direction. Vitamins direct the building of various tissues from food....They are subtle electricity stored to replete the body battery with fresh energy. They are tabloids of energy.[26]

With the presence of any chronic ailment in the body, it shows the best of judgment to stop eating everything except raw foods – vegetables in their raw state, also fruits and finely ground-up nuts. Don't complain of stomach troubles, colds, headaches. These are always the outcome of lack of physical exercise or a faulty diet.[27]

Diet was such an important concern that Yogananda enshrined it as the fourth point of the "Aims and Tenets" of his organization:

Intelligently maintaining the physical body on unadulterated foods, including a large percentage of raw fruits, vegetables, and nuts.[28]

———— *Affirmation* ————

I shall make myself healthier every day by eating more raw food and ground nuts.[29]

## Your daily diet

Yogananda gave the following specific recommendations for foods to include and avoid in the regular diet.

# Choose from this list [30]

Your daily food intake should be chosen from the following list of foods which contain all the elements needed for the proper maintenance of the body:

- 1 apple
- ¼ grapefruit⁺
- 1 lemon
- 1 lime
- 1 orange⁺
- 1 tsp. olive oil
- 1 glass milk or
- 1 hard-boiled egg
- 1/8 glass cream
- 1 tsp. honey
- 1 tbsp. clabber ♦
- 1 piece of whole wheat bread with a nut butter
- A glass of almond milk or any nut milk °
- 1 baked, or half-boiled or steamed vegetable with its juice
- 1 raw carrot, including part of green top
- 6 leaves raw spinach
- ¼ heart of lettuce
- 1 glass orange juice with a tablespoon of finely ground nuts
- 1 small piece fresh pineapple
- 6 figs, dates, or prunes (these fruits are wholesome only when they are unsulphured)
- 8 leaves of raw spinach
- 1 handful of unsulphured raisins
- 1 tbsp. cottage cheese
- 1 small piece of cheese

---

⁺ These foods are not to be taken in cases of arthritis.

♦ Milk which has been allowed to stand in a warm place, preferably in an earthen vessel, for a day or longer, until it has soured or curdled.

° Grind two tablespoonfuls of nuts thoroughly and mix with water.

Eat at least some of the above foods every day, distributing them over your three meals. For instance, you may take the milk at breakfast, bread, egg and salad at noon, and the ground nuts and fruits at night.

Individual food habits may be taken into consideration, but if they are bad, gradually change them. At any rate, add *some* of the foods in the above list to what you are used to eating. Omit those foods mentioned above which do not agree with you, eating only very lightly when you feel the need of nourishment, and gradually accustoming yourself to a more wholesome diet. You may increase or decrease the quantities given above, in accordance with your individual needs. It is, of course, obvious that the person doing strenuous muscular work requires more food than the sedentary worker.

Make it a point to remember the following articles to include in your daily food, and you will say good-bye to disease.[31]

1. A carrot a day *
2. A lemon a day
3. An orange a day
4. An apple a day
5. A glass of almond milk or any nut milk. (Grind two tablespoonfuls of nuts thoroughly and mix with water.)
6. Chopped green-leafed vegetables daily
7. Unsulphured dates and raisins – one handful daily
8. Avoid white flour and over-eating.
9. Keep colon clean.
10. Whole wheat bread, fresh cheese, and a glass of milk are beneficial if you work hard during the day.

---

* Eat the carrot with a part of the stem and roots – unscraped – only thoroughly washed. Chew it well. Nature made it hard to strengthen your teeth by chewing. It is sweet and luscious once you get used to the taste. You will soon find cooked carrots absolutely tasteless, in addition to their being only the corpse of the carrot from which the vitamin soul has departed.

## *About rice* [32]

Rice has been called the Father of all Cereals. It was the original cereal food of the American Indians. To this day it is the chief cereal food of most Oriental countries....

After washing rice, always cook it in a double boiler. To one cup of rice add two cups of hot water. Then put the double boiler on a medium gas flame for half an hour. It is not good to eat rice all mushy or with the water drained from it after boiling....

Natural, brown, unpolished rice gives physical stamina and mental strength and concentration. White polished rice is practically worthless, most of its precious nutritive elements having been removed.

## Foods to avoid

Do not eat too much white sugar. The ingestion of excessive quantities of sweets causes intestinal fermentation. Remember, foods prepared from white flour, such as white bread, white-flour gravy, etc., also polished rice and too many greasy fried foods, are injurious to your health.[33]

Try, as much as possible, to do without white bread and foods made of white flour. Use graham, brown, whole wheat, vitamin, or rye bread. Don't eat too much even of whole grain bread; it acts like glue in the intestines. Substitute potatoes.

A little salt is fine, but too much salt contributes to hardening of the arteries.

Always use sea salt or mix powdered sea kelp with ordinary salt. You can mix ground sun-dried, pulverized vegetables with salt.[34]

## Eat according to your needs

A man of sedentary habits, like a writer or office worker, should eat small quantities several times a day rather than a few large meals a day – and should fast occasionally. A man working in the mines should eat more, of meat substitutes, nuts, milk, etc. Adding one or two boiled eggs or one quart of milk a day or six tablespoonsful of almonds with water or milk would help the gathering of strength to fight hard work.[35]

#### —————————— An ideal breakfast [36] ——————————

1. Orange juice and ground nuts, or orange juice with a beaten yolk of one egg
2. Grapefruit and ground nuts
3. Two hard-boiled egg yolks in orange juice
4. Tomato juice and egg yolk
5. Watermelon juice and ground nuts (for laxative effect)
6. Bran, milk, honey, and ground nuts
7. Cantaloupe and bran and milk and ground nuts
8. Berries, ground nuts, cream, and honey
9. Pineapple juice, cream and honey, ground nuts, and chopped pineapple
10. Glassful of milk and honey
11. Ground almonds and honey mixed in glassful of water
12. Use any quantity of these according to appetite.

## Lunch

*should be the heaviest meal of the day.*

- 16 leaves of spinach
- 3 oz. ground pecans
- Any chopped vegetable (raw with salad dressing)
- A cooked vegetable
- A protein
- Whole wheat bread with butter if desired

~ *or* ~

- ½ head of lettuce with boiled eggs
- A big salad
- Hot chocolate

~ *or* ~

- Fish, chicken, or lamb *
- ½ head of lettuce
- Salad of ground carrots and dressing

## Supper

*At night use fruits of any kind and nuts.*

- Sun-dried prunes, honeyed
- Any fruit
- ¼ glassful of cream

~ *or* ~

- Slightly boiled vegetable dinner

~ *or* ~

- Raw food dinner

~ *or* ~

- Milk and honey

~ *or* ~

- Orange juice and nuts and one egg

~ *or* ~

- One vegetable slightly cooked

~ *or* ~

- Two glassfuls of grapefruit juice, honey, and ground nuts

* Chicken, lamb, or fish should be thoroughly baked, stewed, or broiled, and eggs should be hard boiled before eating, in order to destroy any harmful bacteria which they may contain.

## Liquids

When thirsty, drink a glass of orange juice or water (preferably distilled or boiled). However, nature's distilled water – undiluted fruit juice – is best. Do not drink too much ice water with meals. Ice water should be taken sparingly at any time, but especially during and after meals as it lowers the temperature of the stomach, thus retarding digestion. *Never drink ice water when you are overheated.* [37]

> Don't indulge in very hot or cold drinks. Thus you will avoid colds. Drink more orange juice.[38]

**About milk.** Yogananda's dietary guidelines are aligned with the ancient Indian healing science of Ayurveda, in which fresh milk plays an important role in the diet and in medicinal preparations. Many yogis in India do a twenty-one-day rejuvenation fast while taking only milk. People with intolerance to lactose will not be interested in his following suggestions.

> Milk is the only food, excepting eggs, which alone can support human life. The extreme "cooked-food lover" and the "raw-food faddist" both often omit from their diets many elements needed for the proper building of the body, so that no matter what your views may be concerning food problems, you will be safe if you drink plenty of milk. It will help prevent old age and the sudden deterioration of the body, which result from not giving the body all the elements that are necessary for its healthy maintenance. Never drink milk with your meals. Milk taken with a heavy dinner produces indigestion. Drink milk alone (between meals) or with fruits.[39]

> The one chemical element most likely to be lacking in the average diet is calcium, the chemical element of lime. Two great calcium foods are milk and cheese. Calcium is needed for the making of bones; but if it is lacking, the most serious effect is upon the nervous system, causing much illness as well as certain changes in our mental characteristics. Too little calcium makes people changeable, violent, and ill-balanced. Plenty of calcium makes one temperate and well-balanced.[40]

## Food combinations

Just as injudiciously mixing chemicals in a laboratory might cause an explosion, so food when improperly combined can create explosions of gas in the intestinal tract. Here are Yogananda's recommendations for combining foods, from his original lessons and magazine articles: [41]

Drink no ice-water while eating, as it cools down the temperature 30 degrees and may cause indigestion. Do not mix starchy foods with liquids (i.e., eat no bread with milk, et cetera), as liquids dilute the saliva required to assist digestion.

If you eat chicken, lamb, or fish, have a vegetable salad with them.

Fruit should be eaten with bread or some other starchy food, but without sugar; you may add a little honey if you wish. Eat only nature's candies (unsulphured figs, prunes or raisins).

Never drink milk with your meals. Milk taken with a heavy dinner produces indigestion. Drink milk alone (between meals) or with fruits.

Do not eat too much white sugar. The ingestion of excessive quantities of sweets causes intestinal fermentation.

Eat less, and follow dietary rules when you eat. Make sunshine, oxygen, and energy a part of your regular daily diet.

*Advice from Swami Kriyananda*

Not so many people know that it is unwise to combine too many different kinds of foods. Vegetables should not normally be eaten with fruits.... A simple but effective rule is to eat only one basic kind of food at one time – whether carbohydrate, protein, or fruits.[42]

### Healthy snacks [43]

- Whenever one is hungry one may take a large tablespoonful of thoroughly ground nuts in half a glass of water or in a glass of orange juice.
- Instead of candy, eat dates and raisins.
- When you are tired or hungry, take a sun bath, and you will find yourself recharged with ultraviolet rays, and revived.

### The weight reducing diet [44]

- Eat mostly raw vegetables and one-half of a boiled yolk of an egg a day.
- Abstain from starchy food, fried foods, and sweets.
- Do not drink water with meals.
- Every three days fast one day on orange juice.
- For greater loss you can benefit from fasting on orange juice for seven days and then going on the nine-day cleansing diet you will find in the third chapter, a normal diet being resumed gradually thereafter. If there is need for further reduction of weight, this procedure can be repeated after an interval of two weeks.
- Fasting, or eating raw foods and drinking less liquids, is good for reducing flesh. People don't get results because they are not regular. One day they fast, and the next day they feast. In order to get noticeable results, follow the raw food diet strictly and steadily for months.
- Reducing by fasting sometimes upsets the stomach. This condition can be prevented by frequent drinking of a small glass of buttermilk or orange juice mixed with a small amount of lemon juice.
- Do these energy recharging exercises, commanding your will, during tension, to burn up the superfluous tissues.
  - Practice the Life Force Full Body Recharge (p. 282) six times, twice a day.
  - Walk in place 200 steps, and then run in place 200 steps, outdoors or near an open window.

– Do Stomach and Digestion Exercises 1 and 2 (p. 307) twenty times, three times a day.

## The weight "fattening" diet [45]

The following foods, which are to be added to the usual diet, are of high nutritive value and have been found beneficial for those who wish to gain weight.

- Bananas with cream
- 2 eggs
- Oatmeal with cream
- 1 large raw vegetable salad

- ¼ glass cream
- 1 tbsp. olive oil
- 2 slices whole wheat bread
- 3½ oz. butter

Weight can also be gained by eating bananas in abundance, and for one month drinking two glasses of water (moderately hot or cold, *not iced*) with each meal.

## The Magnetic Diet: oxygen and sunrays [46]

Material food is only one source of nourishment, one that requires a considerable expenditure of energy in terms of time and money. More immediate and economical sources of energy are readily at hand in the oxygen we breathe and in the rays emanating from the sun. Yogananda writes:

- Oxygen and sunshine should have a very important place in people's lives, because of their direct energy-producing quality…. The life force can assimilate oxygen more quickly than it can assimilate solids or liquids….

- The man of the future will draw nourishment from the ether and from the ocean of invisible Cosmic Energy in which he moves and has his being… [He will] draw his energy requirements, so far as possible, from air and sunlight. The nourishment derived from these two sources can be most easily converted into energy within the body….Just as electricity passes through a rod made of a conductive substance, and electrifies it, so the body battery becomes fully charged with life force derived from oxygen. People who perform breathing exercises always have shining, magnetic eyes.

- Practice the following exercise three times a day: Exhale slowly, counting from 1 to 6. Now, while the lungs are empty, mentally count from 1 to 6. Inhale slowly, counting from 1 to 6. Then hold the breath, counting from 1 to 6. Repeat eleven times.

- Inhale and exhale deeply from six to twelve times every hour, filling the lungs with fresh air down to the lower lobes. This method may be practiced outdoors for twelve hours, while alternately slowly walking and resting. When weather conditions necessitate indoor practice, the windows should be kept wide open.

Exercises for drawing prana from the sun have already been given in Part IV. Here is another powerful exercise you can do at any time during the day – best done with closed eyes so as not to look directly at the sun:

A technique for drawing energy into the body is to stand facing the sun. Raise your hands above your head. Feel the warmth of the sun striking your forehead at the point between the eyebrows, and the palms of your hands. Feel that you are drawing warmth and energy into your body through those "windows." After some time, turn your back to the sun, and feel its warmth upon the area of the medulla oblongata (at the base of the brain). Keep your hands raised above the head. Again, draw the sun's rays into your body.[47]

## When, where, and how to eat

The energy that we absorb from the food does not depend entirely on the quality of the food itself. Our state of mind influences our ability to digest a meal. When we are hurried or in an emotional state, the body is occupied with hormonal reactions, and the food cannot properly digest. To get the most nutritional and vibrational value from a meal, we want to make the act of eating a conscious and enjoyable activity.

## Before eating

I have found it a good practice to do some of the Energization exercises before eating to prepare both the body and mind for the pleasures and benefits of the meal. Once you learn them, or if you already know them, do the complete cycle, or an abbreviated cycle that includes Number 34, the stomach exercise, or the Full Body Recharge, which can be done in just a few minutes.

The first exercise on page 293 is specifically for improved digestion. It stimulates the gastric juices and prepares the body to digest. You can do it before the meal, while the food is cooking, or before you leave to dine out. This same exercise can be done after eating, with a reduced level of tension.

> All worry, care and thought of difficulties
> should be put aside... while eating....
> see that there is only calmness and
> pleasantness at meal time if the digestive
> system is to function normally. [48]

## Eat when hungry

When we are hungry, the body is preparing itself to digest and absorb the nutrients and vibrational qualities of the meal. Yogananda suggests: [49]

- Never eat unless you are hungry.
- Eat moderately if you are hungry.
- Eat less if you are a little hungry.
- Eat nothing if you are not hungry at all.
- Omit the meals that you may try to eat with little hunger, and this will sharpen your hunger for the next meal... Omit lunch or dinner as often as you can (whenever you are not hungry).
- If you are very hungry and are working hard, you may safely eat three light meals daily, but if you don't do much manual labor, then two meals a day are plenty.

## Dangers of over-eating

All machinery, including the physical body, is designed to bear a certain amount of activity. When we push it beyond its limits, it works less efficiently and eventually could stop working altogether. Especially as the body ages, its systems become slower and less able to sustain a heavy load.

There is a Syrian proverb: "The enemy of man is his stomach." Remember that this bodily machinery has been given to you to enable you to accomplish certain works on this material plane, and that you should guard it and take care of it as your most precious possession. The chief abuse of the body lies in overloading it with unnecessary food. Eat sparingly and notice the great change in your health for the better. [50]

One way to regulate our food intake so as not to overtax the digestive process is to stop eating before the stomach feels full, waiting about twenty minutes before taking that second helping. By then the digestive process will have expanded the contents of the stomach, and the impulse to eat more will have subsided. It is also advisable to refrain from drinking for half an hour before and after meals, so as not to dilute the digestive enzymes. Yogananda suggests:

Use your will power to resist the temptation of eating three meals every day, by which the whole system, including the cells, the heart, the nerves, the stomach, has to work continuously. Give your intelligent machine occasional rest by cutting off breakfast, lunch or dinner every day. [51]

Using self-control to regulate our eating habits may cause short-term frustration, but in the long term it is an investment in our health and longevity.

Remember, you eat to live, but do not live to eat. Greed is a servant of the palate -- and enemy of digestion and health. Greed wants to please itself and the sense of taste at the cost of your happiness.
Greed produces evil habits of eating, utterly disregarding the needs of the body even to the point of death. Greed

says: "Let us eat, drink, and be merry, for tomorrow we die." Self-control in eating, good mastication, plain food and eating only when you are very hungry, develop right habits of eating and destroy greed. Self-control may not seem so alluring as self-indulgence, but it protects your health.

The purpose of self-restraint in eating is primarily the conservation of health, though wholesome food need not be, and certainly should not be, unpalatable. Eat often, eat less, think of your health and digestion, and do not concentrate on your palate, if you want to conquer greed. [52]

## Develop "Won't Power"

If you haven't enough will power, try to develop "won't power." When you are at the dinner table and Mr. Greed lures you to eat more than you should and tries to chloroform your self-control and cast you into the pit of indigestion, watch yourself. After partaking of the right quantity and quality of food, say to yourself, "I won't eat any more," and get up from the table and run. When somebody calls, 'John, come back and eat some more. Don't forget the delicious apple pie,' just call back, 'I won't.'" [53]

## The environment in which we eat

We are greatly impacted by the environment: at home, at work, and never so than when we are eating.

> The place where one eats is important...
> At the time of eating, one is opening himself
> to the inflow of vibrations from without.
> If the vibrations of the room in which he eats
> are harmonious, they can be helpful,
> but if not they can affect one more adversely
> than at other times. Paramhansa Yoganandaji did
> not like for us to eat in public places, amid the
> heterogeneous vibrations of worldly people.[54]

When we eat in the car, or in front of the TV or computer monitor while talking about politics and the news, in a noisy pizzeria while watching a sports event – all of the sounds, colors, thoughts, and emotions being expressed or harbored by ourselves and others are being ingested along with the food. Kriyananda's advice: **If possible, eat in a harmonious environment, not in places where there is discord.**[55]

When going to a restaurant, choose wisely, not only for the cuisine, but equally important, for the vibrational quality of the environment. Eat where your mind and body can relax and truly enjoy the food and absorb its nutritional and pranic value. It is possible nowadays to find restaurants with good-quality food and an atmosphere that is conducive to good digestion.

When eating at home, try to make mealtime a special event, a time to stop other activities, turn off the television and other devices, and give thanks for the divine gift of food. Conversation should be uplifting, not of gossip or politics, or work. The Jewish Sabbath meals are an excellent example of the sacrality of eating, with gratitude expressed in prayer, joyful song, and uplifting conversation.

Yogananda requested his monastic disciples to eat their meals in silence. This practice is observed at the Ananda Europa retreat center near Assisi, where the first part of the meal is eaten in silence while listening to inspired music, and the later part of the meal is spent in friendly conversation. Guests who may at first feel uncomfortable with the custom soon come to enjoy the time of silent communion with food, and often continue the practice when they go home.

## Prayers before eating

I recently watched some short videos of people who had developed a loving, reciprocal relationship with all kinds of creatures, including a blue jay, a sparrow, chipmunks, a bat, and even an alligator and a hippopotamus. As animals respond to human affection and appreciation, so does the food we eat. It has made a sacrifice on our behalf, and acknowledging it and the source from which it comes gives the act of eating a deeper meaning.

All religious and spiritual traditions teach prayers of gratitude to be recited before eating. When we say these prayers consciously, acknowledging the divine source of our food, we become more open to receive its true value.

## Yogananda's Prayer
## before taking food [56]

Heavenly Father, receive this food. Make it holy.
Let no impurity of greed ever defile it.
The food comes from Thee. It is to build Thy temple.
Spiritualize it. Spirit to Spirit goes.
We are the petals of Thy manifestation, but Thou art
  the Flower,
its life, beauty and loveliness.
Permeate our souls with the fragrance of Thy presence.

Every line of the prayer contains deep teachings about the source of our food, about the food itself, and about ourselves and our relationship to the food and to its Giver.

In the prayer before eating by Swami Kriyananda, which is meant to be sung, we ask that the material food be transformed into cosmic food.

## Swami Kriyananda's
## prayer-song before meals

Receive, Lord, in Thy Light
The food we eat for it is Thine.
Infuse it with Thy love, Thy energy,
Thy life Divine. Aum.

##  The Indian food offering ritual

Many Hindu homes include a "puja room" with images of Indian gods and goddesses. Before serving a meal, the woman of the house arranges small portions of food on a ceremonial plate and offers them, with appropriate mantras, to the deities. Only then is the meal served, together with a small quantity of the "prasad" for each person. This ritual symbolically reminds us to offer our activities to be blessed by God in gratitude for His blessings.

### How to eat

The frenetic pace of modern life, and the hurried, unconscious way we generally eat, bolting down our food without chewing it, detracts from the healing value of the food. As with all our daily activities, the greater the awareness we bring to what we are doing, the greater the benefits we will receive. Our health can be greatly improved simply by eating more consciously, slowly, with an intention to draw prana and nourishment from each meal.

A significant portion of digestion happens in the mouth by mixing the food with salivary enzymes that break up the large particles and begin to break down carbohydrates, starches, and triglycerides in order to speed the digestive process.

Since some of these essential enzymes are not present in other parts of the digestive process, if the food is not thoroughly mixed with saliva, it will not be adequately digested. Ayurveda insists that each mouthful be chewed thirty-two times; the science of yoga says that we should "drink our solid foods and chew our liquids," mixing liquids as well as solids with saliva. Yogananda observes:

- Indigestion generally occurs from lack of proper mastication, quick swallowing, and overeating of rich foodstuffs.[57]

*He advises:*

- Eat less, chew well. Think not of your taste alone but of your health.[58]

- Develop right habits of eating: self-control, frugal eating, good mastication, plain food, eating only when you are very hungry.[59]

- Diseased teeth produce many ills. Rinse your mouth out ten times with water after each meal if you have no toothbrush handy. That is what the Hindu pundits prescribe.[60]

### When cooking

The thoughts and emotions of the person preparing the meal contribute to its vibrational value. One reason that "mother's cooking" is so fulfilling is because she cooks with love.

When preparing food for family and friends, or for yourself, do so with an appreciation of the divine energy present in the food and the effort required to bring it to you. As Yogananda says in his prayer before eating: "The food comes from Thee, it is to build Thy temple."

Listening to inspiring music while you cook will elevate your vibrations and those of the environment. If you must cook for a long time, keep your energy high by doing the Double Breath Power Snack (p. 296) or the Full Body Recharge (p. 282). When serving the food, keep in mind that an appealing presentation will help to activate the digestive juices. "Eye appeal is stomach appeal."

## *Effects of food on the mind*

In Part VI we will consider the important role that the mind plays in our self-healing process. In order for the mind to do its job, it needs to be properly nourished, physically and vibrationally. Certain foods create "mind fog," a state where the mind is unable to think clearly or creatively. Foods that take a long time to digest rob energy from the mind, and toxins from polluted foods and intestinal fermentation cloud the mind.

In addition to its nutritional value, foods impart certain qualities:

> Material foods impress the mind with certain good or bad qualities, and people's thoughts, actions, and health generally are determined by the foods they eat.[61]

### Does our diet affect our disposition?
#### *Yogananda responds*

*Answer:* Our diet affects our disposition to a great extent. It affects our state of mind either favorably or unfavorably, and whatever affects our state of mind affects our disposition. It is necessary to eat the proper food in order to make a proper brain as well as a proper body. All food has some relation to the mind.

The human machine is not unlike an automobile or a steam engine. The efficiency and general behavior of mechanical engines are largely dependent upon the fuel supplied to them; similarly, the condition of the human machine is largely dependent upon the food that a person eats. Food has much to do with developing character, ability, social habits, and so forth.[62]

## The three vibrational qualities of food

Every part of creation is composed of a mixture of three qualities. In Sanskrit these are called the *gunas*. We will explore them in depth in Part XII. For now let us look at the qualities as they relate to food.

**Sattwa** is the highest, most refined vibration. It manifests purity, calmness, and nobility. Foods with a sattwic vibration aid our moral and spiritual development and enhance longevity.

In this category Yogananda includes: fruits, fruit and vegetable juices, unpolished cereals, peanut and almond pastes, honey, milk or coconut milk, nuts, celery, lettuce, and many of the foods listed below.

**Rajas** is the activating quality. It manifests as restlessness, material desires, and strong emotions. Foods that have these stimulating vibrations include meat, eggs, grains, onions, garlic, horseradish, pumpkin, potatoes, pickles, and spices. These foods can have some medicinal uses.

**Tamas** is the energy-depressing heavy quality. It manifests as inactivity, laziness, greed, pride, and similar attitudes. Tamasic foods include foods that are putrefied; those with strong, unpleasant smells; foods that are old and without vitality; liquor; stale meats; processed and artificially made foods; and some fermented foods – Yogananda specifically mentions moldy cheeses such as Roquefort.

Sattwic foods are cooling to the brain and nervous system, while rajasic and tamasic foods produce heat.

Yogis emphasize the importance of food that is cooling to the system. Harmful food, they say, heats the system by introducing impurities into it that block the normal flow of *prana* in the body.... Heat is only a symptom of a system that is not working as freely and harmoniously as it should....

Excessively spiced foods, alcoholic beverages, too many carbohydrates, artificial stimulants, and stale or devitalized foods are unnatural to the body and are said to have a heating effect on it. Overcooked foods have a similar effect.

Fresh fruits, nuts, raw or lightly cooked vegetables,
milk or fresh milk products, and also whole grains
are said to be cooling to the nervous system.
Anything that excites the body is heating to it;
anything that relaxes it is cooling.[63]

## SPIRITUAL QUALITIES *of* SPECIFIC FOODS

### FRUITS
*Develop heart and spiritual qualities*

| | |
|---|---|
| **ALL CITRUS FRUITS** | Banish melancholy, stimulate the brain |
| **ORANGES** | Reforming zeal |
| **APPLES** | Self-control |
| **PEARS** | Peacefulness |
| **BANANAS** | Calmness, Humility |
| **BERRIES** | Purity of thought |
| **CHERRIES** | Cheerfulness, Joy |
| **COCONUTS** | Generally spiritualizing |
| **DATES** | Tenderness, Sweetness |
| **FIGS** | Softens a too-strict sense of discipline |
| **GRAPES** | Devotion, Divine Love |
| **PEACHES** | Selflessness, Concern for others |
| **PINEAPPLES** | Self-assurance, Courage |
| **STRAWBERRIES** | Dignity |
| **RASPBERRIES** | Kindheartedness |
| **HONEY**[64] | Self-Control |

### VEGETABLES
*Give power to management the body;*
*Adjust physiological imbalances*

| | |
|---|---|
| **AVOCADOS** | Good Memory |
| **BEETS** | Courage |
| **CORN** | Mental vitality |
| **LETTUCE** | Calmness |
| **SPINACH** | A simple nature |
| **TOMATOES** | Mental strength |

# NUTS
*Help deep thinking; good for brain-power and concentration*

**ALMONDS** Vital Strength, Sexual Self Control
**PEANUTS** Elimination, General Strength
**PINE NUTS/CASHEWS** Harmonious Development of the Body
**PISTACHIOS** Brain Development, Memory

# OTHER FOODS
*These are helpful rajasic foods*

**ALMONDS** Vital Strength, Sexual Self Control
**COW'S MILK/EGGS** Enthusiasm, Fresh Spiritual Energy
**EGG YOLK** Outwardly Directed Energy
**RICE** Mildness
**WHOLE GRAIN** Strength of Character
**WHOLE WHEAT** Steadfastness to Principle
**ALL GRAINS** Produce strength of character

## CHAPTER 1: *Points to Remember*

- Choose foods that are rich in vitality and endowed with high vibrations.

- Find a suitable diet and stay with it; do not make food your religion.

- Include sunrays and oxygen in your daily diet.

- Prepare and eat your food more consciously.

- Eat in calm, uplifting environments with inspiring companions.

# PART V   CHAPTER TWO

## Exercise

> Don't complain of stomach troubles, colds, headaches. These are always the outcome of lack of physical exercise or a faulty diet. Perform some sort of exercise every day until a perspiration breaks out over your whole body. Your colds and other similar ills will soon disappear.[1]
>
> —YOGANANDA

**Much is known** nowadays about the benefits of physical exercise for children, adults, and seniors. Some experts recommend 150 minutes of exercise per week; others suggest taking at least 10,000 steps per day. Exercise with light weights has proven to be rejuvenating for elderly people living in care facilities. Keeping the muscles fit through exercise is essential for the proper metabolism of food. Exercising the heart daily is important to keep it working at high efficiency throughout life. A sedentary life is inimical to health.

An integral part of Yogananda's health regime is daily exercise. He wrote to Swami Kriyananda: "Keep exercised and body fit for God-realization." For all of us, he recommended and frequently emphasized regular exercise in his writings:

- Right eating, moderation, and exercise will practically banish disease from the face of the earth.[2]

- Walk, run, or take some form of vigorous exercise with deep attention until you perspire, every morning and evening.[3]

- Perform some sort of exercise every day until a perspiration breaks out over your whole body. Your colds and other similar ills will soon disappear.[4]

- Take brisk fresh-air walks daily.

- Slowly walk two miles a day. Remain outdoors.[5]
- Take an early morning run in the park to keep your heart in good condition, otherwise you will find you get out of breath quickly.[6]
- Now that winter and its healthful outdoor sports are here, take time to go skating, skiing, and walking.[7]
- Do you run every day? If, when you run or go upstairs, you feel a pain in the chest or are quickly out of breath, take care. You have a lazy heart, suffering from lack of proper exercise. Begin to take daily walks and increase your speed until you can run without panting. Then run every day.[8]

Any form of physical exercise that you enjoy, such as bicycling, swimming, tennis, soccer, gymnastics, skating, gardening, et al., can be beneficial to your health when it is done consciously "with deep attention until you perspire."

### My health recipe

My health had not been very good of late: my feet, knees, and shoulders were inflamed, I had trouble breathing, and in meditation my concentration was "occasional." Since there wasn't much pleasure in living like this, I decided to take charge of the situation by getting my racing bike out of storage.

Every day I rode from my house to Assisi and back, a round trip of about thirty kilometers (nineteen miles). As I pedaled, I harmonized the movement of my legs with my breathing pattern.

I started to feel my body cells filling with oxygen and prana, and my mind entering a semi-meditative state. I did not feel cold even in winter when the temperature fell below zero (32°F). Without changing my diet, I was losing my excess weight and sleeping soundly, the physical problems were adjusting themselves, and best of all, my meditations improved dramatically. To be honest, this daily regime of physical exercise, which I continue to this day, completely transformed my life. –***Narya***, *Ananda Assisi*

When working long hours at the computer, it is important for our overall health to take regular breaks to exercise and fill our cells with fresh oxygen.

here are times when I experience what I think of as mental constipation – my mind is foggy, I can't think straight, and all I want to do is sleep. A nap will sometimes dispel the brain fog, but most times it just makes matters worse, leaving me feeling mentally hungover.

What works is going out for a run. I can't think of a time when it hasn't worked – it's as reliable as a good-luck charm. The hard part is persuading myself to remember how well it has worked in the past, and getting myself out the door.

Once I set out, the blues vanish, replaced by a sense of well-being, almost a euphoria, a state where the creative thoughts flow so rapidly that I wonder if I can remember them all. Now that I have a smart watch, I press "record" and save those inspirations as voice notes to be transcribed after a refreshing shower. –**Shivani** (*the author*)

✻   ✻   ✻

## Life Force Energy Recharging Exercises

Yogananda developed his "Yogoda" or Energization Exercises as a complete, and very efficient, way to give the body the physical exercise it needs daily.

When "Yogoda" is once learned,
ten minutes' daily practice will give results
unequalled by those of most other
forms of exercise. It avoids the bad effects
of most systems, such as exhaustion of the
heart and other organs and failure to
give an all-round development.[9]

These exercises are the subject of Part IV and can be learned with the instruction videos in the Appendices.

Swami Kriyananda practiced them every day of his spiritual life.

**By practicing these exercises daily, you'll develop exceptional ability to heal your body.**[10]

When you are unable to go outside, you can do the series on a porch or indoors with windows wide open for a complete energy renewal. The two aerobic exercises, walking and running in place, can be done for a longer period within the series, for up to 200 more steps.

Years ago, I prepared for a pilgrimage in the Himalayas with a rigorous training program of long walks at altitude for many months. A friend prepared in another way: she included in her daily Energization practice about 500 steps each of the walking and running exercises. Her training turned out to be as good as mine – we walked the steep mountain paths together.

Don't undervalue the importance to your health of regular exercise, or put it off until you have more time. We will never have more time until we *make* the time for what is important. The quality and even the length of your life will be the better for it.

The Life Force Full Body Recharge is an excellent way to keep your energy tank full. I practice it almost every hour, sometimes standing (when my smart watch tells me to stand) and sometimes sitting. I find that when I do it throughout the day I can maintain a peak level of energy, enthusiasm, and creativity without experiencing up-and-down cyclic energy swings.

Proper exercise is also an integral part of the body's ability to eliminate toxins, an aspect that we will explore in depth in the next chapter.

# Detoxification

> One of the main causes of arthritis,
> rheumatism, and many other diseases is auto-
> intoxication, which is due to faulty elimination.
> Uneliminated, decayed food stays like a paste of
> glue on the walls of the intestines and is absorbed
> into the blood. Disease naturally follows.[1]
>
> —YOGANANDA

**One of the primary causes** of disease is auto-intoxication, when waste matter, toxins, and pollutants build up in the body and are not efficiently expelled. Thousands of environmental pollutants, such as exhaust fumes, tobacco smoke, and urban pollutants enter the body through the air we breathe, the water we drink, and sometimes through the pores of the skin.

Urban dust alone usually consists of 224 toxic chemicals that range from substances such as polyaromatic hydrocarbons to heavy metals and pesticides...One notorious mundane pollutant is cigarette smoke about which scientists have learned contain more than 6,000 chemicals.[2]

Not all of the food we eat is completely digested. Inevitably, there are waste products that need to be eliminated from the body each day. In addition, foods grown with chemical fertilizers and insecticides introduce toxins into the body, which accumulate and are difficult to eliminate. Eating organically grown foods relieves the body of having to process and eliminate these chemical toxins.

The human body is brilliantly designed to eliminate most harmful substances; our part is simply to keep the organs of elimination functioning properly. Given a healthy diet and regular exercise, the body can eliminate waste materials effectively. In this chapter, we will look at various ways to keep the organs of elimination functioning at their best.

The citations in this chapter, except when otherwise indicated, are from Yogananda's extensive writings on internal purification.

## The Liver

This vital organ is the major participant in the detoxification process. It breaks down, deactivates, and removes toxic substances such as food additives, harmful minerals, heavy metals, medications, excess hormones, and more. These waste products are then sent via the blood to the kidneys and intestines to be excreted.

One of the most interesting laboratories in the world is located right within each individual—the liver. Incidentally, it is the largest organ and has a tremendous amount of work to do as well as important duties to perform. Usually the time comes when it has been over-worked; in which event, like an overworked horse or a human being, it rebels and lies down on the job. In the liver, together with the spleen, iron is stored and utilized for its normal supply or for an emergency, when there has been any undue loss of blood. Therefore, it is essential that the liver's health is considered, that overeating is avoided, and that an occasional rest period is given to this important organ. The latter is best accomplished by a strict fast on high-vibrating fruits or vegetable juices, or both.[3]

## The Kidneys

The kidneys cleanse the blood of toxic wastes that arrive from the liver, sending them to the bladder to be eliminated through the urine. To keep the kidneys functioning properly, it is important to drink water and other liquids abundantly throughout the day.

## The Intestines and Colon

The waste materials that are broken down by the liver are carried to the intestines in bile, which breaks down the fat molecules and sends the waste on to the colon where it is excreted through feces. If the intestines are not working properly, toxins can be reabsorbed, causing auto-intoxication. It is said that all sickness begins in the intestines. As Yogananda points out: *"You cannot afford to have constipation."* [4]

Meats, potatoes, starchy foods, and white flour can create constipation, as does over-eating and inadequate liquid consumption. Be sure to drink between meals. Drinking warm water with lemon juice in the morning helps to stimulate elimination. Avoid eating late at night. Even one day without a bowel movement should be taken seriously and remedied by drinking water, fruit and vegetable juices, and eating fresh fruits.

> Meat is concentrated food and is strengthening, but it is highly constipating and acts as a retainer of body poisons and a harbinger of disease....Vegetables and fruits, having a natural laxative action, are conducive to health and to the elimination of diseases.[5]
>
> All fruits are laxative in the following order: [6]
>
> 1. prunes;          6. figs;
> 2. watermelons;    7. raisins;
> 3. melons;          8. grapes;
> 4. passion fruit;   9. olive oil is
> 5. tomatoes            very good.
>
> Another sensible medical recommendation... is to evacuate the intestines and flush the bowels completely once or twice a month by a day of drinking only vegetable juices or two or three quarts of water. This general house-cleaning is helpful. To flush the drains and pipes of the arteries every now and then is to prevent them from becoming clogged with poisons.[7]

The exercises below have been introduced in Part IV and are repeated here. Those who know the Energization Exercises can do extra cycles of the stomach exercise when troubled by constipation or digestive problems.

These stomach exercises will help peristaltic movement and digestion, eliminating constipation, reducing obesity. To be practiced daily in the morning after leaving bed.[8]

## EXERCISE 1

- Stand erect; close your eyes.
- Pressingly place both hands on abdomen one above the other.
- Contract and tense (high) the lower portion.
- Hold while contracting and tensing (high) the upper portion.
- Relax both.
- Repeat 6 times.

## EXERCISE 2

- Stoop forward grasping arms of chair.
- Hold arms straight.
- Exhale completely and quickly.
- Close nostrils and mouth with fingers of left hand.
- With breath expelled, slowly cave in abdomen as far as possible, then push it out as far as possible.
- Repeat twice (holding breath out all the time).
- Then inhale. Repeat the above entire exercise 5 times – in case of stomach trouble, repeat 10 times.

## The importance of water

The human body is composed mostly of water. To maintain the organism in good operating condition, and to flush out toxins, an adequate intake of liquids is essential. Fluids are needed to metabolize proteins and carbohydrates; to lubricate the joints; to insulate the brain, spinal cord, and organs; and to carry oxygen and nutrients to the cells.

Water performs essential work in the organism by bathing the tissues and washing away waste materials. "It mechanically excites peristaltic action and increases intestinal secretions, thus aiding in elimination, especially if taken when the stomach is empty."

When people do not drink enough liquids, the body, in endeavoring to keep its fluid content constant, keeps the needed water from the kidneys and from the digestive glands. In this way constipation and possible urinary disturbances are caused....

Hot water is very quickly absorbed and in many cases is very beneficial to weak digestive systems. It relieves thirst very quickly. Lukewarm water is very useful as an emetic if taken in large quantities."

Water is supplied not only by beverages but also by vegetable and animal foods. Green vegetables contain up to 90 per cent and milk contains about 87 per cent water.[9]

## *The Lungs*

The lungs are major organs of elimination. With inhalation, fresh oxygen nourishes the body cells, and with exhalation carbon dioxide is expelled. Daily physical exercise, the Life Force Energization Exercises, and deep-breathing pranayama exercises maximize the lungs' ability to do their job.[10]

While practicing the breathing exercises, give special attention to the exhalation phase, using the abdominal muscles and diaphragm to force the air from the lungs. To get the best results from deep breathing exercises, it is important to keep the nose and throat clean so that the toxins we breathe are eliminated before they get to the lungs.*

Clearing throat and nose with mixture of a
half teaspoonful of salt and a glassful of water early
mornings and noon, and just before going
to bed, has been found to be very effective.[11]

---

*This technique is known in yoga as "jal neti." Helpful videos can be found on YouTube.

Sadly, much of the air we breathe today pollutes rather than nourishes the body. Air pollution in densely populated urban areas has a serious impact on our health. In New Delhi in 2020, 54,000 premature deaths were attributed to air pollution. The body is hard-pressed to eliminate the chemicals that invade it from the air. If you live in a polluted city, it would be wise to take precautions while outdoors and to have proper air filtration indoors. Certain indoor plants are known to help clean the air from toxins, in addition to adding beauty and elevating the vibrational quality of the environment.*

## The Skin

The skin is the body's largest organ. Water-soluble toxins and metabolic residues from rich foods such as dairy, eggs, and meat are excreted through sweat – thus the importance of keeping the pores of the skin free of obstruction by vigorous daily exercise followed by a shower.

> An ordinary bath cleans the body pores and keeps the sweat glands working properly, eliminating impurities. So the Hindu savants say that the person who bathes daily and keeps the pores of his body open, helps his increased body heat to escape through these pores.[12]
>
> Rubbing the whole stripped body vigorously and rapidly with the palms before taking a bath generates life force and is also very beneficial.[13]

*Author's note:* Because Yogananda recommends a bath with bath salts every evening while doing the Nine-Day Cleansing Diet, as an alternative to taking a bath, I rub Epsom Salts on my body in the shower to get some of the detoxifying benefits.

---

* This excellent article suggests ten indoor plants that are air purifiers: https://www. homesandgardens.com/gardens/best-air-cleaning-indoor-plants. In Part XII you will find suggestions for creating healthful indoor environments.

## Life Force Energization Exercises for detox

Yogananda's Energization Exercises offer an efficient way to eliminate toxins. The double breathing that accompanies many of the Energization Exercises enhances the body's ability to eliminate carbon dioxide. The interplay of muscular tension and relaxation brings fresh blood and oxygen to the cells, and during the relaxation phase relaxes muscular tension, liberating the Life Force to do its cleansing work. At the end of a full session, the entire body is cleansed and rejuvenated.

## The importance of fasting

When we continually engage the organs of digestion and elimination, they will tire in time. All bodily mechanisms require rest. Judicious fasting gives the internal organs the rest they need to operate efficiently. In many of his writings Yogananda encourages fasting on orange juice for one day a week and for three days once a month.

- A twenty-four hour fast once a week will give the digestive system a rest.

- Fast one day a week, or at least a half day. If you feel unable to do that, live for one day on nothing but orange juice. This plan will give needed rest to the body machine, which overworks incessantly through over-eating or wrong eating. Do not think that satisfied hunger means satisfied body needs. Learn the laws of rational, scientific diet, and live on simple and wholesome food.[14]

- Every week you must fast one day on orange juice to rest the organs. You won't die – you will LIVE! Each month fast two or three days consecutively, living only on orange juice.…When you fast on orange juice it scrubs every cell. At least every month you should give a thorough house-cleaning to your body by fasting. Do not let poisons accumulate in your system. When you are suddenly sick you begin to pray to God. Don't let yourself get sick. The greatest way of health and the simplest is, every week fast one day on orange juice and two or three days consecutively a month.[15]

Fast three days consecutively on orange juice every month, or every forty-five days, and meditate long and deeply (two or three hours). This will not only give rest to the body, and eliminate poisons, but it will teach you how to live more by Cosmic Consciousness, and less by food.[16]

Those who never fast do not know that man can live by the word of God, or energy flowing from God. Jesus fasted forty days in order to convince himself that his soul had risen above the bodily conditions. That's why he uttered when he was tempted by the material hunger-consciousness, "Man shall not live by bread alone."

Hence the earlier stages of a week's fasting are marked by hunger, but as the days of fasting multiply, less hunger and more freedom from food are distinctly felt. Why? Because the soul is unconsciously made to depend on the inner source of supply by a forced denial of the external source of supply of food. But this method of fasting is only one of the physical methods of rising above the consciousness of matter.

No spiritual aspirant should indiscriminately indulge in long fasts without expert advice. Partial fasting, by omitting one or two meals a day, or by a day's fasting every week, done with the sole purpose of forgetting food, and followed by deep meditation, is helpful in spiritual realization.[17]

Current research on fasting supports Yogananda's recommendations. In the Endnotes for this chapter, you will find the conclusions of Dr. Mindy Peltz, one of the foremost proponents of fasting regimes for self-healing.[18]

Fasting may be divided into two main groups:
*partial fasting* and *complete fasting.*

## Partial fasting

In this group, four general subdivisions may be mentioned:

- Limiting the diet to certain foods
- Abstaining from certain foods
- Limiting the food intake as to quantity
- Limiting the number of meals to one or two per day

Some of these forms of fasting may be combined. For example, to cure disease or reduce weight, a person may abstain from certain foods altogether and limit the intake of other foods, etc. More specific subdivisions are:

### LIQUID DIET

"Liquid" fasting. For one or two days a week, and whenever one does not feel hungry, the food intake may be confined to (1) milk, or (2) orange juice or any other fruit juice.

### SOLID DIET

"Solid" fasting. This diet is confined to:

(1) Raw fruits
(2) Raw vegetables
(3) Half-boiled vegetables, including the juice in which they were boiled

*Drink plenty of water while on this diet.*

## Fasting and longevity

Confirming Yogananda's recommendations made nearly a century ago, current research in disease prevention and gerontology demonstrates the effects of complete and partial fasting. Refraining from food for

* The following recommendations are from Yogananda's lesson, "The Divine Magnetic Diet," *Super-Advanced Course No. 1,* Lesson 5. The complete article is the Appendices.

between 12 and 72 hours has shown remarkable results in increasing life span as well as preventing and treating disease.

> Intermittent and periodic fasting (IF and PF, respectively) are emerging as safe strategies to affect longevity and healthspan by acting on cellular aging and disease risk factors, while causing no or minor side effects.... In humans, the alternation of fasting and refeeding periods is accompanied by positive effects on risk factors for aging, diabetes, autoimmunity, cardiovascular disease, neurodegeneration and cancer.[19]

Dr. Valter Longo, who has done research for many years in the area of fasting, conducted a study based on people who have done chemotherapy. He observed that at 72 hours of fasting the white blood cells, which were tired and worn out, were reactivated. They reinvigorated themselves and the immune system become stronger. Three-day fasts are now increasingly used not only with the aim of restarting the immune system, but thanks to the massive production of stem cells that are produced during a long fast, the body is able to repair musculoskeletal injuries, increase the efficiency of the neurons in the brain, and dramatically slow the aging process. This impressive healing process happens naturally without any medications or supplements.

## Helpful advice during a fast

- A fasting person who inhales and exhales deeply twelve times, three times a day, recharges his body with electrons and free energy from air and ether.[20]

- Concentrate during fasting. Don't mentally miss food, or dwell on food. Rather feel that you are being charged by Cosmic Consciousness and Cosmic energy, and are learning that your life depends entirely upon it, and that you are getting out of the habit of depending too much upon food.[21]

- Some suitable laxative during an orange juice fast is good.[22]

- The Full Yogic Breath (p. 186) is a good exercise for filling the body with energy, particularly when you are fasting.[23]

- Especially effective is doing the Life Force Full Body Recharge (p. 282) every hour.

I t's been a year now that I have been fasting once a week. I look forward to the day of rest from compulsive eating as a welcome break from my usual eating habits. In the beginning, lemon juice, water and maple syrup helped me dampen the food cravings during the day. Now, I don't even want to eat or drink the whole day. My bowels get a detox every time I fast. I can feel my body thanking me for this day of rest. I do feel subtle changes in body/mind, but I can't explain in words what is happening. I feel I can understand spiritual teachings better and get more insights than when I was not fasting. –**Draupadi**, *Switzerland*

I fasted every Sunday from midnight to midnight for thirteen months. It was a huge leap toward a better spiritual practice, deeper meditation, and finding a stronger connection with the spiritual realms. Over several months I would get really hungry around three p.m., but by the end of a year it got easier. –**Gideon**, *U.K.*

T ogether with a friend we did a three-day fast, in which we drank only the vegetable broth recommended by Yogananda. I felt that my body got rid of toxins, but the most unpredictable thing for me was the extraordinary energy that grew from the third day, and the "bliss" that perhaps I have not experienced even in meditation. I felt joy – there was no room for negative emotions, just love, forgiveness, acceptance. It was a wonderful experience. –**Monica**, *Turin, Italy*

F or a period of two years I fasted for 24 hours once a week, occasionally twice, taking no food, just water, sometimes water with lemon and herbal tea. I would start from lunch on Sunday to Monday lunch. It was difficult at first, more psychologically than physically, as I kept thinking about what I was going to eat first after the fast, but after a couple of weeks it became easier.

*These are the benefits I experienced*:

- I felt lighter, more agile, both physically and mentally.
- I lost some extra weight.
- My skin looked better.
- I looked younger than my actual age.
- There was less puffiness in my face and eyes.
- I had more energy for my Monday morning strength training and sprints workout.
- I had fewer cravings for food, especially sugar.
- I had better, more restful sleep, especially on Sunday night.
- My mind was clearer and sharper.
- I had more self-discipline.
- During the week I had better control of food intake and I felt less hungry.
- I had better meditations. *—Nesha*, *Belgrade, Serbia*

For the past few years I have fasted once every month for three days. When I feel hungry, I drink to fill my stomach, which helps, and I always feel fit during these days. My work can go on, and I can walk for a while. I lose some weight, but that recovers quickly after starting to eat again.

I feel more mental clarity and afterwards I feel myself physically very clean, and I always feel a need to start eating again with only biological (organic) food. I can highly recommend this practice. *—Ellen*, *Netherlands*

My first experience with fasting was in college. I decided to fast every Thursday for a whole year. I realized many things during those fasts – for instance, that hunger is something you can distract yourself from. I'd be starving one moment, my only thought being what I wanted to eat, and then I'd be completely absorbed in something in the next moment, having utterly forgotten about my cravings.

It was like a mini-miracle. But you have to fight in those moments when you feel hungry, and instead enjoy the benefits of a clearer mind, more perceptive senses, and better meditations. Now, anytime I feel that I am starting to get sick, I try to fast for more than twenty-four hours to give my body a break from the work of digestion and to focus my energy on healing.

A notable and often forgotten benefit of fasting is how it enhances one's sense of smell, it seems as much as five-fold! Smell is a sense we often forget because most of the time we probably eat too heavily to be keenly aware of its existence. While fasting, I realized that I was more percep-tive, sensorily, energetically, and intuitively.

I like to think of fasting as a super power. If you can control your impulse to eat and use your willpower to choose what you eat, you gain mastery over many other parts of your life. You have proved to yourself the power of your will. *–Rachel, U.S.A.*

## *Curing Colds and Catarrh*

While the common cold is not usually considered a severe medical condition, it can proceed from the nose to the throat, then to the lungs. Yogananda offers the following advice for eliminating colds and for treating them as quickly as possible.

When you catch cold, fast for two days. Remember that during a cold the extra poisons of your body are being thrown off. If you add more food to your system, you help to obstruct the poison-eliminating system of Nature by clogging up the circulation with extra food chemicals.

If you cannot bear up under a complete fast, eat apples or pears or grapes, but refrain from eating acid fruits. Do not eat anything at night.

Do not drink hot or cold water. Drink only two glasses of tepid warm water daily. I do not believe that to drink too much water during a cold is good, for the extra water taken comes out constantly through the mucous membrane, making the nose run too much, and causing irritation and accumulation of pus there. Fasting during a cold is very good, for it helps Nature to effect her own cure without interruption from any source. It is very good to use some laxative suitable to your system at the beginning of a cold.

A good four-hour sun-bath with the rays of the sun falling directly on the epidermis of the body has been known to cure a cold in one day.[24]

&ast;

Catarrh is caused mostly from overeating at night and from neglecting colds.... If you are suffering from catarrh, make your night meals very light. Eat mostly fruits and very little cooked vegetables, some boiled peas or boiled spinach just to satisfy the demands of your acquired habit.

Eat your heaviest meal at noon. Do not drink water nor eat before going to bed at night. Eat very little bread, a small piece of toasted whole wheat bread at noon.

Do not drink iced water with your meals, especially at night. Sleep well covered, open windows wide both summer and winter. Refrain from eating meat as much as possible. Never eat fish, meat, or eggs at night. Drink milk in the afternoon. A fruit diet and ground nuts at night are best. Take long walks in the morning, and especially at night before going to bed. Inhale and exhale all the time when walking.[25]

## Nine-day Cleansing and Vitalizing Diet [26]

In addition to regular fasting, or in place of fasting if it proves overly difficult, Yogananda recommended the following cleansing diet as *"a most effective method for ridding the system of poisons,"* that can be done one or more times in the year.

### INGREDIENTS

- 1½ grapefruit
- 1½ lemons
- 5 oranges
- 1 glass orange juice with 1 teaspoon of ground almonds
- A natural laxative
- 1 cooked vegetable with juice (quantity optional)
- 3 cups of the Vitality Beverage
- 1 raw vegetable salad (quantity optional)

### Vitality Beverage

- 2 stalks chopped celery
- 5 carrots (chopped) including part of stem
- 1 bunch chopped parsley
- 1 quart of water.
- ½ liter chopped dandelion or turnip greens or spinach
- *No salt or spices*

The beverage may be prepared in two ways, the first being preferable:

(1) After putting celery and carrots through a meat chopper [or cutting them finely], lightly boil them in water for ten minutes, then add selected greens and parsley and boil for ten minutes more. Strain by squeezing through cheesecloth.

(2) Use the same ingredients, but do not cook them. After putting them through a meat chopper, strain as above. [*Note*: This was written in 1930 before widely available juicing machines and extractors, which would be the logical modern alternative.]

Drink one cup of the beverage, prepared by either method, at each of the three meals.

This vitality beverage has been found to be a blood tonic and very effective in rheumatism, various stomach disorders (including acute indigestion), chronic catarrh, bronchitis, and "nervous breakdown."

While on the cleansing diet, strictly abstain from spices, candies, pastries, meat, eggs, fish, cheese, milk, butter, bread, fried foods, oil, beans – in fact, all foods not mentioned above. If you feel a need for additional nourishment, you may take a tablespoonful of thoroughly ground nuts in a half glass of water or a glass of orange juice.

Following the nine-day diet, one should be especially careful in the selection and quantity of one's food intake on the first day, and resume a normal diet gradually.

If one is not successful in ridding the body of all poisons during the initial attempt, the cleansing diet may be repeated after an interval of two or three weeks.

While on the cleansing diet, it has been found beneficial, every night just before going to bed, to use two pounds of some good bath salts in one-fourth tub of warm water, and also very helpful to take a bath-salts bath every now and then for several weeks after finishing the cleansing diet.

## Suggestions from those who have undertaken the Cleansing Diet

- You might need to prepare your body before you undertake this diet. If you are a heavy meat-eater or smoke, or use caffeinated drinks, going without these substances for a long period will likely provoke reactions such as headaches, weakness, and irritability. You can ease into the diet by trying it for one day, then after a time, two days, until you feel that your body is ready for the full nine-day cleansing period.

- Another preparation would be to fast occasionally, starting with 18 hours perhaps once a week, building up to 24 hours once a week. After some months you should be ready to try the Cleansing Diet, starting with a three-day trial.

- For breakfast, the citrus can be juiced, diluted with water if preferred, and taken at other times during the day as desired.

- The salad can consist of any quantity of fresh vegetables, and may be eaten either at lunch or dinner. The lemon can be used as a salad dressing. No salt should be used.

- The cooked vegetable, eaten at either lunch or dinner, should be just one kind of vegetable, and the lemon can be used here as well. It is best to avoid potatoes.

- Make the Vitality Beverage in the morning and keep it warm in a thermos so you can drink it throughout the day. If your body likes it, you can drink more than the suggested amount.

- Alternatives for people with gastric conditions: because citrus fruits aggravate conditions of gastritis, stomach ulcers, and hiatal hernia, consider substituting them with additional Vitality Beverage, rose hips tea, vitamin C powder, and kombucha which will alkalize the system and provide vitamins and minerals needed for the cleansing.

- It is probably best to avoid avocado in the vegetable salad.

- Doing the Energization Exercises outdoors two or more times during the day provides prana, lessens the desire for material food, and facilitates the detoxification process.

- The Full Body Recharge, done often, even every hour, will keep the body filled with prana and will hold hunger at bay.

- Take advantage of the sun. It is helpful to do this diet in the summer, when you can spend time in the sun and absorb that source of energy. A big raw vegetable salad is more appealing in warm weather.

- Drink water abundantly, either at room temperature or warm; you can add some of the lemon, if you wish.

- Using a mild natural laxative the evening before you begin, and every evening thereafter, is highly recommended, and is part of the diet itself. If you are so inclined, you can take an enema the evening before and for the first day or two. It is important for the success of the diet, and for our ability to maintain it, that toxins be flushed from the body every day.

n March 2020 I decided to embark on Master's diet. At the beginning I was very doubtful, As I didn't know what to expect, and above all I was afraid of not having enough strength to carry on the service I was following at that time: I was working in the fields to gather and collect heavy stones in order to plant spelt and oats.

The diet began, and in fact my service turned out to be a blessing; I could stay outdoors in the sun and breathe pure air. I noticed that day after day I had more and more energy and I didn't feel any physical fatigue at all. It was a dream! I could lift the heavy weights without feeling tired. It was as if a veil had been lifted and I no longer cared about my body.

The second day, I had a strange experience: I felt that my mind was congested with "toxin-thoughts." Before falling asleep, I felt that my head was getting rid of these thought-forms, that they were being expelled through the skin, from the brain itself. The next morning I woke up recharged and full of energy.

Doing this sacred diet was a gift for me, a way to get in touch with the Spirit that dwells beyond the physical sphere. –**Elisa**, *Venezia Giulia, Italy*

did this diet only once. I would like to do it more often, but at least with one other person to have some moral support. The miracle that happened was that something subtle changed in me and motivated me to want to fast once a week. If I had not done this nine-day diet, I am sure I would not have tried fasting. –**Draupadi**, *Switzerland*

have done the Master's purification diet four or five times, two or three times for nine days, the others with the five-day "abbreviated ritual." Each time it takes great determination to decide to do it, but once you have decided and convinced your mind that it is a necessary operation, carrying out the program is not difficult.

The diet is not easy: the first days can produce lots of headaches because of the toxins that are being released, plus weakness, and feeling cold. But then there is an improvement. On the other hand, it is very satisfying to know that you are doing something really useful for your body and mind.

I've realized that to counteract the discomfort resulting from toxins, we must not disregard Yogananda's advice to take a laxative in the evening. Many people may think "I don't need it" but the laxative serves to cleanse the bowels more thoroughly and eliminate the toxins as soon as possible. If this is not done, these toxins can be reabsorbed by the intestine, generating a vicious cycle of malaise that cannot be overcome. For the same reason, it can be of great help to do an enema. Certainly, drinking lots of water can also be of great help. –*Clarita*, *Ananda Assisi*

I 've done the nine-day cleansing diet at least four times, and each time I felt happy, bright, perky, positive, and ready to take on the world. Through this experience I have come to realize that there is a force beyond mere material food that sustains us. We needn't be slaves to our desire for the food that is not really good for us.

*My advice to those who want to try this cleansing diet*:

**The Vitality beverage is of great importance.** I like to both juice and cook the ingredients – juicing the vegetables for their nutritive properties like vitamins and raw enzymes, while also making the cooked beverage, which I think gives more minerals and a more "yang" feeling that grounds you and gives you more natural salts, making the diet easier to keep up when the going gets tough.

**The salad.** You can make the salad more appealing by cutting the vegetables in different ways. You can use a vegetable peeler to make long strips or spirals or other shapes.

You can make a salad dressing using some of the lemon juice and blending a few of the vegetables, like some cucumber and parsley, maybe a pinch of onion to make it more tasty, even blend in a small piece of ripe avocado to help you get over the rough patches.

Also to make the food more appealing I use beautiful dishes, sometimes a wooden bowl or a glass bowl for the salad, an elegant glass for the beverage. *–Rachel*, *U.S.A.*

T he medication I had been taking was causing me more pain and discomfort than the disease. I had been diagnosed with a severe chronic condition, and the specialists prescribed immunosuppressive medications that caused me to vomit profusely and have terrible headaches. After two and half years I knew that my body could no longer support these heavy medications.

I showed my doctor Yogananda's Cleansing Diet Vitality Beverage, and she suggested that I should try a seven-day liquid fast, using the Vitality Beverage for the first four days, then only water. During this time I would not take the medication.

The seven days were a combination of heightened well-being on a subtle energetic level, coupled with the physical challenges of purifying a toxic system. The calm that the fast created in my nervous system was remarkable. One of the most important results was the strengthening of my will. My mind was so set on living for seven days without food, that during this time I could joyfully cook for my family without a pang of hunger or a desire to partake of the meal I had prepared for them.

The experience was the beginning of the end of my taking immunosuppressive drugs and freedom from their secondary effects. It also showed me that "I am master of my body, I am master of myself,' and that when I put my mind to something, I can accomplish anything. *–Jenny*, *Switzerland*

# CHAPTER 3: *Points to Remember*

- A proper diet, daily vigorous exercise, and judicious fasting are the keys to good health, disease prevention, and longevity.

- The organs of elimination are easily compromised by overeating, and by external and internal toxins.

- Drink a sufficient amount of water and other liquids to support the digestive system and to process waste matter effectively.

- A daily routine of deep breathing exercises helps eliminate toxins.

- To support the body's ability to eliminate toxins, Yogananda recommends fasting one day per week and three consecutive days once a month.

- The Nine-Day Cleansing and Vitalizing Diet should be done at least one or more times a year.

- Life Force Energization Exercises are an efficient way to both recharge and purify the body cells.

*Affirmation*

Today I will rise above the consciousness
of food and know that I live by the pure peace
of Silence. I will feed my Soul constantly
with the Divine Manna of Peace.[27]

# Your recipe for improved health

**In the previous** three chapters we have relished a cornucopia of Yogananda's suggestions for improving our physical health – so many, that it may be difficult to know where to start and how to proceed. Thus we offer the following summary of important points. Taking into account your current health habits, begin your journey to better health with one of the suggestions in these chapters that appeals to you. As you experience the benefits, you may be motivated to do more.

*A proper diet, daily vigorous exercise, and judicious fasting are the keys to good health, disease prevention, and longevity.*

### ☀ Diet ☀

- Choose foods that are rich in vitality and imbued with high vibrations.
- Find a suitable diet and stay with it – don't make food your religion.
- Include sunlight and oxygen in your daily diet.
- Prepare and eat your food more consciously.
- Eat in calm, uplifting surroundings, alone or with inspiring companions.

### ☀ Exercise ☀

- Every day walk, run, or take some form of vigorous exercise until you perspire.

### ☀ Detox ☀

- Fast one day a week and three days once a month on orange juice, adding ground almonds if necessary.
- Once a year, do the Nine-Day Cleansing Diet.

### ☀ Life Force Energy Recharging Exercises ☀

The complete set of exercises, done one or more times a day, and the Life Force Full Body Recharge practiced frequently throughout the day, will facilitate digestion, metabolism, and elimination.

# NOTES PART FIVE

## Title Page

1 Kriyananda, *Conversations with Yogananda* No. 104.

## Chapter One

1 Yogananda, "Recipes," *East-West*, July–August 1926.
2 Yogananda, "The Divine Magnetic Diet," *Super-Advanced Course No. 1*, Lesson 5. You will find this Lesson in the Appendices.
3 Yogananda, "Diet and Disposition," *Inner Culture*, February 1940.
4 Dennett, Carrie, "You Are What You Eat," Chicago Health, December 4, 2015, *https://chicagohealthonline.com/you-are-what-you-eat-let-food-be-your-medicine-too/.
5 Choudury, Ruchira Roy, "The Four Pillars of Ayurvedic Healing," The Art of Living, https://artoflivingretreatcenter.org/blog/the-four-pillars-of-ayurvedic-healing/.
6 "Nutrition in Medical Education," McGovern Medical School, https://www.uth.tmc.edu/nutrition/history.htm.

   See also the research being done by David Sinclair at the Harvard Medical School on the relationship between diet and longevity. LaMotte, Sandee, "The Benjamin Button Effect," CNN Health, July 15, 2022, https://edition.cnn.com/2022/06/02/health/reverse-aging-life-itself-scn-wellness/index.html].

   "Focus on plants for food, eat less often, get sufficient sleep, lose your breath for ten minutes three times a week by exercising to maintain your muscle mass, don't sweat the small stuff and have a good social group.

   All these behaviors affect our epigenome, proteins and chemicals that sit like freckles on each gene, waiting to tell the gene "what to do, where to do it, and when to do it," according to the National Human Genome Research Institute. The epigenome literally turns genes on and off.

   What controls the epigenome? Human behavior and one's environment play a key role. Let's say you were born with a genetic predisposition for heart disease and diabetes. But because you exercised, ate a plant-focused diet, slept well and managed your stress during most of your life, it's possible those genes would never be activated. That, experts say, is how we can take some of our genetic fate into our own hands."

7 Kriyananda, "Music, Creativity, and Mystical Experience," from a talk given in March, 1996
8 Kriyananda, *The New Path*, 446.
9 Kriyananda, *Conversations with Yogananda* No. 141.
10 Yogananda, "Meat Eating Versus Vegetarianism," *Inner Culture*, April 1935.
11 Yogananda, *Super-advanced Course,* Lessons 4 and 5.
12 Yogananda, *New Super Cosmic Science Course*, Lesson 4.
13 Yogananda, "Recipes," *East-West*, July–August 1927.
14 Yogananda, *Super Advanced Course No. 1*, Lesson 5.
15 Yogananda, *Advanced Course on Practical Metaphysics*, Lesson 11.
16 Yogananda, "What Is Perfect Diet?" *Inner Culture*, October 1940.
17 Yogananda, *New Super Cosmic Science Course*, Lesson 4.
18 Yogananda, Lesson 4.
19 Yogananda, *Super Advanced Course No. 1*, Lesson 5.
20 Yogananda, "Recipes," *East-West*, September–October 1927.

21  Yogananda, "Recipes," *East-West*, June 1933.
22  Kriyananda, *The Art and Science of Raja Yoga*, 180.
23  Yogananda, "Message to My Los Angeles Yogoda Students," *East-West*, March–April 1926.
24  Yogananda, *Super Advanced Course No. 1*, Lesson 5.
25  Yogananda, "Recipes," *East-West*, July–August 1928.
26  Yogananda, "Recipes," *East-West*, May–June 1929.
27  Yogananda, "Recipes," *East-West*, September–October 1926.
28  Yogananda, "Aims and Tenets of the Yogoda Sat-Sang Society," *East-West*, May–June 1929.
29  Yogananda, "Meditations and Affirmations," *East-West*, January 1933.
30  Yogananda, *Super Advanced Course No. 1*, Lesson 5.
31  Yogananda, Recipes," *East-West*, May–June 1929.
32  Yogananda, "Recipes," *East-West*, November–December 1927.
33  Yogananda, *Super Advanced Course No. 1*, Lesson 5.
34  Yogananda, *New Super Cosmic Science Course*, Lesson 4.
35  Yogananda, "Recipes," *East-West*, May–June 1929.
36  Yogananda, *New Super Cosmic Science Course*, Lesson 4.
37  Yogananda, *Super Advanced Course No. 1*, Lesson 5.
38  Yogananda, "Message to My Los Angeles Yogoda Students," *East-West*, March–April 1926.
39  Yogananda, "Recipes," *East-West*, April 1932.
40  Yogananda, "Diet and Disposition," *Inner Culture*, February 1940.
41  Yogananda, "Recipes," *East-West*, September–October 1927, and the *Super Advanced Course No. 1*, Lesson 5.
42  Kriyananda, *The Art and Science of Raja Yoga*, Diet, 275.
43  Yogananda, *Super Advanced Course No. 1*, Lesson 5.
44  Yogananda, Lesson 5.
45  Yogananda, Lesson 5.
46  Yogananda, Lesson 5.
47  Kriyananda, *The Art and Science of Raja Yoga*, 120.
48  Yogananda, *Praecepta Lessons*, Vol. 4:80
49  Yogananda, "Recipes," *East-West*, January–April 1927.
50  Yogananda, "Recipes," *East-West*, November–December 1927.
51  Yogananda, "Recipes," *East-West*, January–April 1927.
52  Yogananda, *Super Advanced Course No. 1*, Lesson 9.
53  Yogananda, "Recipes," *East-West*, September 1933.
54  Kriyananda, *Art and Science of Raja Yoga*, 373.
55  Kriyananda, *Secrets of Radiant Health and Well-Being*, 1.
56  Yogananda, *Whispers from Eternity*, No. 15.
57  Yogananda, "Recipes," *Inner Culture*, September 1934.
58  Yogananda, "Recipes," *East-West*, March–April 1928.
59  Yogananda, "Diet and Disposition," *Inner Culture*, February 1940.
60  Yogananda, "Value of Occasional Fasting," *East-West*, January–February 1926.
61  Yogananda, *Super Advanced Course No. 1*, Lesson 5.
62  Yogananda, "Diet and Disposition," *Inner Culture*, February 1940.
63  Kriyananda, *Art and Science of Raja Yoga*, 67-68.

## Chapter Two

1  Yogananda, "Recipes," *East-West*, September–October 1926.
2  Yogananda, "Recipes," *East-West*, May–June 1929.

**3** Yogananda, "Art of Living," *East-West*, May 1933.
**4** Yogananda, "Recipes," *East-West*, September–October 1926.
**5** Yogananda, *Praecepta Lessons*, Vol. 3:70.
**6** Yogananda, "Recipes," *East-West*, July–August 1926.
**7** Yogananda, "Recipes," *East-West*, November–December 1926.
**8** Yogananda, "Recipes," *East-West*, July–August 1927.
**9** Yogananda, "Yogoda: or Tissue-Will System of Body and Mind Perfection," 1923 edition.
**10** Kriyananda, *Awaken to Superconsciousness*, 149.

## Chapter Three

**1** Yogananda, "Recipes," *East-West* magazine, November–December 1928.
**2** "Skin Affected By Air Pollution," Environmental Pollution Centers, January 28, 2019, https://www.environmentalpollutioncenters.org/news/skin-affected-by-air-pollution/.
**3** Yogananda, *Praecepta Lessons*, Vol. 1:15.
**4** Yogananda, "Resurrection," *East-West*, May–June 1929.
**5** Yogananda, "Meat Eating Versus Vegetarianism," *Inner Culture*, April and May 1935.
**6** Yogananda, *New Super Cosmic Science Course*, Lesson 4.
**7** Yogananda, "Recipes," *East-West*, November–December 1928.
**8** Yogananda, *Yogoda Course*, Lesson 1.
**9** Yogananda, *Praecepta Lessons*, Vol. 5:121.
**10** Vol. 3:70.
**11** Vol. 3:70.
**12** Yogananda, "Health Recipes," *East-West*, March–April 1930.
**13** Yogananda, *Super Advanced Course No. 1*, Lesson 5.
**14** Yogananda, "Recipes," *East-West* magazine, January–February and May–June, 1926. Also: "It is highly advisable to fast one day a week. The Hindus claim that the 11th day of the New Moon and the 11th day of the Full Moon are the best days on which to fast, because of certain electrical, pranic influences that operate on these days to keep the body supplied with subtle vitality. – "Spiritual Food," *Advanced Course on Practical Metaphysics, Lesson 11.*
**15** Yogananda, "Resurrection," *East-West*, May–June 1929.
**16** Yogananda, "Second Coming of Christ," *East-West*, January 1933.
**17** Yogananda, "Christian Science & Hindu Philosophy, Part 2," *East-West*, July–August 1926.
**18** Research on fasting has shown that it has the following beneficial effects:
- Increases the GH anti-aging hormone; this happens after thirteen hours of fasting.
- Activates metabolism.
- Activates autophagy, a cleaning mechanism within the cells that removes damaged parts; this happens at fifteen hours of fasting.

*A 24-hour fast has these results:*
- Reduction of amyloid plaque with neuron regeneration.
- Production of endogenous ketones.
- Reduces inflammation.
- Increases the production of stem cells in the intestines.
- Increases antioxidants.
- Increases serotonin.
- Reduces candida.

- Reduces SIBO (small intestinal bacterial overgrowth, a serious condition affecting the small intestine).
- Increases BDNF which **regulates the growth, protection, maintenance, and repair of neurons in the brain.**
- Stimulates the production of oxytocin which improves glucose absorption, reduces appetite, and reduces levels of the stress hormone cortisol.

*A three-day fast delivers these important additional results:*

- Remarkable increase in production of stem cells.
- Resets the entire immune system.

See this excellent video by Dr. Peltz: https://www.youtube.com/watch?v=6_MJrJrL5-Q&ab_channel=Dr.MindyPelz; and visit her website: https://drmindypelz.com. Also of interest: Mattson, Mark P. et al., "Intermittent metabolic switching, neuroplasticity and brain health," National Library of Medicine, June 30, 2020, https://www.ncbi.nlm.nih.gov/pmc/articles/PMC5913738/.

**19** Longo, Valter D., et al., "Intermittent and periodic fasting, longevity and disease," Nature Aging, January 14, 2021, https://www.nature.com/articles/s43587-020-00013-3#Abs1.

**20** Yogananda, *Super Advanced Course No. 1,* Lesson 5.

**21** Yogananda, "Second Coming of Christ," *East-West,* January 1933.

**22** Yogananda, *Praecepta Lessons,* Vol. 4:83.

**23** Kriyananda, *Art and Science of Raja Yoga,* 85.

**24** Yogananda, "Healing Colds by Proper Diet," *East-West,* May 1932.

**25** Yogananda, "Recipes," *East-West,* April 1932.

**26** Yogananda, *Super-Advanced Course No. 1,* Lesson 5.

**27** Yogananda, "Meditations and Affirmations," *East-West,* July 1933.

## ❀ HEALING LIGHT OF GOD ❀

The perfect light is divinely present in all my body-parts.
Wherever that healing light is manifest, there is perfection.
I am well, for perfection is in me.

His healing light has been shining within me, around me,
but I have kept the eyes of my inner perceptions closed
so that I beheld not His transmuting light.

I will plunge the gaze of my faith through
the window of the spiritual eye and baptize my body
in the healing light of Christ Consciousness.

Father, teach me to remember and be grateful
for the years of health that I have enjoyed.

Teach me to open my closed eyes of unbelief and
behold Thine instantaneously healing light.

Heavenly Father, Thou are present in every atom,
every cell, every corpuscle, in every particle
of nerve, brain, and tissue.

I am well, for Thou art present in all my body parts.

❀　❀　❀

# GLOSSARY

**Ahankara**. The ego, from the Sanskrit, meaning "I act."

**Aum**. The all-pervading sound emanating from Cosmic Vibration, also known as the Pranava, the Amen, and the Amin.

**Babaji**. Called "Mahavatar" ("Great Avatar") by Yogananda, Babaji reintroduced the ancient science of Kriya Yoga in the modern age. In *Autobiography of a Yogi*, Yogananda writes: "Babaji's mission in India has been to assist prophets in carrying out their special dispensation."

**Bhagavad Gita.** The major scripture of Hinduism, the teachings of Lord Krishna to his disciple Arjuna, delivered on the battlefield of Kurukshetra, as told in the epic story, Mahabharata.

**Chakras**. Plexuses or centers in the spine, from which energy flows out into the nervous system, and through that system into the body, sustaining and activating the various body parts.

**Chitta**. The feeling aspect of consciousness.

**Christ Consciousness.** Consciousness of Spirit as immanent in every unit of vibratory creation.

**Cosmic Consciousness.** Consciousness of Spirit transcending finite creation.

**Day of Brahma.** The aeons-long period of cosmic manifestation. At the dawn of a Day of Brahma, all creation, remanifested, emerges from a state of unmanifestation – the Night of Brahma.

**Dharana**. One-pointed concentration.

**Dharma**. Virtue, righteousness, right action.

**Dhyana**. Absorption in deep meditation.

**Ego.** The soul identified with and attached to the material body and the material creation.

**Gunas**. The three basic qualities that comprise the universe: *sattwa guna*, the elevating quality, that which most clearly suggests divinity; *rajas*, the activating element in nature; *tamas*, the darkening quality, that which obscures the underlying unity of Life.

**Guru.** The spiritual preceptor who introduces the disciple to God and guides his inner journey from the darkness of ignorance to the light of Self-realization.

**Ida**. One of the two parallel nerve channels in the astral spine, *ida* begins and ends on the left side of the spine. The energy passes upward through it and causes inhalation.

**Karma**. Action that is motivated by the ego, and which at some time, in one form or another, returns to the one who initiated it.

**Krishna**. One of the incarnations of Lord Vishnu, Krishna was a king at the time of the war of Kurukshetra, as told in the epic, Mahabharata. He is the guru of the warrior Arjuna, and his instructions to his disciple at the beginning of the war form the Bhagavad Gita, India's principle scripture.

**Kriya Yoga**. An ancient science developed in India for the use of all God-seekers. Its technique is referred to and praised by Krishna in the *Bhagavad Gita,* and by Patanjali in the *Yoga Sutras*. It consists of the careful, conscious circulation of energy around the spine in order to magnetize it and redirect the mental tendencies toward the brain.

**Kundalini**. Life Force which lies dormant at the base of the sushumna in the astral body. Spiritual enlightenment requires that this force be awakened and through specific practices caused to rise upward and reunite with Spirit at the *sahasrara chakra*, the thousand-petalled lotus.

**Kutashta Chaitanya**. The state of Christ Consciousness, or the awareness of the presence of Spirit in every atom of creation. Located at the Spiritual Eye, the Kutastha, is a reflection of the medulla oblongata: a field of dark blue light surrounded by a golden halo, in the center of which is a five-pointed star. The golden aureole represents the astral world; the blue field inside it, the causal world and the omnipresent Christ consciousness; the star in the center, the Spirit beyond creation.

**Lahiri Mahasaya**. Yogananda's "param guru," Lahiri Mahasaya was the guru of Swami Sri Yukteswar. He initiated thousands into the practice of Kriya Yoga.

**Mahabharata**. One of the two major Sanskrit epics of ancient India, the Mahabharata is both historical and allegorical. It contains an account of the war of Kurukshetra and also the Bhagavad Gita.

**Maya**. The instrument with which material manifestation was created, separating the creation from the Creator. It is a conscious force that perpetuates creation and keeps its inhabitants in ignorance of their true identity. Often referred to as Maha Shakti.

**Medulla oblongata**. The approximate physical location of the negative pole of the sixth chakra. It is the point at which cosmic energy enters the physical body.

**Nadis**. Subtle channels of life force in the astral body, comparable to the nervous system in the physical body.

**Patanjali**. An enlightened sage who described the science of Raja Yoga in his *Yoga Sutras*. He lived approximately in the second century BCE and is reputed to have written numerous spiritual treatises. Yogananda refers to him as an ancient Indian avatar, "the greatest of Hindu Yogis."

**Pingala.** One of the parallel nerve channels in the astral spine, pingala begins and ends on the right side of the spine. Energy passing downward through it causes exhalation.

**Prana.** Life force as it manifests in the human body and in all living creatures.

**Pranayama.** Control of the senses through withdrawal of energy.

**Sanatan Dharma.** The "Eternal Religion." The immutable truths that form the basis of religious and spiritual theologies, and moral and ethical codes.

**Satchidananda.** The description of the state preceding and beyond manifestation by India's great philosopher-saint, Swami Adi Shankaracharya: *Ever-existing, ever-conscious, ever-new Bliss.*

**Swami Sri Yukteswar.** Yogananda's guru, and a direct disciple of Lahiri Mahasaya, often mentioned in *Autobiography of a Yogi.*

**Samadhi.** Divine ecstasy. Union of the individual soul with the infinite Spirit.

**Samskaras.** Past tendencies. The traces of past karmas, both positive and negative, that carry over from life to life.

**Spiritual Eye.** The point midway between the eyebrows, within the frontal lobe of the brain, is described as the seat of the intellect, of willpower, and—in superconsciousness—of ecstasy and spiritual vision.

**Sushumna.** The astral spine, through which kundalini, having been magnetized to flow upward, begins its slow ascent toward enlightenment.

**Vasana.** A tendency or talent from past incarnations that influences current behavior.

**Vedas.** The four ancient scriptural texts of Sanatan Dharma: Rigveda, Samaveda, Yajurveda, and Atharvaveda.

**Vritti.** Eddies or whirlpools of energy that accompany ego-motivated thoughts and actions.

**Yugas.** Ages or cycles of time. The four ages are Kali Yuga (the age dark with ignorance), Dwapara Yuga (an age of energy), Treta Yuga (an age of awareness of the power of mind), and Satya Yuga, also called Krita (an age of high spiritual awareness).

**Yamas and Niyamas.** Described by Patanjali in his Yoga Sutras, the first two branches of the soul's journey to enlightenment, which consist of guidelines for conserving vital energy and directing it into constructive attitudes and actions.

# BIBLIOGRAPHY

Becker, Robert. *The Body Electric: Electromagnetism and The Foundation of Life*. New York: William Morrow Paperbacks, 1998.

Clarity Magazine. Ananda Church of Self-Realization, Nevada City, California. Winter 2011.

*East-West*. Self-Realization Fellowship. Monthly and bimonthly issues, November/December 1925–March 1934.

Graeber, Nalini. *Transitioning in Grace: A Yogi's Approach to Death and Dying*. Nevada City, CA: Crystal Clarity Publishers, 2019.

*Inner Culture*. Self-Realization Fellowship. Monthly issues, April 1934–December 1941.

Kriyananda, Swami. See also Walters, J. Donald.

    *Affirmations for Self-Healing*. Nevada City, CA: Crystal Clarity Publishers, 2005.

    *Ananda Yoga for Higher Awareness*. Nevada City, CA: Crystal Clarity Publishers, 2004.

    *Art as a Hidden Message*. Nevada City, CA: Crystal Clarity Publishers, 1997.

    "Astral Ascension Ceremony." Online Appendix.

    *Awaken to Superconsciousness*. Nevada City, CA: Crystal Clarity Publishers, 2000.

    "Baptism Ceremony." Online Appendix.

    *Cities of Light: A New Vision for the Future*. Gurgaon, India: Ananda Sangha Publications, 2009.

    *Conversations with Yogananda*. Nevada City, CA: Crystal Clarity Publishers, 2003.

    *Eastern Thoughts, Western Thoughts*. Nevada City, CA: Crystal Clarity Publishers, 1975.

    *Education for Life*. Gurgaon, India: Ananda Sangha Publications, 2006.

    "A Festival of Light." Online Appendix.

    *God Is for Everyone*. Nevada City, CA: Crystal Clarity Publishers, 2003.

    "Grace vs. Self-Effort." Speaking Tree, *Hindustan Times*, January 29, 2004. https://www.hindustantimes.com/india/grace-vs-self-effort/story-CiQ5zfaJykdwz8uOKUeprN.html

    *Guidelines for Conduct of Members of the Ananda Sevaka Order*. Nocera Umbra, Italy: Ananda Sangha Publications, 2020.

*A Handbook on Discipleship.* Nevada City, CA: Crystal Clarity Publishers, 2010.

*The Hindu Way of Awakening: Its Revelation, Its Symbols.* Nevada City, CA: Crystal Clarity Publishers, 1998.

*Hope for a Better World!* Nevada City, CA: Crystal Clarity Publishers, 2002.

"How Old Are You?" Speaking Tree, *Times of India*, date unknown.

"How Well Do You Get Along with Others?" *Clarity Magazine*, Ananda Church of Self-Realization, Winter 2011.

*In Divine Friendship: Letters of Counsel and Reflection.* Nevada City, CA: Crystal Clarity Publishers, 2008.

*Intuition for Starters.* Edited by Devi Novak. Nevada City, CA: Crystal Clarity Publishers, 2002.

*Keys to the Bhagavad Gita.* Nevada City, CA: Crystal Clarity Publishers, 1979.

"Lahiri Mahasaya's Birthday." Talk at Ananda Village, California, September 30, 1995.

*Letters to Truth Seekers.* Nevada City, CA: Crystal Clarity Publishers, 1973.

*The Light of Superconsciousness.* Edited by Devi Novak. Nevada City, CA: Crystal Clarity Publishers, 1999.

*Living Wisely, Living Well.* Nevada City, CA: Crystal Clarity Publishers, 2010.

*Material Success Through Yoga Principles.* Nevada City, CA: Crystal Clarity Publishers, 2005.

*Meditation for Starters.* Nevada City, CA: Crystal Clarity Publishers, 1996.

*Money Magnetism: How to Attract What You Need, When You Need It.* Nevada City, CA: Crystal Clarity Publishers, 1992.

*The New Path: My Life with Paramhansa Yogananda.* Nevada City, CA: Crystal Clarity Publishers, 2009.

*Out of the Labyrinth.* Nevada City, CA: Crystal Clarity Publishers, 2001.

*A Place Called Ananda.* Nevada City, CA: Crystal Clarity Publishers, 1996.

*The Promise of Immortality.* Nevada City, CA: Crystal Clarity Publishers, 2001.

"Radiant Health and Well Being." YouTube video, Ananda Sangha Worldwide. https://www.youtube.com/watch?v=jRx_U2JS8HE

*Rays of the One Light.* Nevada City, CA: Crystal Clarity Publishers, 2007.

*Rays of the Same Light.* Nevada City, CA: Crystal Clarity Publishers, 1988.

*Religion in the New Age.* Gurgaon, India: Ananda Sangha Publications, 2010.

*A Renunciate Order for the New Age.* Nevada City, CA: Crystal Clarity Publishers, 2010.

*The Road Ahead.* Nevada City, California: Ananda Publications, 1973.

*The Road Ahead.* Nevada City, CA: Crystal Clarity Publishers, 1974.

*Sadhu, Beware! A New Approach to Renunciation.* Gurgaon, India: Ananda Sangha Publications, 2005.

"The Science of the Future." Talk at Unity in Yoga Conference, May 27, 1995.

*Self-Expansion Through Marriage.* Nevada City, CA: Crystal Clarity Publishers, 2012.

*Space, Light, and Harmony: The Story of Crystal Hermitage.* Nevada City, CA: Crystal Clarity Publishers, 2005.

*Twenty-Six Keys to Living with Greater Awareness.* Nevada City, CA: Crystal Clarity Publishers, 1989.

"Wedding Ceremony." Online Appendix.

"Whisper to God." Speaking Tree, *Times of India*, date unknown.

"You Don't Have to Be Sick." YouTube video, Ananda Sangha Worldwide. https://www.youtube.com/watch?v=V9ApjBHI29U&abchannel=AnandaSanghaWorldwide

*Your Sun Sign as a Spiritual Guide.* Nevada City, CA: Crystal Clarity Publishers, 2013.

*Yours—the Universe!* Nevada City, CA: Hansa Publications, 1967.

Laubach, Frank. *Letters by a Modern Mystic.* London, United Kingdom: SPCK Publishing, 1937.

Sivananda, Swami. *Japa Yoga.* Rishikesh: The Sivananda Publication League, 1942.

Walters, J. Donald. *How to Be a Channel.* Nevada City, CA: Crystal Clarity Publishers, 1987.

*Secrets of Friendship.* Nevada City, CA: Crystal Clarity Publishers, 1992.

*Secrets of Health and Healing.* Nevada City, CA: Crystal Clarity Publishers, 2018.

*Secrets of Success and Leadership.* Nevada City, CA: Crystal Clarity Publishers, 2017.

Yogananda, Paramhansa. *The Attributes of Success.* Los Angeles, CA: Self-Realization Fellowship, 1944.

*Autobiography of a Yogi.* Gurgaon, India: Ananda Sangha Publications, 2004. Reprint of the 1946 first printing, published by The Philosophical Library, Inc., New York, New York.

*The Bhagavad Gita According to Paramhansa Yogananda.* Edited by Swami Kriyananda. Nevada City, CA: Crystal Clarity Publishers, 2008.

*The Essence of the Bhagavad Gita, Explained by Paramhansa Yogananda, As Remembered by His Disciple Swami Kriyananda.* Nevada City, CA: Crystal Clarity Publishers, 2006.

*The Essence of Self-Realization: The Wisdom of Paramhansa Yogananda, Recorded, compiled, and edited by his disciple Swami Kriyananda.* Nevada City, CA: Crystal Clarity Publishers, 1990.

*How to Love and Be Loved.* Nevada City, CA: Crystal Clarity Publishers, 2007.

*The Rubaiyat of Omar Khayyam Explained.* Edited, with occasional comments, by J. Donald Walters. Nevada City, CA: Crystal Clarity Publishers, 1994.

"Spiritual Interpretation of the Bhagavad Gita." *Inner Culture,* August 1938– December 1941.

*Whispers from Eternity.* Edited by Swami Kriyananda. Nevada City, CA: Crystal Clarity Publishers, 2008.

Yogananda, Swami. "Advanced Course on Practical Metaphysics, 1926." Lessons 1-12. Los Angeles, CA: Self-Realization Fellowship, 1926.

"Advanced Super Cosmic Science Course, 1934." Lessons 1-6. Los Angeles, CA: Self-Realization Fellowship, 1934.

*Cosmic Chants.* Los Angeles, CA: Self-Realization Fellowship, 1938.

"Interpretation of the Bhagavad Gita." *East-West,* April 1932–March 1934.

"Interpretation of the Bhagavad Gita." *Inner Culture,* April 1934–February 1936.

*Metaphysical Meditations.* Los Angeles, CA: Self-Realization Fellowship, 1932.

"New Super Cosmic Science Course, 1934." Lessons 1-6. Los Angeles, CA: Self-Realization Fellowship, 1934.

*Praecepta Lessons, Volumes 1-5.* Los Angeles, CA: Self-Realization Fellowship, 1934–1938.

*Psychological Chart.* Los Angeles, CA: Self-Realization Fellowship, 1925.

*Scientific Healing Affirmations.* Los Angeles, CA: Self-Realization Fellowship, 1924.

*Songs of the Soul.* Los Angeles, CA: Self-Realization Fellowship, 1923.

"Spiritual Interpretation of the Bhagavad Gita." *Inner Culture,* May 1937– July 1938.

"Super Advanced Course No. 1, 1930." Lessons 1-12. Los Angeles, CA: Self-Realization Fellowship, 1930.

"Yogoda Course, 1925." Lessons 1-12. Los Angeles, CA: Self-Realization Fellowship, 1925.

*Yogoda, Tissue-Will System of Body and Mind Perfection.* Boston, MA: Sat-Sanga, 1923.

*Yogoda, Tissue-Will System of Body and Mind Perfection.* Boston, MA: Sat-Sanga, 1925.

# PHOTO & ILLUSTRATIONS

# PARAMHANSA YOGANANDA

Born in 1893, Paramhansa Yogananda was the first yoga master of India to take up permanent residence in the West.

He arrived in America in 1920 and traveled throughout the country on what he called his "spiritual campaigns." Hundreds of thousands filled the largest halls in major cities to see the yoga master from India. Yogananda continued to lecture and write up to his passing in 1952.

Yogananda's initial impact on Western culture was truly impressive. His lasting spiritual legacy has been even greater. His *Autobiography of a Yogi*, first published in 1946, helped launch a spiritual revolution in the West. Translated into more than fifty languages, it remains a best-selling spiritual classic to this day.

Before embarking on his mission, Yogananda received this admonition from his teacher, Swami Sri Yukteswar: "The West is high in material attainments but lacking in spiritual understanding. It is God's will that you play a role in teaching mankind the value of balancing the material with an inner, spiritual life."

In addition to *Autobiography of a Yogi*, Yogananda's spiritual legacy includes music, poetry, and extensive commentaries on the Bhagavad Gita, the Rubaiyat of Omar Khayyam, and the Christian Bible, showing the principles of Self-realization as the unifying truth underlying all true religions. Through his teachings and his Kriya Yoga path millions of people around the world have found a new way to connect personally with God.

His mission, however, was far broader than all this. It was to help usher the whole world into Dwapara Yuga, the new Age of Energy in which we live. "Someday," Swami Kriyananda wrote, "I believe he will be seen as the avatar of Dwapara Yuga: the way shower for a new age."

*"As a bright light shining in the midst of darkness, so was Yogananda's presence in this world. Such a great soul comes on earth only rarely, when there is a real need among men."*

– HIS HOLINESS THE SHANKARACHARYA *of* KANCHIPURAM –

# SWAMI KRIYANANDA

A prolific author, accomplished composer, playwright, and artist, and a world-renowned spiritual teacher, Swami Kriyananda (1926–2013) referred to himself simply as a close disciple of the great God-realized master, Paramhansa Yogananda. He met his guru at the age of twenty-two, and served him during the last four years of the Master's life. He dedicated the rest of his life to sharing Yogananda's teachings throughout the world.

Kriyananda was born in Romania of American parents, and educated in Europe, England, and the United States. Philosophically and artistically inclined from youth, he soon came to question life's meaning and society's values. During a period of intense inward reflection, he discovered Yogananda's *Autobiography of a Yogi*, and immediately traveled three thousand miles from New York to California to meet the Master, who accepted him as a monastic disciple. Yogananda appointed him as the head of the monastery, authorized him to teach and give Kriya initiation in his name, and entrusted him with the missions of writing, teaching, and creating what he called "world brotherhood colonies."

Kriyananda founded the first such community, Ananda Village, in the Sierra Nevada foothills of Northern California in 1968. Ananda is recognized as one of the most successful intentional communities in the world today. It has served as a model for other such communities that he founded subsequently in the United States, Europe, and India.

*"Not only did Kriyananda walk in the footsteps of an enlightened master, it [is] obvious that he himself became an embodiment of Yogananda's teachings."*
– MICHAEL BERNARD BECKWITH, author, *Spiritual Liberation* –

*"Swami Kriyananda is a man of wisdom and compassion in action, truly one of the leading lights in the spiritual world today."*
– LAMA SURYA DAS, Dzogchen Center, author of *Awakening the Buddha Within* –

# ABOUT THE AUTHOR

**SHIVANI LUCKI** left her legal studies and a promising career in Washington, D.C. when she realized her quest for truth and justice would not be fulfilled in the classroom or courtroom. Her gypsy journey across the United States eventually led to California where she began a serious practice of yoga and meditation with Swami Kriyananda, who introduced her to the idea of intentional communities through his book, *Cooperative Communities — How to Start Them and Why.*

With a small backpack, a sleeping bag, and a heart full of hope, she arrived on June 22, 1969, at the fledgling Ananda community. She was twenty-four years old. Recognition was instantaneous: This was the way of life she had long been seeking. She resolved to dedicate her life to Yogananda's ideal of "World Brotherhood Colonies," for "plain living and high thinking."

Her special passion has always been the self-healing techniques of Yogananda, taking as her unique mission to find and share these mostly out of print or never published teachings. One day she hoped to found an institute for healing based on Yogananda's methods.

Shivani has earned a worldwide reputation as one of the foremost teachers of meditation, specifically Kriya Yoga, an ancient method Yogananda re-introduced to the world in modern times. She helped establish two Ananda communities—one in California, and one near Assisi, Italy—and the Yogananda Academy of Europe. Fulfilling her dream, she founded the Life Therapy School for Self-Healing. Since 1985 she and her husband have lived in the Ananda Assisi community.

*"Shivani possesses a luminosity that disperses all self-doubt and fear. To know her is to exchange endless ego traps for clarity, joy, and inner security."*
—**Jagadish**, *Thailand*

# In Appreciation

very creative endeavor is a journey. We may believe we know where we are headed and how to get there – but it doesn't always work out that way. Inspiration is never static, and the creative process, like life itself, develops through many stages.

While my goal was crystal clear for me at the outset – to present the full scope, depth, and practical healing power of Paramhansa Yogananda's techniques for achieving physical vitality, mental peace, and spiritual realization – the path to the goal became a profound process or personal discovery. Discoveries came, of course, through meditating on the principles and practicing the techniques, and through the many people who kindly commented on the text, and shared their personal stories of healing. As the book grew from infancy to adulthood, it gradually discovered its destiny as a trilogy instead of a single encyclopedic tome.

I have acknowledged the true authors of these books in the Dedication. Here, I add my deep appreciation to **Nandini Cerri**, director of Yogananda Edizioni in Italy, who for years encouraged me to write, and supported me at every step of the way.

Many friends, teachers, and healthcare practitioners read parts of the book, offering their thoughtful insights and suggestions. My thanks to them all, especially to: **Jagadish Photikie**, **Jennifer Hansa Black**, **Hana Mukti Božanin**, **Dr. Donatella Caramia**, **Dr. Abhilash Kumar**, **Latha Gupta**, **Nayaswami Lakshman**, and **David Sanjaya Connolly**.

Of exceptional note, I offer my deepest appreciation to my Aquarian brothers: **Rambhakta Beinhorn**, who sensitively and expertly edited the books; and **Tejindra Scott Tully**, whose inspired design for the covers and text makes the book a pleasure to read and a brilliant examplar of graphic artistry.

Let me not forget my husband, **Arjuna Lucki**, who endured long absences while I was sequestered in my writing hideaway; and my many friends and colleagues who, during my absence from usual duties, took the helm and taught my classes with masterful skill.

May I presume to thank you as well, **dear reader**, for sharing the inspiration you garner from these pages with those in need of healing?

*Together may we bring Light and Healing to the world!*

## Autobiography of a Yogi
*Paramhansa Yogananda*

*Autobiography of a Yogi* is one of the world's most acclaimed spiritual classics, with millions of copies sold. Named one of the Best 100 Spiritual Books of the twentieth century, this book helped launch and continues to inspire a spiritual awakening throughout the Western world.

Yogananda was the first yoga master of India whose mission brought him to settle and teach in the West. His firsthand account of his life experiences in India includes childhood revelations, stories of his visits to saints and masters, and long-secret teachings of yoga and Self-realization that he first made available to the Western reader.

This reprint of the original 1946 edition is free from textual changes made after Yogananda's passing in 1952. This updated edition includes bonus materials: the last chapter that Yogananda wrote in 1951, also without posthumous changes, the eulogy Yogananda wrote for Gandhi, and a new foreword and afterword by Swami Kriyananda, one of Yogananda's close, direct disciples.

Also available in Spanish and Hindi from Crystal Clarity Publishers.

## Scientific Healing Affirmations
*Paramhansa Yogananda*

Yogananda's 1924 classic, reprinted here, is a pioneering work in the fields of self-healing and self-transformation. He explains that words are crystallized thoughts and have life-changing power when spoken with conviction, concentration, willpower, and feeling. Yogananda offers far more than mere suggestions for achieving positive attitudes. He shows how to impregnate words with spiritual force to shift habitual thought patterns of the mind and create a new personal reality.

Added to this text are over fifty of Yogananda's well-loved "Short Affirmations," taken from issues of East-West and Inner Culture magazines from 1932 to 1942. This little book will be a treasured companion on the road to realizing your highest, divine potential.

## How to Achieve Glowing Health and Vitality
THE WISDOM OF YOGANANDA SERIES, VOLUME 6
*Paramhansa Yogananda*

Yogananda explains principles that promote physical health and overall well-being, mental clarity, and inspiration in one's spiritual life. He offers practical, wide-ranging, and fascinating suggestions on having more energy and living a radiantly healthy life. Readers will discover the priceless Energization Exercises for rejuvenating the body and mind, the fine art of conscious relaxation, and helpful diet tips for health and beauty.

### Meditation for Starters
*Swami Kriyananda*

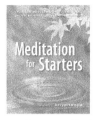

Have you wanted to learn to meditate, but just never got around to it? Or tried "sitting in the silence" only to find your mind wandering? Do you wish you had a meditation guidebook that explained clearly what to do, step-by-step? If so, *Meditation for Starters* is for you.

Learn meditation from a true expert, with more than 60 years of experience. Swami Kriyananda has helped tens of thousands of people successfully start a regular meditation routine.

This award-winning book provides everything you need to begin a meditation practice. Easy-to-follow instructions teach you how to relax the body, focus your attention, and interiorize your mind. With only a little practice you will experience the enhanced awareness and joyful calmness that was missing in your life.

### The Hindu Way of Awakening
ITS REVELATION, ITS SYMBOLS:
AN ESSENTIAL VIEW OF RELIGION
*Swami Kriyananda*

Hinduism, as it comes across in this book, is a robust, joyful religion, amazingly in step with the most advanced thinking of modern times, in love with life, deeply human as well as humane, delightfully aware of your personal life's needs, for the teaching in this book is no abstraction: It is down-to-earth and pressingly immediate.

This book brings order to the seeming chaos of the symbols and imagery in Hinduism and clearly communicates the underlying teachings from which these symbols arise - truths inherent in all religions, and their essential purpose - the direct inner experience of God.

### Intuition for Starters
HOW TO KNOW & TRUST YOUR INNER GUIDANCE
*Swami Kriyananda*

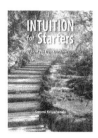

Is there a way to know how to make the best choice? Yes! through developing our faculty of intuition.

Often thought of as something vague and undefinable, intuition is the ability to perceive truth directly not by reason, logic, or analysis, but by simply knowing from within.

This book explains how within each of us lies the ability to perceive the answers we need and shows how to access the powerful stream of creative energy which lies beneath the surface of our conscious mind: the superconscious.

Step-by-step exercises, advice, and guidance reveal intuition to be an ally and an accessible fountain of wisdom to be found within each of us.

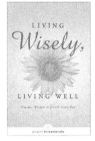

### Living Wisely, Living Well
*Swami Kriyananda*
*Winner of the 2011 International Book Award*
*for Self-Help: Motivational Book of the Year.*

Learn the art of spiritual living, and discover hundreds of techniques for self-improvement. Living Wisely, Living Well contains 366 practical ways to improve your life—a thought for each day of the year.

• A step-by-step guidebook for manifesting your higher Self • The distillation of a lifetime of wisdom • A call to dynamic inner growth

Take a year off from the "same old you." Read this book, put into practice what it teaches, and in a year's time you won't recognize yourself.

### Affirmations for Self-Healing
*Swami Kriyananda*

These 52 affirmations—one for each week of the year—will help you strengthen positive qualities in yourself such as willpower, forgiveness, happiness, courage, contentment, and kindness.

This inspirational book is the ultimate self-help manual—a powerful tool for personal transformation. Swami Kriyananda teaches that negative thoughts exist in the subconscious mind, mentally whispering thousands of times each day, "I am afraid, I am tired, I am angry . . ." To be successfully overcome, these thoughts must be faced in their own territory.

Affirmation is a proven method of influencing the subconscious mind and replacing those negative thoughts with positive statements of well-being. Each affirmation and prayer combination in this book is a tool that reaches the depths of the subconscious in a language it can hear and understand. Where other methods fail, these affirmations can succeed.

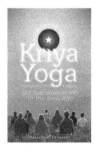

### Kriya Yoga
SPIRITUAL AWAKENING FOR THE NEW AGE
*Nayaswami Devarshi*

Both instructive and inspiring, *Kriya Yoga: Spiritual Awakening for the New Age*, is a roadmap for the already practicing Kriya Yogi. Through real-life stories from long-time Kriyabans, you will learn what attitudes and practices can help or hinder your progress on the spiritual path.

Simultaneously, this book is a signpost to the aspiring devotee on how and why to take up the lifelong practice of Kriya Yoga. You will discover what pitfalls to look out for along the way, and how to reach ultimate success on your journey to Self-realization.

He added, "The time for knowing God has come!"

## APPENDICES

*cA treasure trove of inspiration awaits you!*

The online Appendices for this volume are reserved just for you. Scan the QR code or enter the internet address below, and discover many additional resources to help deepen your understanding on your path to self-healing and Self-realization.

*Included are:*

- Instruction videos in Life Force healing techniques, taught by the author
- Instruction and guided practice of pranayama and meditation
- Articles—many of them available for the first time—from the original writings of Paramhansa Yogananda and from the writings and talks of Swami Kriyananda.

### www.healinglifeforces.com/volume-1/

## HEALING LIFE FORCE COMMUNITY

*Sign up today and you will receive:*

- Healing Tips videos by the author
- Live sessions with the author
- Blogs on healing techniques in daily life
- Insights, invitations and much more.

Scan the QR code or enter this internet address to join!

### www.healinglifeforces.com

## Your **HEALING JOURNEY** with **PARAMHANSA YOGANANDA** continues!

HEALING WITH LIFE FORCE
VOLUME TWO

# MIND

Our mind is the most important self-healing instrument that we possess – once we learn to be its master. In Volume Two you will be introduced to its multi-dimensional capacities that can be developed and used to prevent illness and reverse symptoms of disease.

SUPERPOWERS OF THE CONSCIOUS MIND:
**Concentration, willpower, visualization**

SUPERPOWERS OF THE SUBCONSCIOUS MIND:
**Memory and Habit development**

SUPERPOWERS OF THE SUPERCONSCIOUS MIND:
**Intuition**

*Using these superpowers, you will learn to:*

- *Eradicate unhealthy habit grooves and establish good ones*
- *Create a positive mental outlook with the use of scientific healing affirmations*
- *Attract divine grace and receive inner guidance for aspects of your life*
- *Channel healing life force to others*

"All disease has its roots in the mind. If the mind can produce ill health, it can also produce good health."
—YOGANANDA

HEALING WITH LIFE FORCE
VOLUME THREE

# MAGNETISM

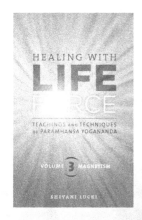

This volume reveals how the Law of Attraction operates in our lives: how it draws us into contact with friends from past lives; and how we can use it to attract the economic and human resources for a successful career. The final chapter of the trilogy demonstrates how we can attune ourselves to the subtle, vibratory healing frequencies of mantra and music; of nature, holy places, and inspiring people.

Important techniques are given to reinforce the magnetic aura which protects us from negative influences that threaten our physical, mental, emotional, and spiritual health and well-being. *Chapters include:*

**The Relationships Challenge**
**Characteristics of Healthy and Unhealthy Relationships**
**Soulmates**
**Separation and Divorce**
**Prosperity and Success**
**Healing Habitats**
**Transition and Transcendence**

"A strong, positive magnetic aura around your body will prevent not only people's negative thoughts from affecting you, but also negative § or harmful circumstances and happenings, even disease."
—YOGANANDA

Available at CrystalClarity.com in October, 2024

Printed in the USA
CPSIA information can be obtained
at www.ICGtesting.com
JSHW010859190224
57562JS00005B/13